W9-ADO-050

THE WALTER LYNWOOD FLEMING
LECTURES IN SOUTHERN HISTORY
Louisiana State University

Other Published Lectures in This Series

THREE
CARPETBAG
GOVERNORS

Richard N. Current

THREE

CARPETBAG

GOVERNORS

LOUISIANA STATE UNIVERSITY PRESS—BATON ROUGE

WINGATE COLLEGE LIBRARY
WINGATE, N. C.

Copyright © 1967 by
Louisiana State University Press

Library of Congress Catalog Card Number: 67–26971

Manufactured in the United States of America by
The Colonial Press

Designed by Robert L. Nance

To my brother Eugene

47076

PREFACE

A PERCEPTIVE CRITIC who read this book in manuscript, and whose identity remains unknown to me, expressed three general reservations about it.

"For one thing," he wrote, "it gives, I believe, a rather more lurid picture of events in the South during Reconstruction than many historians presently paint. Since Professor Current is dealing with political figures, who were always having to face problems of race riots, murders, and the like, he necessarily must deal with the more dramatic, or melodramatic, aspects of Southern life during the period. But perhaps it might be worth noting somewhere that all the political warfare chronicled in his pages made very little difference in the pattern of life of most Southerners, white or black."

The point is well taken. I therefore note here that the careers of my three men—Harrison Reed, Henry Clay Warmoth, and Adelbert Ames—form only a small part of Reconstruction history. Even with respect to their careers, my lectures deal only with certain phases and make no pretense of comprehensive coverage. I wonder, however, whether the outcome of the political warfare, especially in the case of Ames, did not make considerable difference for the pattern of life that was ultimately to be set for Southerners, black and white. And surely the violence and bloodshed constitute a very important theme, though admittedly not the only one, of the Reconstruction period in the South.

"Second, the total effect of his book is to exculpate the carpetbag governors. I know that in the case of both Reed and Warmoth he speaks of weaknesses and defects, but the total impression of the manuscript is that on the whole these carpetbaggers were decent, average fellows, who, for all their faults, did about as well as could be expected of anybody. This seems a little bland to me."

Bland or not, that is precisely the impression I wish to give. It is hard for me to believe that any of these three men was essentially any less decent or less able than most politicians of his time and place. The reputation of each of them suffers from the stigma of the term "carpetbagger," a term that still has remarkable power to evoke an aura of evil, bringing to mind the familiar image of a low-class, poverty-stricken, ignorant, greedy, utterly unscrupulous adventurer and exploiter from the North. The term has become fixed in the vocabulary of American history, and yet, I submit, it is nothing more than a smear word that stuck and continues to stick. That Reed, Warmoth, Ames, and other Northern Republicans in the South should have come to be hated by most white Southerners is perfectly understandable. A present-day historian, however, ought to put aside the stereotype when viewing any of the men called carpetbaggers. To be sure, none of my three, not even Ames, can be plausibly presented as a genuine hero. But none of the three, not even Warmoth, deserves to be characterized as a real villain.

"Third, I wish Professor Current had stuck rather more closely to the very significant questions he posed early in the first essay. In fact, he does not, except perhaps in the case of Ames, get very far into his men, does not tell us why they went South, and does not analyze what they thought they were doing as governors."

Touché! No reader can sense more keenly than I do my failure in this regard. Before actually sitting down to write these lectures, I had aspired to do "psychographs" of my three men which would be at least remotely comparable to those that Gamaliel Bradford did so well with his subjects in *Damaged Souls* and other books. This kind of thing, as it turns out, was not in me, nor, I suspect, was it in the available sources. Nevertheless, I hope other readers may discover that, even though there is little or no explicit analysis of motivation, these pages do, after all, provide some clues and inferences making it fairly clear why each man went South and what he thought he was doing as governor.

I am grateful to the anonymous critic for his searching comments on the manuscript, for certain flattering things he also said about it, and for the helpful suggestions he offered in regard to a number of details. I also owe thanks, for aid and encouragement of one kind or another, to my friends T. Harry Williams, John Loos, Frank Freidel, Kenneth M. Stampp, and Joseph Logsdon, and to my wife, Rose Bonar Current. I am indebted, moreover, to the Research Council of the University of North Carolina at Greensboro for a grant assisting part of the research on which the lectures were based.

R. N. C.

Contents

THREE
CARPETBAG
GOVERNORS

The Carpetbagger as Conservative:

HARRISON REED

EVERYONE KNOWS what the carpetbaggers were, at least by reputation. They were Northern men who went south after the Civil War to take advantage of the defeated and impoverished states of the former Confederacy. Mere adventurers, these men were so poor that each of them could carry all his possessions with him in a carpetbag (a then common kind of valise covered with carpeting material). Once arrived in the South, the newcomers got themselves elected to office by means of the Negro vote and maintained themselves in office with the support of the federal army. They had the cooperation of some white Southerners, the so-called scalawags. For several years the carpetbag officials misruled and robbed the Southern people, while setting blacks against whites and thus destroying the harmony that otherwise would have prevailed between the races. Such, at least, is the view that still passes as true history.

During the Reconstruction period, from 1867 to 1877,

3

men known as carpetbaggers held offices of practically
every kind. Hundreds served as legislators, judges,
sheriffs, and other state and local officials. A total of at
least forty-five sat, at one time or another, in the national House of Representatives, and seventeen in the
United States Senate. Ten were state governors. Six
of the former Confederate states never suffered the ig-
nominy of a carpetbagger in the governor's mansion,
but the other five had to endure two carpetbag
governors apiece. These five states were Arkansas,
South Carolina, Florida, Louisiana, and Mississippi.
Arkansas had, as its two carpetbag governors, Pow-
ell Clayton of Kansas and Joseph Brooks of Iowa. South
Carolina had Robert K. Scott of Ohio and Daniel H.
Chamberlain of Massachusetts. Florida had Harrison
Reed of Wisconsin and M. L. Stearns of Maine. Louisiana had two with such distinguished names as Henry
Clay Warmoth and William Pitt Kellogg, both from Illinois. Mississippi had R. C. Powers of Ohio and Adelbert Ames of Maine. Included in this group of ten are all
but one of the most important and conspicuous of the
entire lot of officeholding carpetbaggers. The one exception is the famous, or infamous, Albion W. Tourgée,
who went from Ohio to North Carolina and became
not a governor but a judge.

The reputations of the carpetbag governors have been
based almost entirely upon the writings of their critics
and enemies, especially the writings of those William A.

Dunning students who turned out dissertations on Reconstruction in various Southern states. Seldom has the carpetbaggers' side of the case been presented, and when it has been, the presentation has had comparatively little effect on historiography. As yet, no scholarly biography of any of the carpetbag governors has been published.

As a preliminary step toward the reconsideration of carpetbaggers, it may be worth while to look briefly into the characters and careers of three of the governors. The object will be, so far as possible, to get inside each man and find out why he went south, what he thought he was doing as governor, and whether, as judged by his motives and deeds, he quite fits the familiar stereotype of the plundering adventurer. The three to be considered—Harrison Reed, Henry Clay Warmoth, and Adelbert Ames—rank among the five or six most prominent of them all. Reed is reputed to have been "something of a hypocrite and everything of a scamp," one of the "odious parasites" who fastened themselves on the state of Florida. Warmoth is remembered as a "dashing young soldier of fortune" who somehow managed, on an eight-thousand-dollar salary, to accumulate a million dollars during his four years as governor of Louisiana. Ames, too, is recalled as a soldier of fortune—not a "dashing" one like Warmoth but a "dull" and "flabby" one—whose election gave Mississippi to know that "the negroes would rule the state."

These three men, as we shall see, actually represented quite different types of carpetbaggers.

Harrison Reed was nearing fifty-five when, on June 8, 1868, he took the oath of office as the seventh governor of the state of Florida. Reed was a rather small man with a big, high-domed head, bald on top, and a long face fringed by whiskers on cheeks and chin, though none on the upper lip, which was shaved clean. His drooping eyelids, behind heavy spectacles, gave him an owlish look, and his calm manner and careful speech confirmed the impression of wise deliberation. His enemies described him variously as "characterless," "hypocritical," and a "damn fool." A former associate of his, defending him, once wrote: "Reed is a fussy old granny, but I think he is honest and sincere." An old friend testified that he was generally regarded as a "high-minded, honest, and honorable man." Certainly, as he faced the four years of his governorship in those troublous times, Reed needed all the wisdom and character that had ever been attributed to him—and more.

This man had already completed one career, though hardly a satisfying one, before he first went to Florida. It was a career as businessman, journalist, land speculator, and politician in Wisconsin. He had arrived in Wisconsin as a youth of twenty-two, in search of a new life away from his native New England.

One of a family of five sons and three daughters,

Reed was born in a village near Lowell, Massachusetts, on August 26, 1813. While he was a child, the family moved to a village in Vermont, where his father operated a hotel and traded in cattle and he himself attended the local academy, served as a printer's apprentice, and then clerked in a store. Two of his brothers, having joined the westward flight from Vermont, were living in the boom town of Milwaukee, in Wisconsin Territory. In 1836 young Harrison, along with his parents and the rest of the family, followed the two pioneers to the land of opportunity. In Milwaukee, according to his later recollection, Harrison "opened the first store of general merchandise and organized the first Sunday school." Unfortunately, the Panic of 1837 soon brought ruin to the family business.

The Wisconsin career of Harrison Reed proved to be a succession of ups and downs. After farming for a while, he went to work for the recently founded *Milwaukee Sentinel,* and within a few years he was editor and part owner of the paper. He received help from the rising financier of Wisconsin railroads, Alexander Mitchell, the husband-to-be of one of Reed's sisters. Reed himself, now that he apparently was well established as a newspaper publisher, married a Wisconsin girl, Anna Louise Turner, and borrowed money from Mitchell to set up housekeeping as well as to buy newsprint. To keep going, however, Reed needed more capital than he could get from his wealthy brother-in-law, and before long he had to sell his interest in the *Sentinel*.

Reed then went to Madison and edited another paper, which lasted only a short time. In Madison he acquired an influential friend in the territorial governor, James Duane Doty, for whom he served briefly as a private secretary. With Doty's powerful aid, he managed, despite a rather low bid, to buy the dams, mills, and other property that the federal government had offered for sale at an abandoned school for the Winnebago Indians on the Fox River. When opponents of Doty and Reed raised the cry of corruption, the secretary of war compelled Reed to repurchase the property at a higher price. Here, on the Fox, he and a partner subdivided the land and laid out the town of Neenah. After a quarrel with his partner, Reed moved across the river and founded another town, Menasha. He could expect to acquire at least a small fortune from his real estate if only Menasha were given a rail connection with the outside world. In his newspaper, the *Neenah-Menasha Conservator*, he kept calling for the construction of a railroad line. Suddenly the Panic of 1857 struck. Railroad building ceased, land values dropped, and Reed's hopes vanished. He went back to Madison and joined the staff of the *Wisconsin State Journal*, the capital city's organ of the new Republican party.

Reed was already something of a politician, having served as chairman of the first board of county commissioners of Winnebago County and as a delegate to

the convention of 1847–48 which drew up a constitution for the state of Wisconsin. So long as the Whig
party lasted, he was an enthusiastic Whig, confessing
that he had been "wedded from childhood to the principles of the American system," that is, the principles
of government aid to private enterprise through a national bank, a protective tariff, and the improvement
of transportation. When the Republican party arose, he
was one of the first to join it, and he consistently advocated its policy of internal improvements. These, it
seemed to him, were desperately needed in a develop-
ing state like Wisconsin. He and his fellow Republicans
were frustrated, however, throughout the Democratic
administration of James Buchanan, whom they viewed
as an obstructionist and a tool of the Southern, pro-
slavery interest. Reed, in his frustration, became more
and more extreme in denouncing slaveowners and their
political power.

The Civil War marked an ending and a beginning for
Harrison Reed, as it did for many another man, both
North and South. With his wife and family, now
consisting of two sons and a daughter, he moved to
Washington soon after Abraham Lincoln's inauguration. As a loyal worker in the late Republican campaign,
he was rewarded with a job in the Treasury Department. Before long his daughter died and then, in
September, 1862, his wife also. As he grieved for them,
he looked back upon a disappointing career. "The

ghosts of my own buried hopes would throng me," he
wrote, "until I would give up in despair." In the midst
of his grief, he suddenly got a chance to begin his life
anew.

His opportunity came in consequence of the federal
direct-tax law of 1862 which provided, in effect, for
the confiscation of Rebel property. According to this
law, a tax was to be levied on all real estate in the South,
and a penalty was to be imposed for any delay in payment. If the owner would take a loyalty oath, he could
redeem his property by paying the tax and the penalty.
If he refused to take the oath and to remit the amount
due, the federal government could seize the property
and either hold it or sell it to loyal buyers. Special commissioners, three for each of the seceded states, were to
carry out the law, though in fact they could operate
only in those areas that Federal armies had occupied.

From Secretary of the Treasury Salmon P. Chase,
Reed received an appointment as one of the three commissioners for Florida at the then handsome salary of
$3,000 a year. With his two colleagues he arrived, in
January, 1863, at Fernandina on the Atlantic coast of
northern Florida, well within the Federal lines. Here
he discovered a new frontier, a land still more promis-
ing than Wisconsin once had seemed. Florida, he
thought, possessed "undeveloped resources and latent
wealth" which "could render it one of the finest
states in the Union." Nothing but Northern capital and

enterprise was needed to bring about "a degree of pros-
perity unknown to even the North."

In Fernandina, at the time of Reed's stay, there was
more to interest him than the beauty of the state's resources. There was also the beauty of a woman, one
young enough to be his daughter but attractive enough
to become his second wife—as indeed she was to
do eventually. Her name was Chloe, Chloe Merrick,
and she had come from Syracuse, New York, as an
agent of the Syracuse Freedmen's Aid Society, to set
up schools for the emancipated slaves of Florida. This
pretty schoolteacher was chosen to do the honors when
a banner, with the magic word "Liberty" upon it, was
presented to a regiment of Negro soldiers, whose commanding officer was also to figure prominently in
Reed's later career. The officer's name will come up
again; it was Milton S. Littlefield.

Reed's dreams of sharing in Florida's development—
and his hopes, if he yet entertained any, of sharing in
Chloe Merrick's life—were soon shattered by a quarrel
with one of his fellow tax commissioners, Lyman D.
Stickney. With his own ideas of Northern enterprise,
Stickney had been serving the interests of certain railroad promoters who had their eyes on Florida land.
While Stickney was away, attending to some of his affairs in the North, Reed and the other commissioner
started their work in Fernandina. They assessed
property, collected taxes, and put up unredeemed

land for sale. They also submitted bids of their own and sold some of the land to themselves, Reed acquiring two blocks of town property for himself and a town lot for each of his two sons. A number of Negroes attended the auctions, and about thirty families were able to obtain homes at prices they could afford, or so Reed later said. Things were going splendidly—when all at once Stickney reappeared. He denounced his associates for proceeding without his knowledge or consent, accused them of defrauding the government by selling property for less than it was worth, and insisted that they cancel all the sales they had made. Unable to agree among themselves, the three commissioners took their dispute from Fernandina to Washington. When Reed called at the Treasury Department, Secretary Chase refused even to listen to his side of the matter, but was quite willing to accept his resignation.

Desperate, Reed appealed to friends who might exert political influence in his behalf. To Congressman J. F. Potter, who was then at home in Wisconsin, he sent a particularly long and revealing letter (November 14, 1863), written in his remarkably neat hand. "I often indulge myself in communion with the loved & lost," Reed began, "& feel sometimes anxious to close this rough pilgrimage & be with them. It will not be long & may the light that comes from those mansions where our loved ones dwell cheer & lighten our pathway & keep us from wandering after the things that 'perish

with the using.'" With a rather abrupt transition from
the other world to this one, Reed continued: "A year
ago I went out as an officer of the government, to find
relief from an overburdened heart, in a new field, where
I thought to be useful in assisting in the great mission
of freedom & civilization which has been forced upon
the nation. I know I have cherished no purpose of
self-aggrandizement nor indulged in any schemes un-
worthy an honest Christian heart." Reed recounted the
villainies of Stickney—"a wily, sharp, dangerous man
in any position & particularly to one who is naturally
confiding like myself"—and then referred to the atti-
tude of the secretary of the treasury. "Now I cannot get
a word with Chase & he is surrounded by a cordon of
unprincipled men—a secret league to make him next
President—at the head of which stands this man Stickney as the representative of Florida!" Reed begged Potter to get the Wisconsin congressmen together, take
them as a group to visit Chase, and persuade him to
see that justice was done. "You know how devotedly I
have advocated the principles of which he is regarded
the chief in the Cabinet & how earnestly I have supported him for the Presidency," Reed wrote. He insisted that he simply must get back to Florida, saying:
"I have embarked in schemes for the benefit of
the freedmen & I want to live in Florida to assist in
bringing it in as a free state & in regenerating the slavery accursed territory." Besides, he concluded, "I need

WINGATE COLLEGE LIBRARY
WINGATE, N. C.

the salary & I may say I deserve the place. . . . But if they insist on accepting my resignation, then I want to obtain the appointment of Surveyor Genl of Florida. . . ."

Despite Reed's desperate appeal, his Wisconsin friends failed to put him back on the direct-tax commission or, for the time being, to place him in any other Florida position, though they did secure for him a Post Office Department job in Washington. There he bided his time until he could return to where his heart was. Through the influence of Alexander W. Randall, formerly governor of Wisconsin and now assistant postmaster general, he finally got an appointment as chief postal agent for Florida. In the summer of 1865, two years after his first visit, he found himself again in Fernandina.

Andrew Johnson now was President of the United States, and Salmon P. Chase was Chief Justice of the Supreme Court. Though Chase's presidential boom for 1864 had fizzled out, Chase looked hopefully to the election of 1868, and he still had the support of a host of Treasury Department employees, including Lyman D. Stickney and others in the South. Chase also had opponents there, and none more determined than Harrison Reed. No longer did Reed even pretend to back Chase in his presidential ambitions or his Radical principles. Reed now was a Conservative Republican and a Johnson man. When Chase visited Fernandina on a Southern tour and invited Stickney aboard his revenue cutter, only a few days after Reed's arrival, Reed sped off a warning to one of Johnson's closest advisers, Montgomery Blair. He wrote: "I wish to bespeak your immediate & earnest assistance to rescue Florida from the hands of Chase & his corrupt agents now holding lucrative positions under the govt. His late visit here was for no other purpose than to revive the effort to secure this state for his future purposes & against the policy of the administration. . . . He has advised his friends here to organize the colored men & prepare them to vote & that their action shall be sustained by the Supreme Court—holding that there is no legal authority or power to deny suffrage to any citizen. Secret organizations of blacks & non-resident outsiders imported here as agents of the Treasury &c have been commenced. . . . The intention is to override the resident white citizens under the plea that they are all disloyal. . . . We want a Military Governor in the interest of the Administration & not one who will seek to place the control of the state in the hands of enemies of constitutional govt. . . . I am told Judge Marvin, late of Key West & now of New York, would like the place & [I] believe he would be a good man. But for God's sake don't let the President send any man in Chase's interest or that can be used for his corrupt purposes. . . ."

After receiving Reed's letter, Blair turned it over to

Johnson with the endorsement: "This is from a reliable
source." Johnson took Reed's advice and named William Marvin, a Florida resident for twenty-five years,
as provisional governor of the state. From then on,
Reed was a power in Florida politics by virtue of his
friendliness with the Johnson administration, his position as mail agent, and a new venture in journalism
as publisher of the *Florida Times*. His influence was increased when, in the summer of 1866, his Wisconsin
friend Alexander W. Randall was elevated from assistant
postmaster to postmaster general and thus was given a
key position in Johnson's cabinet.

When the Radicals in Congress frustrated Johnson's
program for the South and in 1867 launched their own
Reconstruction plan, with suffrage for Southern Negroes, Reed continued to labor against the Radicals
and in behalf of the President. He joined the Jacksonville Republican club along with about two hundred planters and businessmen, Northerners and
Southerners, all of them interested in promoting eco-
nomic development rather than Negro rights. He led in
the formation of a new party, which he wanted to call
Conservative so as to attract as many white Southerners as possible, but which came to be known as Un-
ion-Republican. It included practically all of the federal officeholders in the state. A congressional campaign
committee and the National Union League, however,
sent money and men to Florida to organize the Ne-

groes and form a Radical party in opposition to the
"Reed party."

The two Republican factions came into conflict when,
early in 1868, a convention met in Tallahassee to draw
up a reconstructed constitution for Florida. At the out-
set, three Radicals known as the Mule Team were con-
fident of controlling the convention. The Mule Team
consisted of two white men, former Union officers from
Illinois and New Hampshire, and a Negro who once
had been a barber in Baltimore. These men rented a
house and provided free rooms, meals, and drinks for
impoverished delegates. Under the lead of the Mule
Team, the convention drafted a constitution which
guaranteed the political rights of freedmen and denied
political rights to former Confederate leaders.

All along, however, the Reed forces threatened to
purge the convention of its Radical leaders and undo
their work. Reed himself, though not a delegate, was
on hand in Tallahassee to caucus frequently with his
allies. They denounced the members of the Mule Team
as "political adventurers" from the North, though a
New York *Tribune* correspondent pointed out that
there also were "Yankee adventurers" in the opposing
group, among them the "great power behind the throne,
Harrison Reed." The Reed men, too, provided food,
liquor, and lodging for needy delegates, and they had
much more money to spend than did their opponents.
Indeed, it was rumored that Postmaster-General Ran-

dall had told Reed to "draw on him for $13,500 at any time he might think best." Reed and his followers finally drew off enough of the delegates to deprive the convention of a quorum, then proceeded to expel three Radical leaders (on the ground that they were not bona fide residents of the state) and to adopt a different constitution. This one gave political rights to former Rebels as well as former slaves. It also limited representatives in the legislature to four from each county, so as to minimize the influence of the predominantly Negro counties, and it gave the governor the power of appointing practically all local officials, so as to keep down the number of Negroes in local offices.

After the adjournment of the convention, the majority of its members remained together to nominate a Republican ticket. At the head of it they put Reed as their candidate for governor, and they filled out the ticket with other federal officeholders. The Reed men, according to a prominent Radical, had "pledged themselves to all the leading rebels in the State that the Constitution should be entirely satisfactory to them, and they in turn agreed to support it. But when the officers were to be provided for, and the Reed party did not even give them a smell, . . . this created an 'unpleasantness'. . . . The Rebels then put another ticket in the field," and they declared against ratification. This "Rebel" or Democratic ticket, the Radicals at first thought, was put up only as a trick to keep them from dividing the Republican vote with a slate of their own. The Radicals nevertheless organized an Independent Republican party and presented a separate ticket.

Thus, in the spring of 1868, Reed faced the opposition of both Democrats and Radicals as he campaigned for the governorship and for the adoption of the new constitution. Not that all the former Confederates had turned against him. "The leading rebels in the country here take an active part in getting up Reed meetings," a Radical reported during the campaign. Nor did all the Negroes remain in opposition to Reed. His group heightened its appeal to them when it induced the Negro member of the famous Mule Team to desert the Radicals. The Reed faction had many other electioneering advantages. It controlled the mails, the telegraph lines, the railroads, and most of the newspapers of the state. It had on its side the Union military forces and the Freedmen's Bureau, upon which thousands of Negroes depended for their lives. "And," according to one of the Radicals, "the provisions furnished for these poor starving people have been given or withheld by the agents of [the] Bureau as the applicants were for or against the Reed Constitution and ticket." When the election was over and the returns were in, that constitution and ticket had won by an overwhelming majority.

By the time of his inauguration as governor, in Tallahassee, Harrison Reed had already passed the high point of his political influence. As the federal postal agent, he had been a powerful Republican boss of Florida. "But for his Mail Agency," his persistent foe Stickney remarked, "he could never have figured at all in the politics of the State." Reed was soon to strike back at Stickney once more, by vetoing a bank bill that Stickney had asked the legislature to pass. Nevertheless, the mail agency had done more for Reed than the governorship was to do.

True, the governor had tremendous powers of patronage, with some five hundred state and local jobs to fill. But Reed failed in his attempt to distribute these in such a way as to assure himself the broadest possible support. He appointed more than twice as many Southern as Northern whites, and he confined the Negroes, at first, to rather humble jobs. Negroes were offended because he put none of them in his original cabinet. White Radicals as well as Negroes complained because he appointed so many ex-Confederates, including a cabinet member who was said to be a "very vile and bitter rebel" and a circuit judge who was "one of the vilest and bitterest." Many former Confederate leaders, however, were still debarred from office by the Fourteenth Amendment, and these men, seeing Negroes in the legislature and in state and local offices, looked upon the governor as a Yankee meddler and an instrument of "negro domination and supremacy."

Great though his appointing power was, Reed no longer controlled the federal patronage, and that was far more important than state patronage. Though there were fewer federal than state positions to be disposed of, the federal jobs were the more desirable, for the holders were paid in good United States' money while state employees were paid in depreciated Florida scrip. The federal patronage fell into the hands of the new United States senators from Florida, mostly into the hands of Senator Thomas W. Osborn. Once a soldier from New Jersey, and then a Freedmen's Bureau officer in Florida, Osborn had cooperated with Reed during the constitutional convention and the subsequent state election. From his powerful post in Washington, however, Senator Osborn soon began to direct his Florida forces in an attack on Governor Reed.

Reed antagonized Osborn and many other Republicans by getting in the way of various of their desires. He refused to go along with Osborn and a henchman, Lieutenant-Governor William H. Gleason, also a Wisconsinite, when these two proposed a secret deal to exchange state bonds for scrip at a handsome profit, which they promised to share with Reed. He also declined to use his influence to obtain for Osborn a large tract of state timberland. He vetoed a number of bills, including one to raise the legislators' pay and another to require that hotels and railroads accept Negroes on the same terms as whites. The Osborn men accused him of deserting to the "rebel" Democrats, but in fact he was losing support even among the native white Republi-

cans. He offended many of them by attempting to organize Negro as well as white militia to resist the Ku
Klux Klan. Through a friend in New York, he bought,
on credit, 2,000 rifles for the militia, but Klansmen (or
"regulators") threw most of them off the train bringing
them to Tallahassee.

Within a few months after Reed's inauguration, his
rapidly multiplying enemies undertook to get rid of
him, first by threatening him with assassination, in the
hope that he would resign, and then by impeaching
him. All this, he later said, was "a conspiracy formed
by Osborn and his military satraps," and the real mo-
tive for it was Reed's "refusal to obey their dictation
to vandalize the State." Certainly, he was no more
guilty of "high crimes and misdemeanors" than was his
old patron Andrew Johnson when, earlier that year,
Johnson's opponents had set the fashion of impeachment.

When the legislature began its impeachment proceedings, Lieutenant-Governor Gleason claimed the
legal right to take over the gubernatorial duties. With
the cooperation of the secretary of state, Gleason got
hold of the Great Seal of Florida and set up a governor's
office in the City Hotel, across the street from Reed's office in the capitol. Fortunately for Reed, he had friends
among his appointees on the state supreme court,
especially the chief justice, who was another Wisconsin man, a brother of Alexander W. Randall. The court

handed down two decisions in Reed's favor, the first one denying Gleason's pretense as acting governor and the second disqualifying him as lieutenant-governor on the grounds that he had not been a citizen of Florida for three years before his election. Reed, having dismissed the defecting secretary of state, replaced him with a distinguished Negro, Jonathan Gibbs, and began to favor the senatorial ambitions of the white Radical who once had led the Mule Team. "Governor Reed seems now to fully comprehend the necessity of making terms with us," this leader of the Radicals wrote, "so as to have a party to back him in the future." The impeachment effort failed, and a second impeachment resolution was voted down. At the end of the first year, Reed was still in office, but he was pretty much a man without a party.

The harassed governor enjoyed a happy interlude in the summer of 1869, when he took a trip to Wilmington, North Carolina. There lived Chloe Merrick, keeping up the good work of Negro education she had begun six years earlier in Fernandina, Florida. Reed and Chloe now were married, and he brought her back to Tallahassee as Florida's first lady. The honeymoon was short. Reed had to keep an eye on the hostile legislature during three more years of conflict and renewed and repeated impeachment efforts. During these three years, the most important questions of policy confronting the governor and the legislature were those that

had to do with Negro rights and public finance, especially the financing of railroads.

Reed took no more steps to protect Negroes or whites
from Klansmen and other terrorists after his one ill-
fated attempt to organize and arm the militia. During
1869, Klan-like "regulators" continued to roam through
counties where Negroes were numerous, and especially
through Jackson County, in western Florida below the
Alabama border. There the regulators undertook systematically to kill off or drive out all the leaders of
Negroes. One night in Marianna, the county seat, a
bullet killed the scalawag county clerk and wounded a
carpetbag state senator, W. J. Purman, as the two
crossed the public square together. A few days later,
near Marianna, assassins fired into a Negro picnic,
gunning for the Negro constable but missing him and
killing another man and a small boy. Negroes, retaliat-
ing, shot at a prominent Democrat one evening as he
sat in front of the town hotel; they hit his daughter instead. Regulators then went to the home of a Negro
(whom they implicated in the young woman's death),
took him and his wife and son away, and shot them all.
Terrorists ordered a Jewish merchant out of town because he questioned their sense of justice; his corpse
was afterwards found on the highway. Murder followed murder, and from time to time the bloated
bodies of Negroes could be seen floating in the placid
and beautiful Chipola River.

In Tallahassee the Radicals, black and white, demanded that Reed ask for federal troops or else declare
martial law and send state militia to stop the outrages
in Jackson County. Reed refused to use force, though
the War Department, in response to a direct request
from the Radicals, moved small detachments to both
Marianna and Tallahassee. The governor sent two men
to Marianna, both of them conservative white Southerners, to investigate and conciliate. They reported that
the wounded carpetbagger Purman and his associates
were themselves to blame for all the trouble, for they
had been "stirring up Negroes against whites." Reed
endorsed this view.

Though Jackson County quieted down considerably,
occasional beatings and shootings took place during
1870. Reed blandly told the legislature: "In several
counties organized bands of lawless men have combined to override the civil authorities, and many acts of
violence have occurred; but these have been incidental
to the State in all its past history, and arise less, perhaps, from special enmity to the present form of government than from opposition to the restraints of law in
general." Here Reed the carpetbagger was repeating
a stock argument of white supremacists—that the
bloodshed was more or less normal and had no significant political connotations.

A new climax in Jackson County came in 1871. The
sheriff, who often had been threatened and then had

been assaulted by several men, resigned on the grounds that he could no longer enforce the laws. A few days later the county clerk, the most important carpetbagger in the area, was shot and killed as he walked across the same square where the previous county clerk had been assassinated. The Radicals were disgusted by Reed's reaction to these events. "We have a reputed republican governor in this state; he has the appointing power, and he appoints all county officers except constables," Purman testified before a congressional committee, and yet: "After the resignation of the sheriff, and the murder of the clerk, the democratic citizens met and dictated to the governor the appointment of certain democrats, and he made those appointments."

Near the end of Reed's term of office, in 1872, Purman demanded in the state senate that the governor remove the Democratic officeholders in Jackson County and replace them with good Republicans—or face a new impeachment. Reed is said to have replied: "Impeach and be damned." This fourth and final impeachment was based primarily on charges of corruption, particularly in the governor's handling of railroad matters.

From the beginning of his governorship, as for many years before that, Reed had been deeply interested in the improvement of transportation; and he and his fellow carpetbaggers were not alone in this desire. Florida businessmen and planters, old residents as

well as newcomers, were eager for railroad construction, and since private capital was scarce, they were
quite willing to resort to state aid. Nor did the state's
involvement with railroads begin with Reconstruction
or with Reed. It went back to 1855, when Florida
adopted a plan for building and operating its own rail
system. In 1866, while former Confederates were still
in power, the government abandoned the policy of state
ownership and operation. On the assumption that the
lines could be completed more expeditiously by private
enterprise, with state aid, the government began to sell
them to private companies and to assist these with
tax exemptions, mortgage loans, and land grants. When
Reed became governor, he followed the recently established policy, disposing of the last of the state's railroads in 1868.

Most of these railroads came, directly or indirectly,
into the possession of an amazing pair of Reconstruction financiers—George W. Swepson, who until recently had been nothing more than a small-town North
Carolina banker; and Milton S. Littlefield, that erst-
while Union officer whose acquaintance Reed and
Chloe Merrick had made in Fernandina during the
war. Swepson and Littlefield, already playing a reck-
less game with railroads in North Carolina, were ex-
panding their operations into Florida. Littlefield, with
his smooth talk, his winning ways, and his free spend-
ing habits, was in Florida during the election of 1868,

and he contributed heavily to Reed's campaign. He was there again in 1869, passing out money freely among the Tallahassee legislators. Not satisfied with having acquired the Florida railroads for a song, Littlefield and Swepson now were seeking additional favors from the state. They wanted to swap railroad bonds for state bonds—which presumably they could sell at a better price—in order to obtain funds for improving and extending the lines. The legislature responded by authorizing the governor to issue state bonds totaling $4,000,000 in exchange for railroad bonds.

For about a year, Reed declined to make any bond exchanges. He held to the position that, under the law, he could issue the state bonds only in installments, as sections of railroad line were actually completed. Then, in June, 1870, Littlefield visited Tallahassee and talked with Reed. Within a few days the governor issued the full amount of the bonds, with a face value of $4,000,-000. Littlefield, Swepson, and their associates later disposed of them for $2,800,000. Of this sum, only about $300,000 was ever applied to the construction or improvement of Florida railroads.

Meanwhile, the Osborn faction in the legislature had begun an investigation with the object of showing that Reed was guilty of an impeachable offense, the taking of bribes. The investigators made much of a letter that Swepson purportedly had written to Reed before the passage of the laws providing for the exchange of

bonds. The Swepson letter, dated May 31, 1869, read:
"You remember . . . our agreement was this: You
were to call the legislature together, and use your influence to have our bills passed as drawn by us, and if
you were successful in this you were to be paid twelve
thousand five hundred dollars in cash, out of which
amount was to be deducted the seventy-five hundred
dollars you have heretofore received, leaving a balance
of five thousand dollars to be paid at an early date." In
all probability, this incriminating letter was spurious.
Senator Osborn himself apparently had composed it
and had demanded Swepson's signature as a condition of the Osborn men's voting for the Swepson-Little-
field bills in the 1869 legislature.

Reed's relationship with Littlefield remains something of a puzzle. Reed, it seems, had indeed received
money from him, a total of $7,500, but viewed this as a
loan and intended to repay it. He must have been
shocked when he learned of the trumped-up Swepson
letter, which Littlefield never publicly disavowed.
Reed must have been deeply distressed, moreover,
when the exchange of bonds proved so disadvantageous
for the state. Yet he never seemed to lose his trust in
Littlefield. When the governor of North Carolina called
upon the governor of Florida to hand the man over for
trial on charges of conspiracy and embezzlement, Reed
refused to do it. And, instead of blaming Littlefield for
the poor return on the bonds, he gave the following

public explanation: "It appears that [the] bonds were entrusted by the company to one of the firms of swindlers who abound in New York, which, by fraud and villainy, have diverted much of the proceeds from the work for which they were issued." Apparently the charms of Littlefield, together with the ties of old acquaintance, were more than Reed could resist. He seems more gullible than guilty.

In any case, Reed persisted in maintaining that Florida's railroad affairs were not nearly so bad as his enemies pictured them. The loss on the sale of the state bonds, he explained, was a loss to the company and not to the state. The state continued to hold the company's bonds, with a mortgage on the railroad properties themselves as security for the ultimate payment of interest and principal. Moreover, he pointed out, the railroads were no longer exempted from taxation, as they had been before 1869, and the state would, in the future, derive a sizable revenue from taxes on the railroads' income as well as their lands and other property.

Reed was also criticized for other policies of public finance. He helped to bring about a great increase in both tax rates and tax assessments, and the taxes were laid on corporations as well as individual property owners. Nevertheless, the public debt grew considerably. How much it grew is hard to say, for there are tricky problems of accounting involved in determining its actual size at any given time; certainly, his enemies exaggerated its growth. Reed justified the taxes and the debt by pointing to the "inheritance bequeathed" to his administration by seven prior years of what he called "anarchy and misrule"—an inheritance of an "empty treasury," a large indebtedness, and inadequate revenue laws, "with no schools or school system, no benevolent institutions, no almshouses, no penitentiary, and scarcely a jail." But school expenditures, which had reached a total of only about $70,000 a year by 1870, could account for only an insignificant fraction of the taxes or the debt. And Reed's opponents asserted that other public facilities had improved little if at all. For instance, a Jacksonville hotel owner, who had come from Boston shortly after the war, complained in 1871 that taxes were six times as high as when he arrived. "Yet there are no improvements here, no court-house, and no jail fit to put a hog in."

Again and again Reed urged the legislature to economize, and it responded by proposing a constitutional amendment to reduce state salaries. In this respect, the Republicans under Reed proved to be less extravagant than the Democrats had been before them. Between 1865 and 1867, the Democrats had raised the pay of the governor and other public officials. When the Republican amendment took effect in 1871, the governor's salary was lowered from $5,000 to $3,500. This, along with the other salaries, was still paid in scrip, and the next year Reed told the legislature that the scrip had depreciated so much that his own salary was worth no more than $1,000, the department heads' pay was equivalent to only $700, and the judges' remuneration left them at the "starvation point."

When Reed left the governorship, in 1872, he and his wife, Chloe, settled down on his farm, with its thirty-two-acre orange grove, along the St. Johns River near Jacksonville. From his four years in office he had acquired no fortune; far from it, he had accumulated enduring debts.

In 1874, in the midst of a nationwide depression, Reed petitioned the legislature to reimburse him for money he had spent out of his own pocket, and for bills he had run up on his personal account, while serving the state as governor. He requested $10,000 for attorney's fees he had paid in defending himself against unjust impeachment charges, and $30,000 for "extraordinary expenditures" for which he had obligated himself in maintaining peace and order (as, for example, in hiring secret agents and in procuring arms for the militia, the arms that Klansmen intercepted). His petition further set forth: "That he is now largely indebted and his property encumbered, on account of his expenditures, and he is now subject to a heavy interest which, if not speedily arrested, will absorb the accumulation of years of frugal industry." The state never repaid him a cent.

To supplement his income, Reed turned once more to journalism. He began to edit *The Semi-Tropical,* a monthly magazine which he filled with Florida promotional literature. He dedicated the magazine, as he said, to "dispersing the gloom of the lost cause" and "infusing new energy and courage by instilling the real advantages and recuperative powers we possess." This venture lasted only three years, from 1875 to 1878.

After another decade Reed was still in dire financial straits. A mortgage on his farm was about to fall due, and to his dismay he found that he could get no extension of the loan. "The place has cost me $20,000 & the orange crop the current year will probably net $2,000 on the place," he wrote in 1889 to his nephew John S. Mitchell in Wisconsin. "I want you to find me a loan of $5,000 on it to clear off the old mortgage & enable me to meet the controversy which now seeks to crush me personally & financially." The controversy he referred to was a family quarrel which had estranged him from his sister, the wealthy widow of the Wisconsin financier Alexander Mitchell. She was ill and under the care of a woman friend. Reed hoped that her son, his nephew, would intercede with her and persuade her to move to Florida and live with him and Chloe, but the ailing Mrs. Mitchell refused to have anything to do with either of the Reeds. "I see no way," Reed told his nephew, "that I can enter the barrier so carefully guarded by the designing & unprincipled woman who holds the key to her purse & who for years has poisoned her mind against all who would honestly minister to her happiness. My good wife yearns to be by her bedside & would be a 'ministering angel' of spiritual & bodily comfort, from the promptings of a warm, unselfish & loving heart." But the Reeds made no headway in what he called "this mission of humanity, mercy & justice."

Reed obtained some relief when, in 1889, the Republicans returned to power in Washington and the Benjamin Harrison administration rewarded him with the job of Jacksonville postmaster. This lasted until 1893, when another major depression began. Before many more years, the Reeds' worries were over. Chloe died in Jacksonville on August 5, 1897, leaving one son. Reed, nearly eighty-six, followed her on May 25, 1899, twenty-seven years after the end of his term as governor.

In retrospect, Harrison Reed seems a rather unappealing person, what with his unctuous and self-righteous manner, his frequent wheedling after money, and his unconvincing references to high moral and religious principles. As governor, however, he was much less a villain than he sometimes has been painted. He sought to give Florida an efficient and economical administration, and if he fell short, this was mainly due to his trust in untrustworthy friends and to his helplessness in the face of numerous foes. Certainly, in Florida politics, he was no demagogue who aroused Negroes against whites. He was a Republican, but a conservative one, not a Radical. Nor was he a mere adventurer who came and went without concern for the future of the state. He made Florida his home, and he identified himself, or hoped to do so, with the substantial men, Northern and Southern, who sought to develop the state's resources and enrich themselves in the process. In Florida he was trying to do essentially what he had already tried and failed to do in Wisconsin. He was one of thousands of Northerners who, during or after the Civil War, discovered a new frontier in the South. This is the real significance of his career.

The Carpetbagger as Corruptionist:

HENRY CLAY WARMOTH

AFTER THE END of Reconstruction, conservative white Louisianians looked back upon eight years of what they called "Warmothism," which to them was synonymous with "political gypsyism." Warmothism, they said, had operated for eight long years. The man for whom they named it, Henry Clay Warmoth, was governor for only half of that time (from 1868 to 1872), but his carpetbag successor, William Pitt Kellogg, only carried on the system that Warmoth already had set going. Or so they said.

According to the conservatives' account, this "political gypsy" Warmoth had made himself the "idol and hero of the negro race" and, thereby, governor. He then proceeded to set up a dictatorship. With the aid of a compliant legislature, he concentrated all the registration and election machinery in his own hands. His most ingenious creation was the Returning Board, which could sift the election returns from every parish and throw out those that, in its judgment, had been in-

validated because of bribery or intimidation at the
polls. Governor Warmoth also secured the passage of
police and constabulary laws which created, both in
New Orleans and in the parishes, what amounted to a
standing army under his personal command. He
further reinforced his position by seeing to the establishment of Republican newspapers throughout the
state and giving them a monopoly on printing the laws
and public advertisements.

While concentrating all power in himself, Warmoth,
according to the conservatives' indictment, organized
a system of spoliation which "raised the taxation to the
highest limits ever known in America, swelled the state
debt to many times what it had been before, and reduced the proud commonwealth to unexampled pov-
erty." Among the Republicans in the Reconstruction
legislature, only ten were taxpayers. "Corruption and
bribery reigned supreme, and the knaves, to avoid any
possible danger, refused to pass any bribery law, so that
it was no crime to bribe a public official." Expenditures
that caused taxation and the debt to increase—expenditures on railroads, levees, and other public works—
also provided excellent opportunities for graft. The full
extent of the peculation came to light only when the
vulturous Republicans quarreled over their prey and
turned their talons on one another. One of these men,
testifying about the bribes his fellows had received,
said it had cost more to get Governor Warmoth to

sign a certain railroad subsidy bill than it had cost to get the legislature to pass it. The governor's share of all the plunder, it was widely believed, had made him a rich man within a year of his taking office.

Thus Warmoth has been pictured as a demagogue, a dictator, and a corruptionist. From some of the things that were said about him, he appears to have been a monster of wickedness, a kind of carrier of moral contagion, who brought with him to Louisiana the germs of a political plague which spread through that otherwise healthy and happy land. Before taking a closer look at this man and his role in Louisiana politics, let us glance briefly at the main facts of his career as a whole.

Henry Clay Warmoth was born on May 9, 1842, the son of a saddle and harness maker, in the village of McLeansboro, Illinois. His mother died when he was a small boy. He got what education he could from the village school, from his experience as a typesetter in the local printing office, and from the miscellaneous law books of his father, who for many years was a justice of the peace. A few days before the firing on Fort Sumter, Warmoth left for Missouri and hung out his lawyer's shingle in the Ozark Mountain town of Lebanon.

Shortly after the first battle of Bull Run, when he was barely eighteen years old, Warmoth obtained an appointment as colonel of a pro-Union militia outfit. Later, as the lieutenant-colonel of a Missouri regiment

and then as an officer on General John A. McClernand's
staff, he took an active part in U. S. Grant's Vicksburg
campaign. When Grant quarreled with McClernand
and removed him from command, he also dismissed
Warmoth from the Army. Warmoth went to Washington, talked with President Lincoln, and was restored
to the command of his original regiment, which he led
in the battle of Chattanooga. Then, as a staff officer of
McClernand's again, he served in the Red River campaign in Louisiana and Texas. Late in the war, the general commanding the Department of the Gulf, N. P.
Banks, detailed him as a judge of the provost court in
New Orleans. By the end of 1864, Warmoth was out of
the Army and was practicing law at the New Orleans
bar. He was in Washington for Lincoln's second inauguration and the inaugural ball, and he was in Rich-
mond, as a tourist, only a few days after Lee's evacua-
tion of it.

From the spring of 1865 to the spring of 1867, while
President Johnson and the congressional Republicans
took their separate courses toward Reconstruction,
Warmoth busied himself with politics in and out
of Louisiana. In November, 1865, he helped to sponsor
an extralegal election in which Negroes voted; he was
thus chosen as Louisiana's "territorial delegate" to Congress. He was given a seat on the floor of the House,
while the regularly elected representatives from the
state of Louisiana had to watch the proceedings from

the gallery, but he failed to gain official recognition as
a territorial delegate. In September, 1866, he attended
the convention of Southern Loyalists in Philadelphia,
and during the fall of that year he campaigned in Con-
necticut, New York, Ohio, Indiana, Illinois, and Missouri to help elect anti-Johnson Representatives to Congress. At the beginning of 1867, in New Orleans once
again, he was enrolling Union veterans, Negro and
white, in the Grand Army of the Republic, of which he
was provisional commander for Louisiana.

By the time the Reconstruction Acts of 1867 were
passed, giving the vote to Southern Negroes, Warmoth
had made himself the most prominent of Louisiana Republicans. In the new state constitution of 1868, they
removed the minimum-age requirement so that he
would be eligible for governor, though only twenty-six
years old. After taking office, he lost the support of
many of those who had helped elect him, and before
long he began to cooperate with the Democrats. In
the election of 1872 he supported the Democrat John
McEnery against Kellogg for governor and the Lib-
eral Republican and Democratic candidate, Horace
Greeley, against Grant for President. Warmoth and his
allies claimed a victory for their state ticket, but their
opponents, with federal backing, took and held the
offices. Confusion and disorder, with frequent bloodshed, prevailed in Louisiana politics until 1877, when
incoming President Rutherford B. Hayes removed the

last of the troops and abandoned the Reconstruction effort.

Meanwhile, Warmoth had taken up the life of a sugar planter, having purchased an interest in a Louisiana plantation. In 1877 he married the daughter of a New Jersey jewelry manufacturer and went to Europe on a wedding trip. After one year as a member of the Louisiana legislature (1876–77), he held no state office but became and remained the Republican boss of the state. In 1888 he ran a hopeless race as a gubernatorial candidate and from 1890 to 1893 was collector of customs at New Orleans. He stayed in Louisiana and lived on and on, long enough to observe the rise of another Louisiana figure who also was called a demagogue, a dictator, and a corruptionist—Huey P. Long. In 1930, Warmoth published a volume of memoirs titled *War, Politics and Reconstruction: Stormy Days in Louisiana.* He died in the course of his ninetieth year, on September 30, 1931.

What kind of person had Warmoth been as a young man? Was he the hideous monster, corrupt at heart, that his later reputation would seem to imply?

Certainly the young Warmoth was far from hideous in appearance; rather, he was a man of striking presence and arresting good looks. He was very tall and very slender, standing well over six feet and weighing no more than 140 pounds. He had appealing brown eyes and a dark mustache (a rather full one in the style of the time), and his skin was said to be "as fair and smooth as a woman's." Wherever he went, he attracted attention, and he was quite aware of it. At one of the many Washington social affairs he attended in 1865–66, a stranger wanted to know who "this fellow Warmoth" was. "He walks with such a lordly air!" When this remark was reported to Warmoth, he put it in his diary, with obvious satisfaction. Not bad, for a small-town boy from Illinois.

The handsome Warmoth was a fun-loving, hell-raising sort, who attracted a great many like-minded friends. He had a number of enthusiasms, among them theatergoing, steamboat-racing, cigar-smoking, and poker-playing. His mission to Washington as a would-be territorial delegate he viewed at times as something of a lark. On a side trip to New York he attended a reception where Horace Greeley and others of the city's notables were among the guests. "Had a jolly time and came home tight," he noted in his diary. He was staying at the New York Hotel, which catered to Southerners. "It is certainly a very sassy thing for a man with my political views to stop at a hotel . . . where all the rebels stop," he wrote. "But anything for fun." On his electioneering tour through the North in the fall of 1866, he found convivial companions among Republican politicians in various places where he spoke. "Jolly bunch," he commented on one occasion. "Had a good time with the Boys of Cleveland." His former comrades in arms remembered him well. One of them, referring to the "historic fields of Dixie," recalled how he had "so often listened with unfeigned pleasure to jokes and narratives" that Warmoth told. "The echo of your clarion voice . . . has not died away. . . . Everybody says bully for Warmoth and more especially your many lady admirers whose names are legion."

Warmoth was indeed attractive to women, old and young, married and unmarried, Northern and Southern. At a wartime ball in New Orleans, when he was just twenty, he met General Banks's wife. "Mrs. Banks complimented me," he confided to his diary, "by saying that when she saw me she was taken back to old times—that I looked talked & acted like Genl Banks when he was young. I blushed. Thanked her and felt better—danced with her." (Less than a week after that, the General asked him to remain in New Orleans as judge of the provost court. Apparently Mrs. Banks had spoken to her husband about him.) In Washington, Warmoth met Mary Harlan, daughter of an Iowa senator and wife-to-be of Lincoln's son Robert. Miss Harlan took the initiative by inviting Warmoth to accompany her to a reception, and thereafter he squired her about a good deal. After his return to New Orleans, he received a letter from a friend in Washington who reminded him of "that little affair of yours with the young creole lady on Canal St," which he said was a "difficult problem. . . . It can't be solved satisfactorily both to Miss Har-

lan and her." From a former comrade, living in Salt
Lake City, Warmoth heard about the insatiable desires
of Mormon women; he was warned: "You would kill
yourself here in about one year." An admiring Louisiana lady, when he was governor, referred in an un-
signed letter to his "grand physical beauty." And so it
went.

When, at thirty-five, Warmoth finally chose to end
his bachelorhood, the lucky girl was a nineteen-year-old
brunette named Sally Durand. "She has very pretty
eyes, a clear, fresh complexion, a neat figure, a graceful
carriage, and dresses modestly and tastefully," according to a news report of the wedding. "She possesses
many accomplishments, and has but recently completed a very finished education." She also had a very
wealthy father.

Not all had been brashness and merriment, however,
with the youthful Warmoth in his bachelor days. He
also had his sensitive, impressionable, idealistic side,
and he could be serious enough when the occasion demanded. A New York *Tribune* reporter, after an inter-
view in 1872, described him as having "a quiet air of
clear-headed determination, and a straightforward but
temperate manner of expressing himself."

Warmoth was deeply impressed by some of his Washington experiences in 1865. At Lincoln's second inauguration, when the sun, the moon, and a bright star
were all at once visible, after days of rain and clouds,

he was moved to exclaim: "Oh! the spectacle! Oh! the omen! May God grant that it is the omen of peace and reunion." At the news of Robert E. Lee's surrender, he told himself: "God bless the country & its people. May peace & good will be speedily restored & swords be beaten into plough shares, & we learn to fight no more. The rebellion is over. God Almighty be praised." On April 15 he wrote: "Yesterday so beautiful & the air so dry & clear with a happy President & a happy people. Today a dead President murdered by a citizen of the United States, a mourning people, & the city, the country & the Heavens mourning & weeping at his loss." That night, Warmoth slept fitfully. "When I would wake up from my troubled sleep, the first thing that would enter my mind would be Sic Semper Tyrannis, the South is avenged, & the description I have of Booth's walking across the stage after the murder of the President." Warmoth's reaction to Lincoln's death may have had something to do with the development of his Radical feelings toward the South.

Again, the following winter, Warmoth had his thoughtful moments in Washington. After hearing a lecture by the famous Henry Ward Beecher, he jotted down the following note: "Beecher's theme was Man's Want of Confidence in Man. He had every confidence in Man. Labor was respectable, and so are laborers. Suffrage for all men, the right to vote a natural right. Radicalism. Discussion interesting." One Sunday, Warmoth

occupied himself with the Bible, reading the entire
book of Matthew. On another occasion he observed to
himself: "Men are foolish things—afraid of God, but
will not acknowledge His power."

Warmoth made a fine impression on many of the
prominent men he met in the North in 1865 and 1866.
These men certainly did not look upon him, when he
became Louisiana's governor, as bringing an evil influence into Southern politics. Just the opposite. As Lincoln's former secretary John Hay wrote, congratulating
him on his "well earned success" in the election of
1868, "It is a most cheering indication for the South
that the fresh young energy of the West is taking so
large a share in the management of civil affairs."

Once he had taken office as governor, did this brash,
energetic, and on the whole attractive young Illinoian
proceed to make himself "dictator" of Louisiana? True,
he attempted to supervise elections by means of the Returning Board, and he tried to enforce the state's authority through the metropolitan police, the parish
constabulary, and the state militia as well. It does not
necessarily follow, however, that either the purpose or
the result of these undertakings was dictatorship.

The original purpose was defensive. Ever since the
end of the war, the Republican party in Louisiana had
faced the hostility of armed gangs of irreconcilable
white men. Republicans, especially Negroes, were at
the mercy of such terrorists. "You will see in the [New

Orleans] Tribune of this morning," the party leader
Thomas J. Durant informed Warmoth, January 13,
1866, "another account of a typical outrage committed
on a poor negro in Terrebonne by the patrol, which is
the name given to the organization of returned Confederate soldiers established by Governor Wells and the
Louisiana Legislature [which then, of course, was
Conservative, or Democratic]." In April of the same
year another Republican wrote to Warmoth from Don-
aldsonville: "It is impossible to convey even a slight suspicion of the dread which prevails among our little
party. Persecutions the most unjust and diabolical are
of every day occurrence. The object seems to be to drive
out of the parish and state every loyal man. . . ."
Warmoth himself witnessed the New Orleans riot of
July, 1866, in which dozens of Negroes were killed and
wounded.

This terrorism did not diminish but increased after
Warmoth and the Republicans had taken office. He
himself promptly received a death threat from the Ku
Klux Klan. During the fall campaign of 1868, the wartime loyalist governor, Michael Hahn, reported from
New Orleans: "Murder and intimidation are the order
of the day in this State. There is now more cruelty
practised towards Republicans than there was against
Unionists during the rebellion. Every night democratic
clubs parade the streets of this city, and violence &
bloodshed almost invariably follow. During the past

two or three weeks Republicans were leaving the country parishes & were seeking protection in this city, but now the prominent men of the party are daily leaving the city for protection elsewhere." The presidential and congressional elections of that year went against the Republicans in Louisiana. "The pistol and the knife are more potent than the ballot," a defeated Republican candidate for Congress explained. "Less than three hundred republicans voted in this city [New Orleans] where we can poll eighteen thousand votes. Men were not only intimidated from voting but were intimidated into voting the democratic ticket."

Given these circumstances, Warmoth and his fellow Republicans certainly had good reason for resorting to some device, such as the Returning Board, to offset intimidation at the polls and for adopting police measures to protect the voters and provide some semblance of law and order. Even if it be granted that the aim was legitimate, however, there still remains the question of the consequences, the question whether Warmoth used the new measures to set up a dictatorship. The plain fact, as will be seen, is that these did not really give him absolute control of the state. They did not even enable him to control his own party, and soon he was fighting for his political life. Among his Republican foes were many of the white Southerners (scalawags), many of the Negroes, and eventually many of the carpetbaggers as well.

Warmoth and his Northern friends antagonized the Southern white Republicans by taking too many offices for themselves. As Michael Hahn, who was one of the disgruntled Southerners, complained in 1868: "Instead of [the Northerners] extending the Republican fold, old citizens of Union and Republican proclivities were ostracized & only new comers were placed in positions of honor & emolument. They were not satisfied with filling the positions of Governor and other State officers and U.S. Senators with 'Carpet-baggers,' but went further: in the present campaign every white man on the electoral ticket [for presidential electors] & every one of the five nominations for Congress is a 'Carpet-bagger.' This greediness naturally excites & inflames the old rebel population, & disgusts the tried old Union citizens."

The same greediness eventually offended many of the Negroes too. "It seems that the negroes have had enough of the 'carpet-baggers,'" the New Orleans *Bee* reported late in 1870. "They say the latter have been profuse in promises to them but sparing in performance —that the 'carpet-baggers' told them their turn would come 'to-morrow' but 'to-morrow' never came. The negroes therefore say they are going in for 'to-day' and are determined to secure their share of the spoils." Some Negroes were displeased also because Warmoth, as governor, had failed to press as hard as they thought he ought to have done for their civil rights.

Far more disastrous to Warmoth than the loss of part of his scalawag and Negro support was the alienation of many of his carpetbag associates and, along with them, President Grant. Warmoth's fellow Illinoian and for a time close personal and political friend, the United States Senator William Pitt Kellogg, turned into a dangerous and implacable enemy. The break between these two resulted mainly from further disagreements over the division of the spoils and, more particularly, over the role of James F. Casey in the spoils system. Casey, the husband of Mrs. Grant's favorite sister, had received from the nepotic President an appointment as collector of customs in New Orleans. Senator Kellogg and other members of the Louisiana delegation in Congress at first opposed Casey's appointment and tried to bring about his removal, but Warmoth, in response to an appeal from Casey, sent a letter to Grant in his behalf. When Grant showed this letter to Kellogg and the others, "they left the President without Collector Casey's scalp," as Warmoth tells the story in his memoirs, "but with 'red blood in their eyes for Governor Warmoth.'" The stands of Governor Warmoth and Senator Kellogg were reversed, however, when, in 1871, the word got out that the President "would like to have Collector Casey sent to the Senate so that he might be near Mrs. Grant." Kellogg now was ready to welcome Casey as a Senate colleague, but Warmoth threw his influence in the legislature against Casey and secured

the election of his own candidate. Thereafter Warmoth
had to contend against a powerful Kellogg faction,
which included the "custom house ring" and had the
full backing of the Grant administration.

During the last two years of his four-year term,
Warmoth found himself constantly on the defensive
against his factional foes. In 1871, with the aid of
United States soldiers, they attempted a coup by which
to oust him as governor and purge the party of his fol-
lowers. The Democratic allies whom he began to culti-
vate were powerless to save either him or themselves in
the 1872 election. After the election the Warmoth Returning Board counted in the candidates of the new
coalition, but the Kellogg men produced a returning
board of their own, and they claimed a majority for
their ticket, including Kellogg himself as their candidate for governor. With federal assistance—a court
order, a marshal, and troops—the Kellogg Republicans
took possession of the state house. They started impeachment proceedings against Warmoth, to hurry
him out before his term was up, and in the confusion at
the end it was hard to know just who really was governor.

All this hardly adds up to a Warmoth dictatorship.
His patronage powers, even if he had used them more
effectively, were unequal to those of Kellogg and the
custom house ring; his state militia and metropolitan
police were no match for the United States Army; and

2

The Solubility Product

If a large enough quantity of silver chloride is mixed with some water, and if enough time elapses so that equilibrium is reached, there results a saturated solution of silver cations and chloride anions in equilibrium with solid silver chloride. This is an example of *heterogeneous equilibrium*, equilibrium involving a homogeneous solution phase and several homogeneous solid crystals which collectively constitute a solid phase. The chemical reaction which permits establishment of equilibrium between the two phases can be written as

$$AgCl(s) \rightleftarrows Ag^+ + Cl^- \tag{2.1}$$

where (s) denotes solid. The equilibrium constant expression is

$$K = \frac{a_{Ag^+} \, a_{Cl^-}}{a_{AgCl}} \tag{2.2}$$

If the solid AgCl is in its most stable crystalline state, the solid will be in its standard state at atmospheric pressure and the activity of the solid will be equal to unity. In this case, Equation (2.2) becomes

$$K = a_{Ag^+} \, a_{Cl^-} = y_{Ag^+} \, y_{Cl^-} \, (Ag^+) \, (Cl^-) \tag{2.3}$$

This equation will be valid for any aqueous solution in equilibrium with solid AgCl in its most stable crystalline form at one atmosphere. Silver ions, chloride ions, and other electrolytes may be added to the solution, and the equation will continue to remain valid. The numerical value of equilibrium constant will be a function of temperature and pressure alone, although the activity coefficients will be functions of the concentrations of all solute species as well as functions of temperature and pressure.

13

Now if the solution is sufficiently dilute, the two activity coefficients will individually approach unity, their product will approach unity, and it is then possible to approximate Equation (2.3) by the simple relation

$$K = (\text{Ag}^+) (\text{Cl}^-) \tag{2.4}$$

Equation (2.4) is commonly known as the solubility product equation, and the equilibrium constant is called the solubility product of silver chloride. In this form the equation has been found to be very useful for both describing and predicting chemical phenomena. It is important to be aware of the fact that this equation is strictly valid only under certain special conditions: the solid must be in equilibrium with a saturated solution of its ions, the solid must be in its most stable crystalline form, and the product of the two activity coefficients must be equal to unity. There may in fact be no set of experimental conditions under which these criteria can be simultaneously satisfied.

Equation (2.4) can readily be generalized for solubility equilibria involving multivalent ions. For the reaction

$$\text{M}_m\text{X}_x \rightleftarrows m\text{M}^{+a} + x\text{X}^{-b} \tag{2.5}$$

the solubility product equation is

$$K = (\text{M}^{+a})^m(\text{X}^{-b})^x \tag{2.6}$$

The *solubility* of a compound is the amount of the solid which is dissolved in a saturated solution under equilibrium conditions. Care must be taken when comparing numerical values of solubilities and of solubility products for a series of compounds. Three tables can be constructed: one giving in numerical order for a variety of salts numerical values of the solubility products, another for the solubilities in grams of salt per liter of solution, and a third for the solubilities in moles of salt per liter of solution. The order of listing of the salts will be different in each of the tables if a variety of different valence types and of different molecular weights is included in the assortment of salts.

Establishment of Solubility Equilibrium. The process of shaking solid crystals of an ionic substance with water will probably produce a saturated solution, but the length of time required is exceedingly long for some substances. The net rate of solution of a solid is dependent on many factors, including temperature, chemical properties of the substance, physical characteristics of individual particles of the solid, and the concentrations of ions in the solution in contact with the solid. Rate of solution would be expected to increase with increasing temperature. The net rate of solution of solid will decrease as the product of ionic concentrations (each concentration raised to the power of the stoichiometric coefficient of that ion) approaches the value of the equilibrium constant. The net rate of disappearance of solid will become zero when this ion product equals K, assuming that an equation of the form of (2.6) is strictly valid. However, no comparative information regarding rates of solution of different compounds can be deduced from the magnitudes of equilibrium constants without additional information.

Many compounds are less soluble in a particular solvent at room temperature than at a higher temperature, and a saturated solution can often be quickly prepared by dissolving solute at an elevated temperature and then allowing the solution to cool. This procedure sometimes yields a supersaturated solution in which the ionic concentrations are greater than those permitted at equilibrium by the solubility product equation. This is a case of metastable equilibrium, or pseudoequilibrium. If enough time elapses, or if a seed crystal is dropped in, precipitation will probably occur and stable equilibrium may be established. Only then does the equilibrium constant expression apply.

Precipitation of a compound can occur as the result of chemical reaction in solution. As expected, the equilibrium constant equation will quantitatively describe the ionic concentrations at equilibrium, but there may be many nonequilibrium conditions persisting for appreciable periods of time. When precipitation occurs rapidly, the resulting solid may not be in the form of large crystals but may instead remain suspended as colloidal particles. If conditions are right, the colloidal particles may form a gel. Sometimes such colloidal systems are stable for months, but usually they exhibit gradual changes in properties via processes collectively termed aging. The activity of these colloidal particles will in general be different from the activity of the most stable crystalline form, and the solubility product equation will not apply until the aging processes have brought the system to equilibrium.

It has often been observed that very small crystals are unstable with respect to the formation of larger crystals, and often equilibrium conditions will not be approximated until these larger crystal sizes have been obtained. Formation of larger crystals from many small crystals is sometimes accomplished by allowing the crystals to stand in contact with the supernatant solution. The dynamic solution and deposition processes at the molecular level favor the more stable crystals, and the processes will be accelerated at elevated temperatures. Heating a mixture of crystals and supernatant solution is called digestion of the precipitate.

Occlusion of foreign ions into the crystal lattice of the precipitate often occurs when crystallization proceeds rapidly from a solution containing ions other than those constituting the desired compound. This produces an impure crystalline substance which will in general have an activity different from that of the pure crystal. A pure precipitate can sometimes be obtained by dissolving and then reprecipitating the crystals, or by digesting the crystals. Often the equilibrium state involves a solid phase which is not a pure stoichiometric compound, and this fact introduces substantial complications into a quantitative description of the system.

It is common for a compound to exist in several different crystalline forms, one of which will be the most stable and consequently the form defined as having unit activity. Occurrence of crystals having several different degrees of hydration is also common, and again the most stable of these several hydrates under the conditions of the experiment (but at atmospheric pressure) is the one used to define the standard state. Transitions in the solid state are often extremely slow. A certain amount of freedom is available to the chemist in picking a particular crystalline form for the standard state when transitions are very slow, but it is essential that experiments be designed so that reproducible conditions can be achieved.

Apparent Equilibrium Constants. Equation (2.2) is a general equation written in terms of chemical activities. It is independent of the concentrations of the various ions in solution, and it is independent of the particular state of the solid precipitate. For many purposes, an equation of the form of Equation (2.4) turns out to be much more useful. Equation (2.4) is valid only under the quite restrictive constraints of unity activity coefficients and unit activity of the solid. One can expect the activity coefficients to remain individually equal to unity only if the environment around each ion is the environment of infinite dilution, and this is an unreasonable expectation for many chemically-interesting solutions.

There is nothing to prevent us from defining an empirical constant, K', as

$$K' = (\text{Ag}^+)\,(\text{Cl}^-) \tag{2.7}$$

This empirical constant K' will be called an *apparent equilibrium constant* or an *apparent solubility product constant*. Unlike K, the apparent constant will be a function of the concentrations of all ions in solution, and its value may indeed not be very constant under certain experimental conditions. The value of K' will approach the value of K in the limit of infinite dilution. Thus K' is very nearly equal to K in the limiting case of a slightly-soluble salt in the absence of added electrolyte. It is also possible for the value of K' to be essentially independent of the concentrations of certain ions under appropriate experimental conditions, in particular under the conditions of constant ionic strength.

Ionic Strength. In 1921 Lewis and Randall[1] introduced the term ionic strength, defined by

$$\text{ionic strength} = \frac{1}{2}\sum_i m_i z_i^2 \tag{2.8}$$

where m_i is the molal concentration of the ionic species i, and z_i is the net charge on species i. The summation includes all species in solution. There will be no contributions from uncharged species or from species having equal numbers of positive and negative charges, since in both cases z_i is zero.

Lewis and Randall proposed that in dilute solution the activity coefficient of any ion depends solely on the ionic strength of the solution. If this is so,

[1]G. N. Lewis and M. Randall, *J. Am. Chem. Soc.* **43**, 1112 (1921).

then in dilute solutions the activity coefficient of an ion will be the same in all solutions having the same ionic strength. There is experimental evidence to indicate that this generalization is valid for solutions of ionic strength as high as a few hundredths and in some cases a few tenths. The ionic strength principle is valid over the greatest concentration range for electrolytes which yield only univalent ions. The ionic strength principle asserts that the individual ionic activity coefficients are explicitly independent of the chemical nature of the environmental ions, that the values of the activity coefficients are functions only of the ionic strength. The principle obviously fails when there is substantial chemical reaction between the species under consideration and the electrolyte species added to maintain constant ionic strength. Alkali perchlorate salts have long been added to aqueous solutions as "inert electrolytes" for adjustment of ionic strength. However, a certain amount of suspicion must be cast even with these salts, since both perchlorate complexes and alkali metal complexes in aqueous solution have been reported.

If individual activity coefficients are constant, then the factor

$$y_{Ag^+} \, y_{Cl^-} \qquad (2.9)$$

in Equation (2.3) is a constant. It is therefore reasonable to expect that at low concentrations K', although not the thermodynamic equilibrium constant, will nevertheless have a constant value if experiments are performed at constant ionic strength. In practice, a chemist almost always determines an apparent equilibrium constant for ionic reactions in solution. The value of the thermodynamic equilibrium constant can then be obtained by determining apparent equilibrium constants at a series of different values of ionic strength. Graphic extrapolation is performed to obtain the value at infinite dilution. The value of the apparent equilibrium constant at infinite dilution is the value of the thermodynamic equilibrium constant.

The concept of individual ionic activity coefficients is a convenient intellectual construction, but it is important to remember that neither the activity coefficient of a single ion nor the activity of a single ion is experimentally measurable. The nonobservability of single ion activities is a direct consequence of the impossibility of performing experiments in which the properties of a solution are studied as a function of the concentration of a single ion, all other concentrations being held constant. Requirement of electroneutrality prohibits an independent concentration change of one ionic species at a time. In recognition of the nonoperational character of single ion activities and activity coefficients, it is sometimes desirable to replace the product in (2.9) by a *mean activity coefficient*, $y_\pm$, defined as

$$y_\pm = y_{Ag^+} \, y_{Cl^-} \qquad (2.10)$$

Correspondingly, a mean activity, $a_\pm$, is defined as

$$a_\pm = a_{Ag^+} \, a_{Cl^-} \qquad (2.11)$$

Theoretical prediction of activity coefficient values at ordinary concentrations (from molarities of a few hundredths to a few tenths and higher) is difficult. Experimental determination of activity coefficients is straightforward for simple solutions in which the important equilibria involved are simple and well characterized. For the more complicated systems in which interesting chemistry is poorly understood, activity coefficient measurements may be nearly impossible.

A helpful generalization, first discovered experimentally, comes from the interionic attraction theory of Debye and Hückel: in quite dilute solutions, the mean activity coefficient varies directly as the square root of the ionic strength.[2] This fact is most useful in performing extrapolations of apparent equilibrium constant values, individually obtained at constant ionic strength, to infinite dilution. The extrapolation is likely to be linear at low concentrations if the data is plotted versus the square root of the ionic strength. Since these considerations apply only at very low concentrations, distinctions between molality and molarity can often be ignored.

Precipitation Titrations. Consider a titration performed by adding a solution of $AgNO_3$ from a burette to a solution of KCl in a flask. We will ask how the concentrations of Ag^+ and Cl^- change as more and more titrant is added and more and more AgCl precipitates. If the titrant is added slowly enough so that equilibrium conditions are always maintained, and if there is always solid AgCl present in the flask, then the system can be described by the following chemical and algebraic equations:[3]

$$AgCl(s) \rightleftarrows Ag^+ + Cl^- \qquad (2.12)$$

$$K' = (Ag^+)(Cl^-) \qquad (2.13)$$

If we forbid transmutations of elements and demand conservation of mass, two *conservation equations* can be written, giving

$$[Ag] = (Ag^+) + \left\{ \begin{matrix} \text{moles of AgCl precipitated per} \\ \text{liter of supernatant solution} \end{matrix} \right\} \qquad (2.14)$$

$$[Cl] = (Cl^-) + \left\{ \begin{matrix} \text{moles of AgCl precipitated per} \\ \text{liter of supernatant solution} \end{matrix} \right\} \qquad (2.15)$$

where [Ag] is the total amount of Ag^+ added to the titration flask, expressed in moles of Ag^+ per liter of solution in the flask, [Cl] is the total amount of

[2]The Debye-Hückel limiting law, the equation valid at lowest values of ionic strength, states that $\ln y_\pm$ is proportional to the square root of ionic strength. However, when the activity coefficient is approximately unity, $\ln y_\pm$ varies approximately as $y_\pm$ itself. For extensive discussions of experimental and theoretical evaluation of activity coefficients, the reader is referred to:

R. A. Robinson and R. H. Stokes, *Electrolyte Solutions*, 2d ed. London: Butterworths Scientific Publications, Ltd., 1959.

H. S. Harned and B. B. Owen, *The Physical Chemistry of Electrolytic Solutions*, 3d ed. New York: Reinhold Publishing Corporation, 1958.

[3]Formation of complex ions is ignored in this derivation. Such complexes certainly do form under the conditions of this titration. For a more complete discussion of this system, see Chapter 12.

Cl^- put in the flask, and (Ag^+) and (Cl^-) are the molar concentrations of ions in the solution. Each of the quantities in Equations (2.13), (2.14), and (2.15) is always positive or zero.

Equations (2.14) and (2.15) are readily combined to yield

$$[Ag] - (Ag^+) = [Cl] - (Cl^-) \tag{2.16}$$

Introduction of Equation (2.13) then produces

$$[Ag] - [Cl] = \frac{K'}{(Cl^-)} - (Cl^-) \tag{2.17}$$

$$[Cl] - [Ag] = \frac{K'}{(Ag^+)} - (Ag^+) \tag{2.18}$$

Equations (2.17) and (2.18) are quadratic equations. They look more like quadratic equations when rearranged into standard form, as

$$(Cl^-)^2 + (Cl^-)\{[Ag] - [Cl]\} - K' = 0 \tag{2.19}$$

$$(Ag^+)^2 + (Ag^+)\{[Cl] - [Ag]\} - K' = 0 \tag{2.20}$$

The *equivalence point* is reached in the titration when the number of moles of $AgNO_3$ added is equal to the number of equivalents of KCl originally in the flask. The condition for equivalence is thus $[Ag] = [Cl]$. Substitution of this condition into Equations (2.19) and (2.20) gives

$$(Cl^-)_e^2 = K' \tag{2.21}$$

$$(Ag^+)_e^2 = K' \tag{2.22}$$

where $(Cl^-)_e$ and $(Ag^+)_e$ are concentrations at the equivalence point.

A directly-measurable experimental variable in a titration is the volume of titrant delivered from the burette. Change of variables is therefore convenient in order to be able to write Equations (2.19) and (2.20) in terms of this volume variable. For the $AgCl$ precipitation titration

$$[Ag] = \frac{V_{AgNO_3} M_{AgNO_3}}{V_{AgNO_3} + V_{KCl}} \tag{2.23}$$

$$[Cl] = \frac{V_{KCl} M_{KCl}}{V_{AgNO_3} + V_{KCl}} \tag{2.24}$$

where M_{AgNO_3} is the molarity of the $AgNO_3$ titrant solution, M_{KCl} is the molarity of the KCl solution originally in the flask, and V_{AgNO_3} and V_{KCl} are the respective volumes of $AgNO_3$ and KCl solutions which have been mixed together in the flask at some point in the titration. It is assumed that the volume of a solution prepared by mixing $AgNO_3$ and KCl solutions is equal to the sum $\{V_{AgNO_3} + V_{KCl}\}$. The assumption of additivity of volumes is an excellent approximation for dilute aqueous solutions, and is of course valid without approximation in the limit of infinite dilution. The quantities V_{AgNO_3} and V_{KCl} can be expressed in any volume units desired so long as the same units are used for both. All volumes and concentrations are always positive or zero.

During the course of a titration, M_{AgNO_3}, M_{KCl}, and V_{KCl} are constants, and [Ag], [Cl], and V_{AgNO_3} are variables. The effect of the change of variables is to replace the two interdependent variables [Ag] and [Cl] by a single independent variable V_{AgNO_3}. Substitution of relations (2.23) and (2.24) into (2.19) and (2.20) yields directly

$$(Cl^-)^2 + (Cl^-)\left\{\frac{V_{AgNO_3} M_{AgNO_3} - V_{KCl} M_{KCl}}{V_{AgNO_3} + V_{KCl}}\right\} - K' = 0 \quad (2.25)$$

$$(Ag^+)^2 + (Ag^+)\left\{\frac{V_{KCl} M_{KCl} - V_{AgNO_3} M_{AgNO_3}}{V_{AgNO_3} + V_{KCl}}\right\} - K' = 0 \quad (2.26)$$

Table 2.1. NUMERICAL CALCULATION OF TITRATION CURVE
USING EQUATION (2.27)[a]

(Cl^-), Moles per liter	$-\log_{10}(Cl^-)$	Calculated V_{AgNO_3}, ml
0		-25
1.77×10^{-9}	8.75	-8.9×10^3
1.78×10^{-9}	8.75	Indeterminate
1.79×10^{-9}	8.75	$+8.9 \times 10^3$
1.00×10^{-8}	8.00	35.83
2.00×10^{-8}	7.70	29.88
5.00×10^{-8}	7.30	26.85
1.00×10^{-7}	7.00	25.91
1.00×10^{-6}	6.00	25.09
1.00×10^{-5}	5.00	25.00
1.00×10^{-4}	4.00	24.95
1.00×10^{-3}	3.00	24.50
3.00×10^{-3}	2.52	23.54
1.00×10^{-2}	2.00	20.45
1.50×10^{-2}	1.82	18.48
2.00×10^{-2}	1.70	16.67
3.00×10^{-2}	1.52	13.46
4.00×10^{-2}	1.40	10.71
5.00×10^{-2}	1.30	8.33
6.00×10^{-2}	1.22	5.99
7.00×10^{-2}	1.15	4.41
8.00×10^{-2}	1.10	2.78
9.00×10^{-2}	1.05	1.32
1.00×10^{-1}	1.00	2.2×10^{-7}
1.00	0.00	-20

[a]Numerical values for the various parameters used in these calculations are as follows:
$M_{AgNO_3} = 0.100$ moles per liter
$M_{KCl} = 0.100$ moles per liter
$V_{KCl} = 25.00$ ml
$K' = 1.78 \times 10^{-10}$

These last two equations are quadratic in the ionic concentrations, but are linear in the independent volume variable V_{AgNO_3}. The equations can be solved for V_{AgNO_3} to produce the results

$$V_{AgNO_3} = V_{KCl} \left\{ \frac{- (Cl^-)^2 + (Cl^-)M_{KCl} + K'}{(Cl^-)^2 + (Cl^-)M_{AgNO_3} - K'} \right\} \qquad (2.27)$$

$$V_{AgNO_3} = V_{KCl} \left\{ \frac{- (Ag^+)^2 - (Ag^+)M_{KCl} + K'}{(Ag^+)^2 - (Ag^+)M_{AgNO_3} - K'} \right\} \qquad (2.28)$$

Equations (2.27) and (2.28) are in a form well suited for computations. For any value of (Cl^-), for instance, a value of V_{AgNO_3} can be calculated. Calculations are easiest if numbers like 1.00×10^{-1}, 1.00×10^{-2}, and so forth, integral powers of ten, are chosen for values of (Cl^-), since then the multiplications are simplified. Tables 2.1 and 2.2 present some illustrative calculations.

Striking results emerge from these calculations. It is readily apparent that Equations (2.27) and (2.28) do not yield physically reasonable results for all

Table 2.2. NUMERICAL CALCULATION OF TITRATION CURVE USING EQUATION (2.28)[a]

(Ag^+), Moles per liter	$- \log_{10}(Cl^-)$	Calculated V_{AgNO_3}, ml
0		-25
1.00×10^{-9}	9.00	-7
2.00×10^{-9}	8.70	$+1.46$
3.00×10^{-9}	8.52	6.38
5.00×10^{-9}	8.30	11.87
7.00×10^{-9}	8.15	14.86
1.00×10^{-8}	8.00	17.44
3.00×10^{-8}	7.52	22.20
1.00×10^{-7}	7.00	24.13
1.00×10^{-6}	6.00	24.91
1.00×10^{-5}	5.00	25.00
1.00×10^{-4}	4.00	25.05
1.00×10^{-3}	3.00	25.51
4.00×10^{-3}	2.40	27.08
6.00×10^{-3}	2.22	28.20
8.00×10^{-3}	2.10	29.33
1.00×10^{-2}	2.00	30.56
1.00×10^{-1}	1.00	2.8×10^9
1.01×10^{-1}	1.00	-5.0×10^8

[a]Numerical values for the various parameters used in these calculations are as follows:

$M_{AgNO_3} = 0.100$ moles per litter

$M_{KCl} = 0.100$ moles per liter

$V_{KCl} = 25.00$ ml

$K' = 1.78 \times 10^{-10}$

values of the concentrations. This happens because of certain boundary conditions imposed on the mathematics by the experimental conditions of the titration. These equations are valid only if there is precipitate in the flask, and thus the equations fail for very small values of (Ag^+) and for values of (Cl^-) extremely near 0.100 moles per liter; these are the experimental conditions at the very beginning of the titration before precipitation occurs. They again fail if the volume of the solution becomes so great that all precipitate redissolves, although the calculations presented here do not show this point. Experimental conditions in this titration are such that (Ag^+) can never exceed 0.100 moles per liter, since all of the Ag^+ comes from 0.100 molar $AgNO_3$ solution. The equations are hence not valid for (Ag^+) greater than 0.100 moles per liter, the corresponding value of (Cl^-) being 1.78×10^{-9} moles per liter.

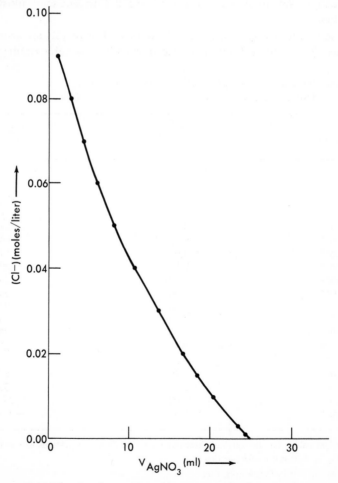

Figure 2.1. Titration Curve Plotted in Terms of (Cl^-) on a Linear Concentration Scale.

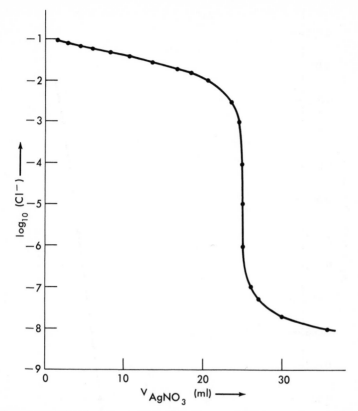

Figure 2.2 Titration Curve Plotted in Terms of (Cl^-) on a Logarithmic Concentration Scale.

Concentrations of Cl^- and of Ag^+ change by many powers of ten, by many orders of magnitude, during the course of the titration. These vast changes are not adequately represented on a graph if the titration curve is plotted using a linear coordinate for the concentration variable. This multipower change of concentration can be satisfactorily represented by use of a logarithmic concentration scale. Comparison of the linear and the logarithmic plots can be made by examining Figures 2.1 through 2.4.

The most characteristic feature of the logarithmic plots is their sigmoid shape with inflection point at the volume corresponding to the equivalence point. Both (Ag^+) and (Cl^-) change by more than a factor of 10^3 upon the addition of 0.2 ml of titrant at the equivalence point. This dramatic concentration change at the equivalence point makes possible accurate methods of detecting the approach to the equivalence point and of locating the equivalence point.

Experimental Precipitation Titration Curve. Experimental curves corresponding to the theoretical titration curves plotted in Figures 2.2 and 2.4 can be obtained if methods are available for determining values of (Ag^+)

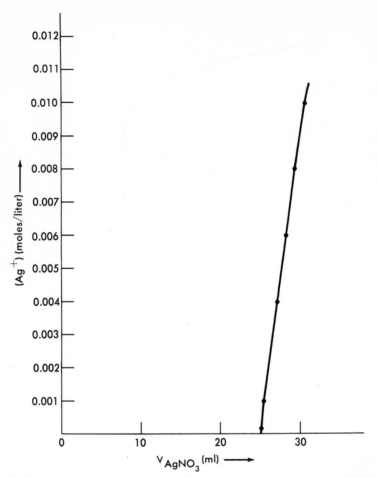

Figure 2.3. Titration Curve Plotted in Terms of (Ag^+) on a Linear Concentration Scale.

and of (Cl^-) after each addition of $AgNO_3$ solution to the initial KCl solution. Electromotive force measurements of these concentrations are particularly straightforward.

Electrodes are available which respond to Cl^- ions or to Ag^+ ions. A metallic silver electrode, carefully coated with a layer of silver chloride, responds to Cl^- ions and is called a silver-silver chloride electrode.[4] A reference electrode must be used to complete the electrochemical cell, and a double-junction calomel—KCl—KNO_3 electrode is convenient.[5] It is

[4]Procedure for making a silver-silver chloride electrode by successively plating silver and then silver chloride onto a platinum sheet or screen is given in D. P. Shoemaker and C. W. Garland, *Experiments in Physical Chemistry* (New York: McGraw-Hill Book Company, Inc., 1962, p. 445). An excellent review of the preparation and use of silver-silver halide electrodes is G. J. Janz and H. Taniguchi, *Chem. Rev.* **53,** 397 (1953).

[5]Construction of a useful double-junction reference electrode from commercially-available components is described by G. Matsuyama, *Anal. Chem.* **32,** 886 (1960).

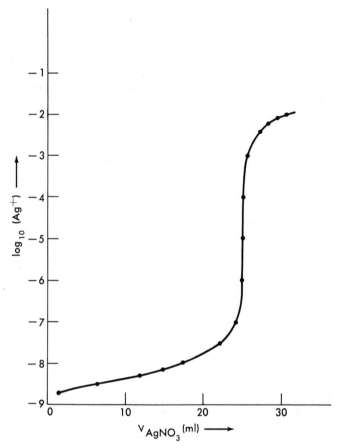

Figure 2.4. Titration Curve Plotted in Terms of (Ag^+) on a Logarithmic Concentration Scale.

important that the electrode does not depend on a chloride-containing electrolyte to make contact between the calomel element of the electrode and the solution in which the titration is taking place, since some flow of contaminating electrolyte into the titration flask will occur, precipitating some Ag^+. Certain glass membrane electrodes respond selectively to Ag^+, subject only to interference by a few other monovalent cations. Figure 2.5 shows the response of one commercially available electrode which can be used in the concentration range of $(Ag^+) = 1$ to $(Ag^+) = 10^{-5}$. The solution must be basic enough so that H^+ does not interfere. This particular electrode is 150 times more sensitive to silver than to sodium, but it is advisable to avoid use of sodium salts in such a titration. The electrode is 150,000 times more sensitive to silver than to potassium. Again, a reference electrode must be used to complete the cell.

The emf of the cell can be measured with a precision potentiometer such as a laboratory pH meter. It is to be expected that the emf will be propor-

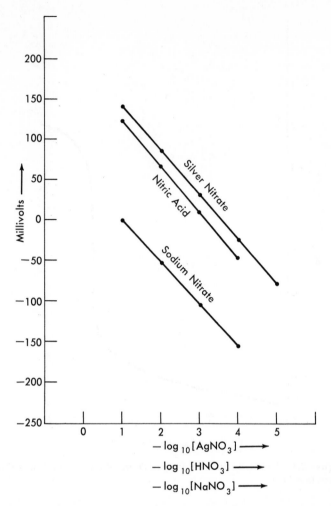

Figure 2.5. Response of a Specific-Ion Glass Membrane Electrode to Aqueous Solutions Containing Ag^+, H^+, and Na^+. SOURCE: *Laboratory Sodium Ion Electrodes*, Beckman Instructions 1155-A. Fullerton, California: Beckman Instruments, Inc., 1962. Redrawn by permission.

tional to $\log_{10} a_{KCl}$ or to $\log_{10} a_{AgNO_3}$. A discussion of why such a dependence is expected is given in Chapter 8.

During a titration of 0.100 molar KCl with 0.100 molar $AgNO_3$, the ionic strength changes from an initial value of 0.100 to 0.050 at the equivalence point and then rises again, asymptotically approaching 0.100 as very large volumes of titrant are added. Titration at constant ionic strength can be accomplished by titrating to the equivalence point with a solution of composition 0.100 moles $AgNO_3$ per liter, 0.100 moles KNO_3 per liter. The portion of the curve past equivalence can be obtained by continuing the titration with 0.100 molar $AgNO_3$ without added KNO_3.

Endpoint Detection. An analytical chemist performing a titration to determine the total concentration of chloride in a solution would like to know the volume of $AgNO_3$ titrant required to reach the equivalence point. He in fact finds the volume of titrant required to reach the titration *endpoint*, the point at which he stops the titration and reads the burette, or the point on a titration curve which he decides approximates the equivalence point. A casual glance at Figures 2.2 and 2.4 shows that there is a sharp inflection in the titration curve very near the equivalence point, and this inflection makes possible a convenient potentiometric method of endpoint detection. The question of whether this inflection does coincide with the equivalence point is considered in Problem 2.7.

Problems

2.1. Derive an algebraic relation between molality and molarity. This equation will probably involve a density. Show from the equation that the values of molality and of molarity approach the same number as the concentration becomes vanishingly small.

2.2. Equation (2.27) can be obtained without explicitly assuming Equations (2.14) and (2.15). Assume instead that the number of positive charges in the solution is equal to the number of negative charges. Using also the facts that $[Ag] = (NO_3^-)$ and $[Cl] = (K^+)$, derive Equation (2.27).

2.3. Find an equation for the relationship between the solubility product constant and the molar solubility of a 1-1 electrolyte, an electrolyte which yields only two univalent ions upon dissociation in solution. Can you then generalize this equation to apply to any salt, regardless of charge type?

2.4. Eversole and McLachlan [*J. Am. Chem. Soc.* **54**, 864 (1932)] reported the solubility of Hg_2Cl_2 to be 4.7×10^{-6} moles per liter at 25°C. in an aqueous solution containing 0.0005 moles per liter $HClO_4$. When the $HClO_4$ concentration was increased to 0.200 moles per liter, the solubility of Hg_2Cl_2 rose to 6.3×10^{-6} moles per liter. Find the apparent solubility product constant of Hg_2Cl_2 for each case, and extrapolate the data to infinite dilution to obtain the thermodynamic equilibrium constant. Use a plot of K' versus ionic strength, and then a separate plot of K' versus the square root of the ionic strength, for the extrapolation. What problems arise? What sort of experiment could yield information about whether the mercury cation is Hg^+ or Hg_2^{++}?

2.5. Derive an equation for the $AgNO_3$-KCl titration curve giving (Ag^+) as a function of V_{AgNO_3} for the initial region of the titration before precipitation occurs. Carefully state the limits of validity of the equation in terms of a range of values of (Ag^+).

2.6. Consider a precipitate which dissolves to yield ν_+ cations and ν_-

anions. If the equilibrium constant is written in terms of single ion activities, a product

$$a_+^{\nu_+} a_-^{\nu_-} = a_\pm^\nu, \quad \nu = \nu_+ + \nu_-$$

appears in the equilibrium constant equation, replacing the a which would appear if the compound dissolved as an uncharged, undissociated molecule. A mean molarity is conventionally defined as

$$m = m_+^{\nu_+} m_-^{\nu_-} = m_\pm^\nu$$

where the m's are molar concentrations. Obtain an equation relating the mean activity coefficient to the single ion activity coefficients.

2.7. Inspection of Figures 2.2 and 2.4 suggests that the inflection point in the titration curve coincides with the equivalence point. Determine if Equation (2.28) has an inflection point at [Ag] = [Cl]. Criterion for inflection is

$$\left(\frac{\partial^2(Ag^+)}{\partial V_{AgNO_3}^2}\right)_{V_{KCl},\, M_{KCl},\, M_{AgNO_3}} = 0$$

Compare the result with the discussion on pages 75 to 77.

2.8. Show that Equations (2.27) and (2.28) fail when the volume of the solution becomes so great that all precipitate dissolves. How great must this volume be?

Bibliographical Note

Compilations of solubility data can be very useful when calculations are being undertaken. Values reported by different investigators are sometimes in substantial disagreement, and hence if the numbers needed are critical, reference should be made to the original scientific paper where details both of experiments and of calculations usually can be found.

A massive compilation of solubility information is A. Seidell, *Solubilities of Inorganic and Metal Organic Compounds*, 3d ed., 2 vols and suppl. Princeton: D. van Nostrand Company, Inc., 1940–1952. Direct references are given to the original papers from which data were taken. A more recent work of comparable scope, compiled under the direction of the U.S.S.R. Academy of Sciences, is H. Stephen and T. Stephen, eds., *Solubilities of Inorganic and Organic Compounds*, 4 vols. London: Pergamon Press, 1963–1964. *International Critical Tables of Numerical Data*, New York: McGraw-Hill Book Company, Inc., 1926 has much data on solubilities, again with references to the primary sources. Solubility data found in these three references is seldom interpreted in terms of equilibrium constants.

Values of solubility product constants are included in L. G. Sillén and A. E. Martell, *Stability Constants of Metal-Ion Complexes*, London: The Chemical Society, 1964. A critical review of solubility equilibria involving oxides and hydroxides is W. Feitknecht and P. Schindler, *Solubility Constants of Metal*

Oxides, Metal Hydroxides and Metal Hydroxide Salts in Aqueous Solution, London: Butterworths, 1963.

It is obvious, but easily overlooked, that any book covers only data published before the compilation of literature references was completed. If recent experimental information is needed, *Chemical Abstracts* should be consulted for references.

An interesting little book which discusses the limitations of the solubility product equations is S. Lewin, *The Solubility Product Principle*, London: Sir Isaac Pitman and Sons, Ltd., 1960. Any chemist preparing to make quantitative measurements should be familiar with J. Timmermans, *The Concept of Species in Chemistry*, trans. by R. E. Oesper, New York: Chemical Publishing Company, Inc., 1963.

An important series in analytical chemistry is I. M. Kolthoff and P. J. Elving, *Treatise on Analytical Chemistry*, New York: Interscience Publishers, 1959–   . Attention is drawn to the following chapters in this multivolume work: D. L. Leussing, "Solubility" (Part I, Vol. 1, Chap. 17); M. L. Salutsky, "Precipitates: Their Formation, Properties and Purity" (Part I, Vol. 1, Chap. 18); J. F. Coetzee, "Equilibria in Precipitation Reactions and Precipitation Lines" (Part I, Vol. 1, Chap. 19); J. A. Hermann and J. F. Suttle, "Precipitation and Crystallization" Part I, Vol. 3, Chap. 32).

3

Acid-Base Equilibria

Categories "acid" and "base" can be made almost as restrictive or as inclusive as is desired. Following Lowry[1] and Brønsted,[2] an acid will be defined as a proton donor and a base as a proton acceptor. Attention is thus focused on proton transfer between two molecules as the fundamental process of acid-base reactions.

One of the most common, most abundant, and most important compounds having potentialities of being either an acid or a base is water. Liquid water has a structure permitting accommodation of extra protons as well as proton vacancies so long as most oxygen atoms have two protons most of the time.

This average oxygen and its two hydrogens can be called a water molecule, symbolized by H_2O. This conventional nomenclature obscures the fact that water is a three-dimensional ordered structure, almost crystalline at temperatures just above the freezing point, held together by labile hydrogen bonds. Bonds involving the relatively very small protons are constantly forming, breaking, and reforming, and a molecule containing a specific oxygen atom and two specific hydrogen atoms has a very short lifetime.

A region which has an extra proton can be represented as H^+, H_3O^+, $H_5O_2^+$, and so forth, depending largely on personal preference. It is clear that a region of space containing several oxygen atoms is involved in deformations of water structure which occur around an extra proton. It is also clear that H^+ is the most compact symbol to use, and this is the symbol which will be employed throughout this book. In the same manner, OH^- will be used to represent a proton vacancy, a region in which a proton is missing

[1] T. M. Lowry, *Chem. Ind.* **42,** 43 (1923); *Trans. Faraday Soc.* **20,** 13 (1924).
[2] J. N. Brønsted, *Rec. trav. chim.* **42,** 718 (1923); *Chem. Revs.* **5,** 231 (1928).

from the water structure. Both H^+ and OH^- will be considered chemical species, distinct from the species H_2O.

Within extremely small percentage limits, the number of positive charges must be equal to the number of negative charges in a beaker of water. Pure water must have equal numbers of H^+ species and OH^- species. The purest water which chemists have been able to prepare has been shown to conduct electricity as if it contained positive and negative ions. In the language of acid-base chemistry, some proton exchange between water molecules occurs in the purest water. Some water molecules have donated protons to other water molecules, and simultaneously the latter molecules have accepted the exchanged protons in a chemical reaction formulated as

$$H_2O \rightleftarrows H^+ + OH^- \tag{3.1}$$

This reaction reaches equilibrium in pure, liquid water without solid or gaseous phases necessarily present, and is an example of *homogeneous equilibria*.

The reverse reaction, corresponding to the reaction of an acid and a base, is extremely fast. If one had an initially homogeneous, unreacted mixture of 1 molar strong acid and 1 molar strong base, neutralization would be essentially complete within 10^{-11} sec.[3] This time is orders of magnitude less than the time required to mix two solutions, and thus in ordinary desk top experiments it is safe to assume that equilibrium has been established with respect to this reaction.[4]

Not much desk top chemistry is associated with pure water by itself. There is nothing much that a chemist can do to change the relative numbers of H^+ and OH^- ions in a beaker of pure water. Except for self exchange of protons, pure water is only potentially an acid or a base, not exhibiting acid-base properties by itself.

Water manifests acidic and basic properties by interaction with other substances. Proton transfer requires simultaneously both a proton donor and a proton acceptor. Two compounds are required for an observable *acid-base couple*. Water starts to be very interesting to chemists when water reacts chemically with some second substance.

This chapter is about acid-base couples resulting from the reaction of pure water with acetic acid, hydrogen chloride, ammonia, and sodium hydroxide. These important chemical solutions are well understood when the amount of solute is so small as to be practically undetectable. Interactions of solvent and solutes are reasonably well understood in simple cases when the total of all solute concentrations is no greater than about 0.1 mole per liter. Details of equilibria inside the familiar reagent bottles of con-

[3] M. Eigen and L. de Maeyer, *Proc. Royal Soc.* **A247**, 505 (1958).

[4] An important exception is the set of equilibria involving the gas CO_2 and the species H_2CO_3, HCO_3^-, and $CO_3^=$ in water. Equilibrium in this system is established slowly. The reactions are catalyzed by certain ions, and by the enzyme carbonic anhydrase [R. P. Davis, "Carbonic Anhydrase," vol. 5, chap. 33 of P. D. Boyer, H. Lardy, and K. Myrbäck, *The Enzymes*, 2d ed. New York: Academic Press, 1961].

centrated acids or in the broth of living protoplasm are subjects of research at the frontiers of chemical knowledge.

Dissociation Constants. The equilibrium constant for the dissociation of water according to (3.1) is given the special symbol, K_w, yielding the equation

$$K_w = \frac{a_{H^+}\, a_{OH^-}}{a_{H_2O}} = \frac{y_{H^+}\, y_{OH^-}}{a_{H_2O}} (H^+)\,(OH^-) \qquad (3.2)$$

It is convenient to define an apparent equilibrium constant, K_w', as follows

$$K_w' = (H^+)\,(OH^-) \qquad (3.3)$$

The product $(H^+)\,(OH^-)$ is often called the ion product of water. Activity of pure liquid water is defined as unity at one atmosphere pressure, and the two ionic activity coefficients individually approach unity in the limit of infinite dilution. Therefore, in extremely dilute solutions Equation (3.2) approaches the limiting relationship

$$\lim_{\substack{\text{[infinite}\\ \text{dilution]}}} K_w = (H^+)\,(OH^-) = K_w' \qquad (3.4)$$

Like all other equilibrium constants, K_w is a function of both temperature and pressure. Its value at 25°C and one atmosphere is 1.008×10^{-14}, and its value increases with increasing temperature. Table 3.1 gives some selected values of K_w at various temperatures.

Table 3.1. Temperature Dependence of K_w

Temperature °C	$-\log_{10}K_w$	K_w
0	14.9435	1.139×10^{-15}
5	14.7338	1.846×10^{-15}
10	14.5346	2.920×10^{-15}
15	14.3463	4.505×10^{-15}
20	14.1669	6.809×10^{-15}
25	13.9965	1.008×10^{-14}
30	13.8330	1.469×10^{-14}
35	13.6801	2.089×10^{-14}
40	13.5348	2.919×10^{-14}
45	13.3960	4.018×10^{-14}
50	13.2617	5.474×10^{-14}
55	13.1369	7.296×10^{-14}
60	13.0171	9.614×10^{-14}

Source: H. S. Harned and R. A. Robinson, *Trans. Faraday Soc.* **36**, 973 (1940). Used by permission.

A *neutral solution* is a solution in which $(H^+) = (OH^-)$. According to Equation (3.3)

$$(H^+) = (OH^-) = (K_w')^{\frac{1}{2}} \qquad (3.5)$$

at neutrality. Since K_w' is a function of temperature, pressure, and solute concentration, the hydrogen ion concentration of a neutral solution will also depend on these variables. Compared to the 55.5 moles of H_2O in a liter of aqueous solution, there are never very many H^+ or OH^- ions in a neutral solution.

Ionization or dissociation of a simple monoprotic acid, HA, in water can be represented as

$$HA \rightleftarrows H^+ + A^- \qquad (3.6)$$

It is convenient to write down a chemical equation like (3.6), and to think of this reaction as if it were an isolated chemical process. There is no experimental way, however, to study reaction (3.6) in water without also having reaction (3.1) occur simultaneously. Both reactions involve H^+, and since the same H^+ ions are taking part in both reactions, this is a case of *simultaneous equilibria*, or *competitive equilibria*, or *coupled equilibria*.

The equilibrium constant for reaction (3.6) is

$$K_{HA} = \frac{a_{H^+}\, a_{A^-}}{a_{HA}} = \frac{y_{H^+}\, y_{A^-}}{y_{HA}} \frac{(H^+)\,(A^-)}{(HA)} \qquad (3.7)$$

An apparent equilibrium constant, K_{HA}', can be defined by

$$K_{HA}' = \frac{(H^+)\,(A^-)}{(HA)} \qquad (3.8)$$

K_{HA}' will in general be a function of concentration, temperature, and pressure, and the numerical value of K_{HA}' will approach K_{HA} in the limit of infinite dilution. Equilibrium constants written like those in Equations (3.7) and (3.8) are *dissociation constants* or *instability constants* of the acid HA. If the reaction is written in the reverse direction to represent association of two ions to yield the protonated acid,

$$H^+ + A^- \rightleftarrows HA \qquad (3.9)$$

then the equilibrium constant is the reciprocal of K_{HA} and is called the *association constant, stability constant,* or *formation constant* of HA.

Hydrochloric Acid. Hydrogen chloride is a diatomic gas which readily dissolves in water. There is strong evidence for the existence of molecular HCl species in concentrated aqueous solution, but most of the HCl molecules dissociate in water according to the equilibrium

$$HCl \rightleftarrows H^+ + Cl^- \qquad (3.10)$$

The apparent equilibrium constant for this dissociation is

$$K_{HCl}' = \frac{(H^+)\,(Cl^-)}{(HCl)} \approx 10^7 \qquad (3.11)$$

BRIAR CLIFF COLLEGE LIBRARY

45315

SIOUX CITY, IOWA

There is ample room for debate regarding the value of K_{HCl}'. Most chemists are agreed that K_{HCl}' is large, and the following discussion is based on the order of magnitude of K_{HCl}', not on its precise value.

A *conservation equation* can be written to express the fact that the total amount of chloride-containing species in solution, expressed in moles per liter, is just the sum of concentrations of all chloride-containing species, each in moles per liter. If [Cl] represents the total moles per liter of HCl put into solution, then

$$[Cl] = (HCl) + (Cl^-) \tag{3.12}$$

The *electroneutrality condition* requires that the number of positive charges in solution must equal the number of negative charges, giving

$$(Cl^-) + (OH^-) = (H^+) \tag{3.13}$$

The qualitative *chemical model* described above for the interaction of the acid HCl and the base H_2O can be summarized in terms of the species present (H_2O, H^+, OH^-, HCl, and Cl^-) and the equilibria involved [reactions (3.1) and (3.10)]. The quantitative *mathematical model* for the same system is composed of Equations (3.3,) (3.11), (3.12), and (3.13). The test to discover if there is correspondence between the models and the actual HCl solution in a beaker is a twofold process. An equation is derived from the mathematical model relating quantities which can be observed experimentally. And an experiment is devised to yield experimental data in the form of numbers which may, or may not, be in accord with the derived mathematical equation.

Equations (3.11) and (3.12) can be combined to give

$$[Cl] = \frac{(H^+)(Cl^-)}{K_{HCl}'} + (Cl^-) = (Cl^-)\left\{\frac{(H^+)}{K_{HCl}'} + 1\right\} \tag{3.14}$$

Equations (3.3) and (3.13) yield

$$(Cl^-) = (H^+) - \frac{K_w'}{(H^+)} \tag{3.15}$$

The quantity (Cl^-) is then eliminated between Equations (3.14) and (3.15) to give

$$[Cl] = \frac{(H^+)^2}{K_{HCl}'} + (H^+) - \frac{K_w'}{K_{HCl}'} - \frac{K_w'}{(H^+)} \tag{3.16}$$

Calculation of points for a dilution curve can be made by assuming values of (H^+) and substituting the assumed values into Equation (3.16). The results of some such calculations are presented in Table 3.2.

The sample calculations reveal some important features of HCl-H_2O equilibria. Since the equilibrium constant is so large, Equation (3.16) can be safely approximated by

$$[Cl] = (H^+) - \frac{K_w'}{(H^+)} \tag{3.17}$$

Table 3.2.   Calculation of Hydrochloric Acid Dilution Curve[a]

$$\frac{(H^+)^2}{K_{HCl}'} \;+\; (H^+) \;-\; \frac{K_w'}{K_{HCl}'} \;-\; \frac{K_w'}{(H^+)} \;=\; [Cl]$$

$10^{-9} + 1.00 \times 10^{-1} - 10^{-21} - 1.00 \times 10^{-13} = 1.00 \times 10^{-1}$
$10^{-11} + 1.00 \times 10^{-2} - 10^{-21} - 1.00 \times 10^{-12} = 1.00 \times 10^{-2}$
$10^{-13} + 1.00 \times 10^{-3} - 10^{-21} - 1.00 \times 10^{-11} = 1.00 \times 10^{-3}$
$10^{-15} + 1.00 \times 10^{-4} - 10^{-21} - 1.00 \times 10^{-10} = 1.00 \times 16^{-4}$
$10^{-17} + 1.00 \times 10^{-5} - 10^{-21} - 1.00 \times 10^{-9} \;= 1.00 \times 10^{-5}$
$10^{-19} + 1.00 \times 10^{-6} - 10^{-21} - 1.00 \times 10^{-8} \;= .99 \times 10^{-6}$
$10^{-21} + 2.00 \times 10^{-7} - 10^{-21} - 5.00 \times 10^{-8} \;= 1.50 \times 10^{-7}$
$10^{-21} + 1.51 \times 10^{-7} - 10^{-21} - 6.62 \times 10^{-8} \;= 8.5 \;\times 10^{-8}$
$10^{-21} + 1.20 \times 10^{-7} - 10^{-21} - 8.33 \times 10^{-8} \;= 3.7 \;\times 10^{-8}$
$10^{-21} + 1.10 \times 10^{-7} - 10^{-21} - 1.00 \times 10^{-7} \;= 1.0 \;\times 10^{-8}$
$10^{-21} + 1.03 \times 10^{-7} - 10^{-21} - 1.00 \times 10^{-7} \;= 3 \;\;\times 10^{-9}$

[a]Only the italicized quantities have been included in the addition of terms to give [Cl].

In fact, for solutions more concentrated than 10^{-6} molar, the equation for the dilution curve is

$$[Cl] = (H^+) \tag{3.18}$$

The two approximate equations (3.17) and (3.18) are plotted together in Figure 3.1. In the most dilute solutions, Equation (3.18) fails to give the chemically-required result that the (H^+) value of an infinitely dilute solution is the same as for pure water. The equations written in terms of molar concentrations would be expected to describe experimental data well at low values of [Cl] when activity coefficients are close to unity and the activity of water is also about unity. A discussion of how activity coefficients do behave in such solutions begins on page 44.

An experiment to test Equations (3.16) through (3.18) would appear to be a titration of a concentrated HCl solution with water, using some method to measure (H^+) as dilution proceeded. Measurement of (H^+) is discussed on pages 41 through 44.

Acetic Acid.   Acetic acid, CH_3-COOH, dissolves in water to produce solutions which contain significant concentrations of both CH_3-COOH and the anion CH_3-COO^-. The fraction $(H^+)^2/K_{HA}'$ will approximate (H^+) during a portion of a dilution titration, and the fraction cannot be ignored as it was in the case of hydrochloric acid. The dilution titration results not only depend on the numerical value of K_{HA}', but they also provide a convenient method for the experimental determination of K_{HA}'.

Equilibria comprising this acid-base couple are

$$H_2O \rightleftarrows H^+ + OH^- \tag{3.19}$$

$$CH_3-COOH \rightleftarrows H^+ + CH_3-COO^- \tag{3.20}$$

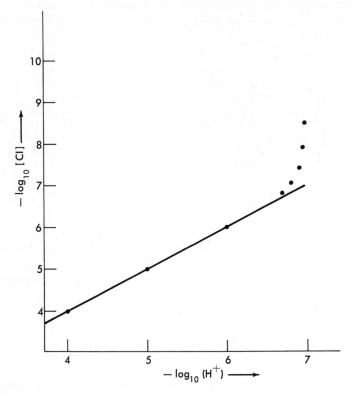

Figure 3.1. Dilution Titration Curve of Hydrochloric Acid, Comparing Approximate Equations 3.17 and 3.18.

There are two acids and two bases in this couple. Both OH^- and CH_3—COO^- can and do act as proton acceptors, and thus are bases. Both H_2O and CH_3—$COOH$ can and do act as proton donors, and hence are acids. Relevant equilibrium constants are the ion product of water and

$$K_{CH_3-COOH'} = \frac{(H^+)\,(CH_3-COO^-)}{(CH_3-COOH)} \qquad (3.21)$$

Conservation equation and electroneutrality equation are

$$[Ac] = (CH_3-COOH) + (CH_3-COO^-) \qquad (3.22)$$

$$(OH^-) + (CH_3-COO^-) = (H^+) \qquad (3.23)$$

where [Ac] denotes the total of all acetic acid species in solution. The chemical model is a statement of the species present (H_2O, H^+, OH^-, CH_3—$COOH$, and CH_3—COO^-) and of the equilibria involved [reactions (3.19) and (3.20)]. The mathematical model consists of Equations (3.3), (3.21), (3.22), and (3.23).

Combination of the two equilibrium constant expressions, the conservation equation, and the electroneutrality equation results in

$$[Ac] = \frac{(H^+)^2}{K_{CH_3-COOH}'} + (H^+) - \frac{K_w'}{K_{CH_3-COOH}'} - \frac{K_w'}{(H^+)} \qquad (3.24)$$

Equation (3.24) is plotted in Figure 3.2. Calculations were made by assuming a value for (H^+) and then computing a value for $[Ac]$. Since the plot

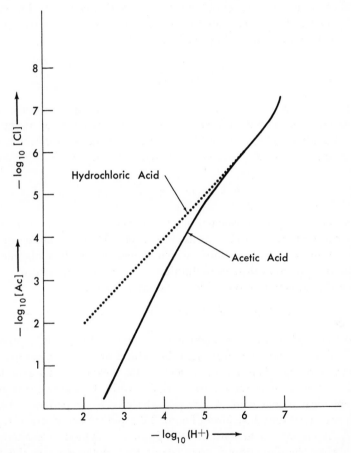

Figure 3.2. Dilution Titration Curves of Acetic Acid and Hydrochloric Acid Compared.

was made in terms of $\log_{10} (H^+)$, it was a matter of substantial saving of mental effort to pick the assumed values of (H^+) to be integral powers of 10 insofar as possible. The value $K_{CH_3-COOH}' = 1.75 \times 10^{-5}$ was used for the calculations.

The question "What amount of acetic acid must be dissolved in a liter of water to produce a certain value of (H^+)?" is readily answered by Equation

(3.24). The plot in Figure 3.2 provides the answer to the question "What is the value of (H^+) in a solution resulting from the mixing of specified amounts of acetic acid and water?"

Comparison of numerical calculations for the graphs in Figures 3.1 and 3.2 reveals a significant qualitative difference between Equations (3.16) and (3.24): never when performing calculations for the HCl dilution curve is it necessary to use the terms containing the acid dissociation constant, whereas for CH_3—COOH the calculation of each value of [Ac] requires the use of at least one term containing the dissociation constant. For values of (H^+) equal to or greater than 10^{-5} an error of less than one part in 10,000 results if Equation (3.24) is approximated by

$$[A] = \frac{(H^+)^2}{K_{CH_3-COOH}}, + (H^+) \tag{3.25}$$

The numerical value of the equilibrium constant for a chemical reaction is not known until some experiments have been performed for its determination. Equation (3.25) can readily be rearranged into a form well suited for the determination of K_{CH_3-COOH}'. Solving for the equilibrium constant,

$$K_{CH_3-COOH}' = \frac{(H^+)^2}{[Ac] - (H^+)} \tag{3.26}$$

Equation (3.26) permits calculation of an experimental value of the equilibrium constant from a single measurement of (H^+) in a solution of known [Ac]. A more reliable method, which makes use of data obtained from solutions of different degrees of dilution, employs the equation obtained by taking the logarithm of both sides of Equation (3.26),

$$2 \log_{10}(H^+) = \log_{10}\{[Ac] - (H^+)\} + \log_{10}K_{CH_3-COOH}' \tag{3.27}$$

This is an equation for a straight line. A plot of $2 \log_{10} (H^+)$ versus $\log_{10} \{[Ac] - (H^+)\}$ should be a straight line with a slope of unity and an intercept equal to $\log_{10} K_{CH_3-COOH}'$. If such a plot of experimental data does not yield a straight line, something is faulty with the experiments or with the chemical model used to interpret the data — or perhaps with both.

Hypothetical data taken from Figure 3.2 is plotted according to Equation (3.27) in Figure 3.3 to illustrate the graphical method of evaluating the equilibrium constant. Solid areas about each point indicate the area in which a point could lie if there were an uncertainty of 0.1 in the experimental value of $\log_{10} (H^+)$. The reliability of this graphical method is enhanced by the fact that the most reliable values of the plotted variables lie closest to the intercept.

Sodium Hydroxide. Sodium hydroxide is an ionic solid substance which dissolves in water to produce the ions Na^+ and OH^-. The chemical model assumed for the reaction of the acid water with the base sodium hy-

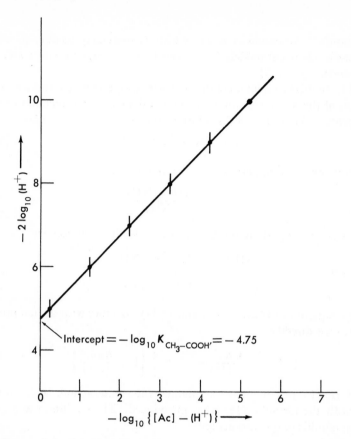

Figure 3.3. Graphical Evaluation of $K_{\text{CH}_3-\text{COOH}}'$ from Dilution Data.

droxide includes no equilibria involving the Na^+ cation. The conservation equation is

$$[\text{Na}] = (\text{Na}^+) \tag{3.28}$$

and the electroneutrality condition is

$$(\text{Na}^+) + (\text{H}^+) = (\text{OH}^-) \tag{3.29}$$

Equations (3.28) and (3.29) can be combined with the ion product of water to give

$$[\text{Na}] = \frac{K_w'}{(\text{H}^+)} - (\text{H}^+) \tag{3.30}$$

There is a different chemical model which will yield this result. Equilibria involving an undissociated NaOH species in solution could have been assumed, and then Equation (3.30) would have resulted for the limiting case of a very large dissociation constant.

Ammonia. Ammonia is a gas which is extremely soluble in water. Two familiar chemical models for the reaction of ammonia with water will be examined.

Model I. In this formulation of the acid-base couple of water and ammonia, formation of the ammonium ion will be considered as the reaction of NH_3 with a proton. Written as a dissociation, this is

$$NH_4^+ \rightleftarrows H^+ + NH_3 \tag{3.31}$$

with a corresponding apparent equilibrium constant

$$K_{NH_4^+}' = \frac{(H^+)\,(NH_3)}{(NH_4^+)} \tag{3.32}$$

The conservation equation and the electroneutrality equation are

$$[NH_3] = (NH_4^+) + (NH_3) \tag{3.33}$$

$$(NH_4^+) + (H^+) = (OH^-) \tag{3.34}$$

Algebraic equations (3.32), (3.33), and (3.34), together with the ion product of water, give directly

$$[NH_3] = \left\{ \frac{K_w'}{(H^+)} - (H^+) \right\} \left\{ 1 + \frac{K_{NH_4^+}'}{(H^+)} \right\} \tag{3.35}$$

Model II. In this model of ammonia-water interaction, an additional species with the formula NH_4OH is introduced. The equilibria and corresponding equilibrium constants are

$$NH_3 + H_2O \rightleftarrows NH_4OH \tag{3.36}$$

$$K_1' = \frac{(NH_4OH)}{(NH_3)} \tag{3.37}$$

$$NH_4OH \rightleftarrows NH_4^+ + OH^- \tag{3.38}$$

$$K_2' = \frac{(NH_4^+)\,(OH^-)}{(NH_4OH)} \tag{3.39}$$

In writing the expression for K_1', no reference to the reactant water is made. The corresponding thermodynamic equilibrium constant is

$$K_1 = \frac{a_{NH_4OH}}{a_{NH_3}\,a_{H_2O}} \tag{3.40}$$

The activity of the solvent water, approximately unity, is assumed constant in writing Equation (3.37). An additional species is included in the conservation equation, which becomes

$$[NH_3] = (NH_3) + (NH_4^+) + (NH_4OH) \tag{3.41}$$

Electroneutrality requires that

$$(H^+) + (NH_4^+) = (OH^-) \qquad (3.42)$$

Combination of the ion product of water with Equations (3.37), (3.39), (3.41), and (3.42) yields

$$[NH_3] = \left\{ \frac{K_w'}{(H^+)} - (H^+) \right\} \left\{ 1 + \frac{K_w'}{(H^+)} \left(\frac{1 + K_1'}{K_2'} \right) \right\} \qquad (3.43)$$

In spite of some different symbols, Equations (3.35) and (3.43) are operationally indistinguishable. They are both of the form

$$[NH_3] = \left\{ \frac{K_w'}{(H^+)} - (H^+) \right\} \left\{ 1 + \frac{const}{(H^+)} \right\} \qquad (3.44)$$

Changes in (H^+) resulting from dilution experiments which are interpreted by Equations (3.35) and (3.43) can give no information about the existence or nonexistence of the species NH_4OH. The experimental data can be interpreted equally well by these two distinct sets of equilibria. The two chemical models are not equivalent in terms of the species postulated, but they are experimentally indistinguishable by such dilution experiments as have been described here.

Logarithmic pH and pK Scales. It was seen in Chapter 2 that use of logarithms facilitated plotting of the silver chloride precipitation titration curve. Logarithmic scales for concentrations, activities, and equilibrium constants are of general utility. An expression like "$\log_{10} (Cl^-)$" takes too much effort to write repeatedly, so a more compact nomenclature was suggested. Sørensen introduced the mathematical operator p into the literature of acid-base chemistry in 1909. The operator p has become generally accepted to mean "take the common logarithm of the quantity following and multiply the result by minus one." Thus

$$p(Cl^-) = -\log_{10}(Cl^-)$$
$$pK_{HA}' = -\log_{10}K_{HA}'$$
$$pH \quad = -\log_{10}H$$

If the value of (Cl^-) is known, there is thus a simple rule for finding $p(Cl^-)$. If K_{HA}' is a well defined quantity, then pK_{HA}' is just as well defined. But what about H and pH?

Hydrogen-Ion Concentration and pH. It would be convenient if experimental techniques were available which made possible an operational definition of pH as

$$pH = -\log_{10}a_{H^+} \qquad (3.45)$$

or

$$pH = -\log_{10}(H^+) \qquad (3.46)$$

Unfortunately, there are no such methods available at present. There is an exceedingly useful instrument called a pH meter which does permit routine and reproducible measurements of this quantity called pH. Readings obtained with a carefully calibrated pH meter define an operational pH scale. This operational pH scale provides an experimental definition of pH.

A pH meter assembly consists of a pH cell connected to a precision potentiometer which measures the emf of the cell. The cell consists of two electrodes dipping into a solution. One electrode responds only very slightly to changes in the composition of the solution and is the reference electrode. The other electrode is electrochemically reversible to hydrogen ions and responds to changes in pH. The difference in response of the two electrodes results in an emf change when the pH of the solution changes. This emf change is measured with the potentiometer, and the emf reading is converted to a reading of pH by an appropriately-calibrated meter scale.

Many different electrode combinations have been used successfully. A simple and sturdy pH cell contains a calomel reference electrode and a glass-membrane electrode. The calomel electrode is composed of mercury in contact with Hg_2Cl_2 which is in turn in contact with a KCl solution. Contact between the KCl solution and the solution on which measurements are being made is by means of a capillary tube or a glass fiber through which KCl solution flows very slowly. Calomel electrodes are available commercially as compact units.

The glass membrane is a thin bulb of pH responsive glass. Inside the bulb is an electrode immersed in a buffered salt solution. The thin glass membrane of the bulb responds to changes in the pH of the medium outside the bulb by exchanging protons at the glass surface. The exact potential of a particular glass electrode immersed in a particluar solution depends on the type of electrode used inside the bulb, the filling solution used inside the bulb, the type of pH responsive glass used for the membrane, and the mechanical properties of the bulb. And of course the potential also depends on the pH of the medium in which the glass electrode is immersed.

An operational definition of pH which has been widely accepted employs the equation[5]

$$pH_{obs} - pH_{std} = \frac{E_{obs} - E_{std}}{2.303\ RT/F} \qquad (3.47)$$

where pH_{std} is a value assigned to a standard buffer solution, E_{std} is the voltage read on a pH meter when the pH cell contains the standard buffer solution, pH_{obs} and E_{obs} are the values of pH and of voltage when the same pH cell contains the solution upon which measurements are to be made, R is the gas constant, and F is the value of the Faraday. This operational definition requires that the meter pH scale be defined by a standardizing procedure in terms of the cell response to some standard buffer solution of defined pH. Standardization is performed before each set of measurements.

[5]For justification of an equation of this form, see Chapter 8.

Then the measurement of pH is made on the set of solutions by converting emf differences into pH differences by multiplying the emf differences by the factor $F/2.303RT$. A properly-calibrated meter scale automatically performs this multiplication by a scaling factor.

It is experimentally an uncomplicated matter to obtain precise and reproducible values for solution pH. But interpretation is not so simple. In fact, there is no satisfactory theoretical meaning which can be attached to experimental pH values. Existence of a liquid-liquid junction between the test solution and the reference electrode filling solution gives rise to a junction potential which is difficult to evaluate. In addition, single ion activities and single ion activity coefficients can be defined only with respect to an arbitrary choice of single ion activity for some reference ion. Thus, although the product $a_{H^+} a_{A^-}$ is a well defined quantity, neither a_{H^+} nor a_{A^-} alone has absolute physical meaning. Single ion activity coefficients can be arbitrarily defined on a conventional activity scale. Guggenheim[6] has suggested that experimental pH is related to (H^+) by an equation of the form

$$pH = -\log_{10} \gamma_? (H^+) \tag{3.48}$$

where $\gamma_?$ is a function of the conventional single ion activity coefficients and is also dependent on various ionic rate processes at the measuring electrodes.

In practice, the pH meter is standardized with a solution to which the National Bureau of Standards (Washington, D.C.) has assigned a value of pH_{std}. Some of the N.B.S. standard buffer solutions are listed in Table 3.3

Table 3.3. NATIONAL BUREAU OF STANDARDS STANDARD pH SOLUTIONS

Composition	Recommended standard pH values (Estimated uncertainty ± 0.005)		
	0°C.	25°C.	55°C.
Potassium tetroxalate (0.05 molal)	1.666	1.679	1.715
Potassium hydrogen tartrate (saturated at 25°C.)	—	3.557	3.554
Potassium acid phthalate (0.05 molal)	4.003	4.008	4.075
Phosphate (0.025 molal KH_2PO_4 and 0.025 molal Na_2HPO_4)	6.984	6.865	6.834
Borax (0.01 molal)	9.464	9.180	8.985
Calcium hydroxide (saturated at 25°C.)	13.423	12.454	11.574

Source: pH standard sample certificates issued by the National Bureau of Standards, U.S. Department of Commerce, Washington, D.C.

along with the pH values which have been assigned to them. The N.B.S. pH scale gives values of pH which are perhaps best regarded as approximately

[6] E. A. Guggenheim, *J. Phys. Chem.* **34,** 1758 (1930).

equal to the quantity "pH" in Equation (3.45), with a_{H^+} a conventional activity. Even though the precise significance of such pH values may be elusive and sometimes obscure, the value of the pH of an aqueous solution is operationally well defined and experimentally easily measured.

Use of Equation (3.26) or (3.27) for determination of the acetic acid apparent dissociation constant requires a knowledge of values of (H^+) for a series of solutions of varying total concentration of acetic acid and acetate. Measurement of the pH values of these solutions yields values not of (H^+) but rather of the more complicated quantity containing an ambiguous activity-coefficient factor. It is current practice in many laboratories to use a *mixed equilibrium constant* which includes factors of concentration for all chemical species except hydrogen ion. The symbol "(H^+)" in this mixed equilibrium constant is not a true concentration but instead is defined by Equation (3.46). This procedure can be thoroughly consistent. There is as much justification for defining a mixed apparent equilibrium as there is for defining an apparent equilibrium constant. In both cases these empirical constants are convenient parameters for analysis and presentation of equilibrium data, and their use can be justified theoretically at low concentrations and at constant ionic strength.[7]

The glass electrode is not specific for H^+. Although effects differ among the various types of commercial electrodes, there is probably always some response to the various other univalent cations. In particular, some response is to be expected to Na^+ at high values of pH, and for certain glass electrodes a significant correction must be made to readings taken at high (Na^+) and low (H^+). Manufacturers of electrodes have recognized this response to a variety of cations, and have experimented with a wide range of membrane glasses. As a result, electrodes have been developed with a low Na^+ error. Other electrodes have been developed with a reasonably specific response to certain cations other than H^+, and these are being used for determinations of such cations as Na^+ and Ag^+. Such an electrode was discussed in Chapter 2.

Reconsideration of NaOH and HCl. Equations (3.16) and (3.30) give (H^+) as a function of solute concentration for aqueous solutions of HCl, a strong acid, and NaOH, a strong base. These equations are simple equations because of the simplicity of the assumed chemical model. It probably comes as no great surprise to discover that neither of these equations describes accurately an actual dilution titration, carried out over the full range of accessible concentrations. Deviations between theory and experiment surely tell something of chemical interest about these solutions, and the interested chemist must set about reconstituting the chemical model so as to make for a closer fit between experiment and predictions of the model. Or alternatively he must redesign the experiments.

[7]Even in very concentrated electrolyte solutions, this procedure can be consistent and useful. Experimental use of the glass electrode to study acid-base equilibria in salt solutions as concentrated as 6 molar $NaClO_4$ and 8 molar LiCl has been reported [D. Rosenthal and J. S. Dwyer, *Anal. Chem.* **35**, 161 (1963)].

There are three reasonably direct ways to bring theory and experiment into better agreement. Since measurement of (H^+) was performed by determination of pH, all problems of pH measurement and interpretation become likely sources of experimental error. This provides one way to rationalize discrepancies between theory and experiment. A second approach is to note that at the higher concentrations the attraction between ions of opposite charge will be altering the environmental conditions about ions by formation of negative-ion atmospheres about cations, and positive-ion atmospheres about anions. As this effect becomes more and more pronounced, activity coefficients of the ions will change and the activity of the solvent water will also change. A quantitative theory can be proposed to deal with these electrostatic effects. A third possibility is to minimize effects due to changing electrostatic environment by designing experiments so as to keep ionic strength (and thus hopefully ionic environment) constant, and then proposing additional equilibria to account for deviations between the predictions of the postulated chemical model and the observed experimental data.

Decisions about which approach to take rest on one's own chemical philosophy and on the pragmatic necessities of a particular chemical problem. Ambiguity of pH measurements can make reasonable an approach in which pH and (H^+) are ignored, and where inquiry is focused on the details of molecular structure in the vicinity of the individual ions. In simple systems, it may be possible to consider interionic attraction effects, ordering of solvent molecules in the vicinity of ions, and the possible existence of additional equilibria in complementary terms. A complete chemical description of a solution must certainly take all effects and all phenomena into account. In practice, chemists working with solutions tend to attack research problems, and in fact to pick research problems, in ways which without much oversimplification place them in three categories, in three schools of research activity.

Interionic Attraction School. Interionic attraction theories attempt to explain properties of electrolyte solutions in terms of deviations from idealized behavior by taking into account the strong electrostatic interactions which exist between charged particles in solution. These theories permit formulation of a continuum of ionic states between the random arrangement of solute particles expected in the absence of attraction and repulsion, and the virtual molecule which is the electrostatically associated ion pair. Theoretical and experimental results are typically presented in terms of activities and activity coefficients. Experiments often used are those which can yield activities, such as electromotive force, conductance, vapor pressure, and osmotic pressure measurements.[8]

Structure School. This group of chemists is concerned with the ordered structure of certain solvents, principally water, and with the ordering and

[8]H. S. Harned and B. B. Owen, *The Physical Chemistry of Electrolytic Solutions*, 3d ed. New York: Reinhold Publishing Corporation, 1958.
R. A. Robinson and R. H. Stokes, *Electrolyte Solutions*, 2d ed. London: Butterworths Scientific Publications Ltd., 1959.

disordering structural changes which occur as results of solution formation. Much use is made of diffraction and spectrophotometric data. Results of this school are typically not presented in activities and equilibrium constants, but rather in the geometrical language of bond angles, bond lengths, and types of molecular symmetry.[9]

Complex-Formation School. This group of solution chemists proceeds as if interpretation of chemistry in solution were conceptually clearest in the language of distinct chemical species. Every effort is made to avoid explicit reference to activity coefficients by experimental use of an approximately constant environment in media of constant ionic strength. Experimental techniques often used are those which can be interpreted by species con-

Table 3.4. ACTIVITY COEFFICIENTS IN AQUEOUS
SODIUM HYDROXIDE SOLUTIONS AT 25°C.

Molality	$\gamma_{\pm}$	Molality	$\gamma_{\pm}$
0.1	0.764	4.5	0.982
0.2	0.725	5.0	1.074
0.3	0.706	5.5	1.178
0.4	0.695	6.0	1.296
0.5	0.688	7.0	1.599
0.6	0.683	8.0	2.00
0.7	0.680	9.0	2.54
0.8	0.677	10	3.22
0.9	0.676	11	4.09
1.0	0.677	12	5.18
1.2	0.679	13	6.48
1.4	0.684	14	8.02
1.6	0.690	15	9.71
1.8	0.698	16	11.55
2.0	0.707	17	13.43
2.5	0.741	18	15.37
3.0	0.782	19	17.33
3.5	0.833	20	19.28
4.0	0.901		

Source: R. A. Robinson and R. H. Stokes, *Electrolyte Solutions*, 2d ed. London: Butterworths Scientific Publications Ltd., 1959, pp. 492, 504. Used by permission.

centrations, particularly absorption spectrophotometry, magnetic resonance, and direct chemical analysis. Formulation of chemical models makes use of two conditions which apply directly to species concentrations: electro-

[9]J. L. Kavanau, *Water and Solute-Water Interactions.* San Francisco: Holden-Day, Inc., 1964.
M. J. Sienko and R. A. Plane, *Physical Inorganic Chemistry.* New York: W. A. Benjamin, Inc., 1963, chap. 4.
K. J. Mysels, *J. Am. Chem., Soc.* **86,** 3503 (1964).

Table 3.5. ACTIVITIES OF WATER IN AQUEOUS SODIUM HYDROXIDE SOLUTIONS AT 25°C.

Molality of NaOH	a_{H_2O}
1.465	0.95
2.726	0.90
3.840	0.85
4.798	0.80
5.710	0.75
6.565	0.70
7.384	0.65
8.183	0.60
8.974	0.55
9.792	0.50
10.64	0.45
11.54	0.40
12.53	0.35
13.63	0.30
14.96	0.25
16.67	0.20
19.10	0.15
23.05	0.10

Source: R. A. Robinson and R. H. Stokes, *Electrolyte Solutions*, 2d ed. London: Butterworths Scientific Publications Ltd., 1959, p. 510. Used by permission.

Table 3.6. ACTIVITY COEFFICIENTS IN AQUEOUS HYDROCHLORIC ACID SOLUTIONS AT 25°C.

Molality	$\gamma_\pm$	Molality	$\gamma_\pm$
0.0005	0.975	0.9	0.795
0.001	0.965	1	0.809
0.002	0.952	2	1.009
0.005	0.928	3	1.316
0.01	0.904	4	1.762
0.02	0.875	5	2.38
0.05	0.830	6	3.22
0.1	0.796	7	4.37
0.2	0.767	8	5.90
0.3	0.756	9	7.94
0.4	0.755	10	10.44
0.5	0.757	12	17.25
0.6	0.763	14	27.3
0.7	0.772	16	42.4
0.8	0.783		

Source: G. N. Lewis and M. Randall, *Thermodynamics*, 2d ed., revised by K. S. Pitzer and L. Brewer. New York: McGraw-Hill Book Company, Inc., 1961, p. 317. Used by permission.

neutrality and mass conservation. Results are usually presented in terms of apparent equilibrium constants.

Tables 3.4, 3.5, and 3.6 present data selected to show that the simplest chemical models will not suffice for complete interpretation of experimental data for HCl and NaOH solutions. Since the mean activity coefficients are far from constant, interpretation of the ion product of water and of pH measurements will be ambiguous. The activity of water is clearly not unity at high electrolyte concentrations. A constant value of K_w' requires constant values of a_{H_2O}, y_{H^+}, and y_{OH^-}. Interionic attraction theories provide theoretical interpretation for activity coefficient values at low concentrations.

A Look Ahead. The remainder of this book places great emphasis on distinct chemical species with constant properties in solutions at constant temperature, pressure, and ionic strength. There is consequently very little discussion of the important results of interionic attraction theories, which owe their power to variability of species identity, a change in properties as average distance between charged species is varied. There is much more emphasis placed on solutes than on the solvent, and the experiments discussed are in many cases designed to find out about the chemistry of the solutes without very much explicit regard for the particular properties of the solvent. Most of the derivations in this book depend for their validity on the existence of experimental situations in which concentrations of reactants can be varied without significantly altering values of the apparent equilibrium constants. A belief in at least approximate validity of the ionic strength principle pervades the entire book.

For each of the derivations in this book, the mathematical consequences of a particular chemical model are expressed in terms of equilibrium constants, an electroneutrality equation, and a set of conservation equations. Each thermodynamic equilibrium constant can be rigorously written in terms of activities, and the electroneutrality and conservation equations can be rigorously written in terms of concentrations. Neither activity nor concentration is a more fundamental quantity for these derivations. By defining an apparent equilibrium constant, and by assuming this constant to have a constant value at constant ionic strength, an approximation is made which permits study, analysis, and quantitative description of the comparatively simple single solute systems of this chapter, and also of the more complicated chemical solutions discussed in the pages ahead.

Problems

3.1. Write down the electroneutrality equation for a solution of HCl, KCl and NaOH in water. Of Na_2SO_4, Na_3PO_4, and KH_2PO_4 in water.

3.2. What is the pH of a neutral aqueous solution at $0°C$.? At $25°C$.? At $60°C$.?

3.3. The equilibrium constant K_{HA} is sometimes called the acidic dissociation constant of HA, and it gets the symbol K_a. The corresponding basic dissociation constant, K_b, is written in terms of (OH^-) instead of (H^+). Give an equation relating K_a and K_b for a monoprotic acid. What is the relationship between K_a and K_b for a polyprotic acid with n dissociable protons?

3.4. The degree of dissociation, α, of a monoprotic acid is the fraction of the molecules present as dissociated species. Thus $\alpha = (A^-)/[A]$. Write the defining equation for K_{HA} in terms of $[A]$ and α. Plot α vs $[A]$ for chloroacetic acid. The dissociation constant for chloroacetic acid can be taken as equal to 1.35×10^{-3}.

3.5. What concentration of HCN in water yields a pH of 6.0? A pH of 5.0? Assume $pK_{HCN}' = 9.32$.

Suggestions for Experimental Investigation

1. Choose some monoprotic acid. Prepare a concentrated solution of this acid. Beginning with a small portion of this solution in a beaker, perform a titration by adding water from a burette. Use a pH meter to determine the pH of the resulting solution after each addition of water. Plot a dilution titration curve, and compare this experimental curve with the predictions made from an appropriate chemical and mathematical model. What explanations can be offered for deviations? What effect would be expected if the pH of the water in the burette is not 7.00? What volume of solution will be in the beaker if 25 ml of an initially 1 molar HCl solution is titrated with water so as to reduce $[Cl]$ to 10^{-6} molar? Is there a better way to design this experiment?

2. Determine an extrapolated K_{HA}' for some weak monoprotic acid by determining dilution titration curves at several values of ionic strength. The values of K_{HA}' obtained at the individual values of ionic strength can then be plotted versus some appropriate function of ionic strength, and a value for K_{HA}' at zero ionic strength (infinite dilution) obtained. Does the specific choice of "inert electrolyte" for maintenance of ionic strength affect the results? To what extent is the extrapolated value of K_{HA}' dependent on the specific function of ionic strength used in the extrapolation plot?

Bibliographical Note

An authoritative monograph on proton-transfer equilibria is E. J. King, *Acid-Base Equilibria*, Topic 15, vol. 4 of *The International Encyclopedia of Physical Chemistry and Chemical Physics* (London: Pergamon Press, 1965). An excellent systematic treatise on acids and bases in solution, which unfortunately employs unconventional nomenclature, is J. E. Ricci, *Hydrogen Ion Concentration* (Princeton: Princeton University Press, 1952).

Further information on the theory and modern practice of pH measurements can be found in: R. G. Bates, *Determination of pH* (New York: John Wiley & Sons, Inc., 1964); A. Albert and E. P. Serjeant, *Ionization Constants of Acids and Bases: A Laboratory Manual* (London: Methuen & Co. Ltd., 1962); G. Mattock, *pH Measurement and Titration* (New York: The Macmillan Company, 1961); and V. Gold, *pH Measurements: Their Theory and Practice* (New York: John Wiley & Sons, Inc., 1956).

The historical development of the pH concept is surveyed by F. Szabadváry, trans. by R. E. Oesper, *J. Chem. Ed.* **41,** 105 (1964).

L. G. Sillén and A. E. Martell, *Stability Constants of Metal-Ion Complexes* (London: The Chemical Society, 1964) summarizes equilibrium constant values reported in the chemical literature up to 1960, with many results also included from the 1961–1963 period. Acid dissociation constants of the various ligands are recorded by including hydrogen ion among the metals as one of the cations with which the ligands associate. Although the compilers do not claim critical evaluation of each result, they have read most papers in the original and have listed experimental conditions with each value. Reference to the original paper, or to an abstract when the paper is in a particularly obscure journal, is given with each reported value. This is a valuable reference book.

G. Kortüm, W. Vogel, and K. Andrussow, *Dissociation Constants of Organic Acids in Aqueous Solution* (London: Butterworths, 1961) is a complete reference to the chemical literature for the chemist in search of a reliable value of an equilibrium constant for an organic acid.

4

Titration of a Monoprotic Acid

Analytical determination of the concentration of an acid in solution is commonly performed by titration of the solution with a standardized solution of a strong base. If experimental conditions are properly arranged, the equivalence point almost exactly coincides with a vivid endpoint detection signal, perhaps the familiar change of color of an acid-base indicator in the solution. Precise endpoint detection is made possible when the characteristically-sigmoid titration curve (a plot of volume of titrant added versus pH) shows a large change of pH when only a fraction of a drop of titrant is added at the equivalence point.

Titration curves can be studied in order to find out about general aspects of the reaction of acids with a strong base in solution. Titration curves can also be studied in detail to reveal characteristics of specific acids and the extent to which the individual chemical nature of a particular acid can affect its titration curve. We will be asking questions about the chemical changes which take place in solution during the course of an acid-base titration.

The least complicated acid is a monoprotic acid, an acid which has only one dissociable proton. Behavior of solutions prepared by mixing together known amounts of water, the acid HA, the salt MA, and the strong base MOH will be examined in detail. It will be assumed that MA and MOH are completely dissociated into the respective ions. The goal is to find an equation which relates (H^+) to the amounts of reagents used to prepare the solutions. A general equation for the reaction in water will be derived, and then it will be shown how the general equation becomes simpler for a variety of special cases. Later there will be an examination of the consequences of having chosen water as the particular solvent.

Equilibria and the associated apparent equilibrium constants which must be considered for a solution prepared from H_2O, HA, MA, and MOH are

$$H_2O \rightleftarrows H^+ + OH^- \qquad K_w' = (H^+)(OH^-) \qquad (4.1)$$

$$HA \rightleftarrows H^+ + A^- \qquad K_{HA}' = \frac{(H^+)(A^-)}{(HA)} \qquad (4.2)$$

A conservation equation can be written to express the fact that the total amount of A-containing species put into solution is equal to the sum of the concentrations of all A-containing species in solution. If [A] represents the total moles per liter of HA and MA put into solution, then the conservation equation is

$$[A] = (HA) + (A^-) \qquad (4.3)$$

A similar conservation equation can be written for the metal cation, giving

$$[M] = (M^+) \qquad (4.4)$$

where [M] is the total moles of MA and MOH put into solution. The electroneutrality condition is

$$(A^-) + (OH^-) = (H^+) + (M^+) \qquad (4.5)$$

Equations (4.1) through (4.5), a set of five simultaneous equations in five unknowns, constitute the mathematical model for this acid-base titration. We seek to eliminate four of these unknowns and thereby obtain a single equation relating the known quantities in [ ]'s to the measurable (H^+). Equations (4.2) and (4.3) can be combined to eliminate (HA), giving

$$[A] = \left\{\frac{(H^+)}{K_{HA}'} + 1\right\}(A^-) \qquad (4.6)$$

Equations (4.4) and (4.5) yield

$$(A^-) = (H^+) - (OH^-) + [M] \qquad (4.7)$$

Upon combining Equations (4.6) and (4.7) and introducing the ion product of water, there results the cubic equation in (H^+),

$$(H^+)^3 + \{[M] + K_{HA}'\}(H^+)^2$$
$$+ \{K_{HA}'[M] - K_{HA}'[A] - K_w'\}(H^+)$$
$$- K_w'K_{HA}' = 0 \qquad (4.8)$$

Equation (4.8) is an equation in three variables, (H^+), [M], and [A]. In a quantitatively-prepared chemical solution, the values of both [M] and [A] are known, and thus the value of (H^+) can be calculated.

Titration Curves. Equation (4.8) is general, permitting calculation of (H^+) in solutions prepared in a variety of ways. For an ordinary titration, a more restricted equation is useful, expressing (H^+) as a function of the volume of MOH solution added to a specific volume of HA solution. If the two solutions contain only the solutes HA and MOH, and if there is no volume change upon mixing reagents, then there exist the relations

$$[A] = \frac{V_{HA} M_{HA}}{V_{HA} + V_{MOH}} \tag{4.9}$$

$$[M] = \frac{V_{MOH} M_{MOH}}{V_{HA} + V_{MOH}} \tag{4.10}$$

where M_{HA} is the molarity of the HA solution, M_{MOH} is the molarity of the MOH solution, V_{MOH} is the volume of MOH solution delivered from the burette at some point in the titration, and V_{HA} is the initial volume of HA in the titration flask. During the course of the titration, only (H^+) and V_{MOH} are variables. Substitution of Equations (4.9) and (4.10) into Equation (4.8) yields

$$(H^+)^3 + \left\{ \frac{V_{MOH} M_{MOH}}{V_{HA} + V_{MOH}} + K_{HA}' \right\} (H^+)^2$$

$$+ \left\{ \frac{K_{HA}' M_{MOH} V_{MOH} - K_{HA}' M_{HA} V_{HA}}{V_{HA} + V_{MOH}} - K_w' \right\} (H^+)$$

$$- K_w' K_{HA}' = 0 \tag{4.11}$$

Regrouping the terms in Equation (4.11) produces the equivalent equation in a form better suited for computation,

$$V_{MOH} = -V_{HA}$$
$$\left\{ \frac{(H^+)^3 + K_{HA}'(H^+)^2 - \{K_w' + K_{HA}' M_{HA}\}(H^+) - K_w' K_{HA}'}{(H^+)^3 + \{K_{HA}' + M_{MOH}\}(H^+)^2 + \{K_{HA}' M_{MOH} - K_w'\}(H^+) - K_w' K_{HA}'} \right\} \tag{4.12}$$

This equation is in a form such that one may compute the volume of base which has been added in a titration, provided that (H^+) is known. Construction of the titration curve proceeds by choosing possible values of (H^+) and substituting them into the equation. The equation is valid only for values of (H^+) within the range accessible in a titration, and if values of (H^+) outside this range are chosen, negative values of V_{MOH} will result. Equation (4.12) is plotted in Figure 4.1 for the titration of 0.100 molar acetic acid with 0.100 molar sodium hydroxide. The initial volume of acid is 25.00 ml, and the equivalence point comes when 25.00 ml of base has been added. The value of the apparent dissociation constant is taken as 1.75×10^{-5}.

In an experiment to determine the shape of a titration curve, an initial volume V_{HA} of HA solution having concentration M_{HA} is titrated with MOH solution of concentration M_{MOH}. After each small addition of MOH solution from a burette, the pH of the resulting solution is determined with a pH meter. The convention will be followed that (H^+) is operationally defined by Equation (3.46). The experimental data forms a set of ordered pairs of numbers, the values of V_{MOH} and pH for each of a series of solutions. The ordered pairs $\{V_{MOH}, pH\}_{exptl}$ are transformed into a set of corresponding pairs $\{V_{MOH}, (H^+)\}_{exptl}$. Equation (4.12) can be used to generate from the

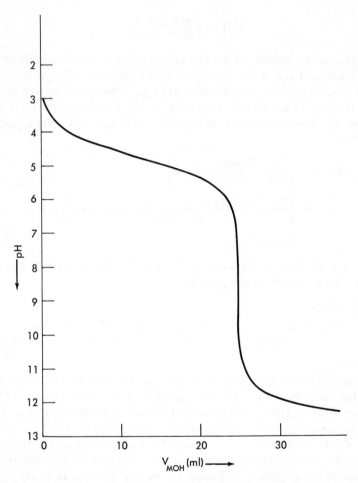

Figure 4.1. Titration Curve of Acetic Acid Calculated from Equation 4.12.

experimental values of (H^+) a set of ordered pairs $\{V_{MOH}, (H^+)\}_{calc}$. The chemical solution being titrated is adequately described by the chemical and mathematical models if there exists a one-to-one correspondence between members of set $\{V_{MOH}, (H^+)\}_{exptl}$ and of set $\{V_{MOH}, (H^+)\}_{calc}$. Experimental uncertainties in the quantities V_{MOH} and (H^+) must be taken into account when deciding if the correspondence is adequate.

Since V_{MOH} is the independent variable and (H^+) is the dependent variable in a titration, for many purposes the preferred solutions to Equations (4.8) and (4.11) are of the forms

$$(H^+) = f([A], [M]) \tag{4.13}$$

$$(H^+) = f(V_{MOH}) \tag{4.14}$$

Such solutions are the next topics of discussion.

Much of the chemistry of a specific acid can be summarized by a graph showing the change of (H^+) or pH during the course of a titration with a strong base. For calculation of points on such a titration curve, Equation (4.12) is in a form which is satisfactory for the entire pH range. But since (4.12) is a ratio of two power series, it is not in a form particularly suited for inspection to learn what is happening in the solution as more and more titrant is added.

Hydrogen-ion concentration in a one molar HCl solution is about 10^{14} times greater than the hydrogen-ion concentration in a one molar NaOH solution. Hence it is not surprising to find that in Equations (4.8), (4.11), and (4.12) some terms contribute significantly only in certain ranges of pH and not in others. Different approximate forms of these equations will be of use in discussing different regions of the titration curve.

High-pH Approximation. In basic solution, a very simple equation describes the titration curve if the hydrogen-ion concentration is low enough to satisfy the inequalities

$$(H^+)^2 \ll K_w' \tag{4.15}$$

$$(H^+) \ll K_{HA}' \tag{4.16}$$

Terms in an algebraic equation may justifiably be disregarded if they are individually small enough compared to other terms to which they are to be added. For example, in the equation

$$\Xi = 1.00 + 1.00 + 0.00101$$

it is justifiable to disregard the third term since the reliability of the first two terms (judged on the basis of the number of significant figures indicated) permits Ξ to be computed with an accuracy of just one part in 100. Examining Equation (4.8) in view of inequalities (4.15) and (4.16), it can be seen by inspection that three terms, $(H^+)^3$, $K_{HA}'(H^+)^2$, and $K_w'(H^+)$, can individually be disregarded with respect to $K_w' K_{HA}'$. There then results the approximate equation

$$[M](H^+)^2 + K_{HA}'[M](H^+) - K_{HA}'[A](H^+) - K_w'K_{HA}' = 0 \tag{4.17}$$

which can be rearranged to give

$$[M]\left\{\frac{(H^+)}{K_{HA}'} + 1\right\} - [A] = \frac{K_w'}{(H^+)} \tag{4.18}$$

Inequality (4.16) requires that $(H^+)/K_{HA}'$ be small compared to unity and the fraction may therefore be neglected in Equation (4.18). This gives the equation desired,

$$[M] - [A] = \frac{K_w'}{(H^+)} \qquad (4.19)$$

$$(H^+) = \frac{K_w'}{[M] - [A]} \qquad (4.20)$$

Introduction of the ion product of water gives

$$[M] - [A] = (OH^-) \qquad (4.21)$$

Change of variables using Equations (4.9) and (4.10) yields

$$(H^+) = \frac{K_w'\{V_{MOH} + V_{HA}\}}{V_{MOH}M_{MOH} - V_{HA}M_{HA}} \qquad (4.22)$$

or, in terms of the volume of titrant added,

$$V_{MOH} = V_{HA} \left\{ \frac{(H^+)M_{HA} + K_w'}{(H^+)M_{MOH} - K_w'} \right\} \qquad (4.23)$$

Function (4.23) is plotted in Figure 4.2 for acetic acid over a wide range of pH values. The concentrations and initial volume of acid assumed for the calculations are the same as used for Figure 4.1.

Equations (4.19) through (4.23) are equivalent equations. Although they obviously fail in neutral and acid solutions, they become better and better approximations to the exact equation as (H^+) becomes smaller and smaller compared to $(K_w')^{1/2}$ and K_{HA}'.

It is significant that Equations (4.19) through (4.23) do not contain K_{HA}' and are therefore independent of the nature of the particular acid in solution. Equations (4.19) and (4.21) say, in effect, that after the value of (H^+) has dropped below a level set by the equilibrium constants, both (H^+) and (OH^-) are determined solely by the excess MOH added beyond equivalence, by the quantity $\{[M] - [A]\}$. In the high-pH region the titration curve will be the same for all monoprotic acids. However, the "high-pH region" begins at somewhat different pH values for different acids, according to inequalities (4.15) and (4.16). If the value of K_{HA}' is too small, it may not be possible to have (H^+) small enough in aqueous solution to satisfy (4.16).

Low-pH Approximation. Next to be considered is the portion of the titration curve in which

$$(H^+)^2 \gg K_w' \qquad (4.24)$$

Again examining Equation (4.8), it is evident that the term $K_w'(H^+)$ can be disregarded with respect to $(H^+)^3$. In addition, the constant term K_w'

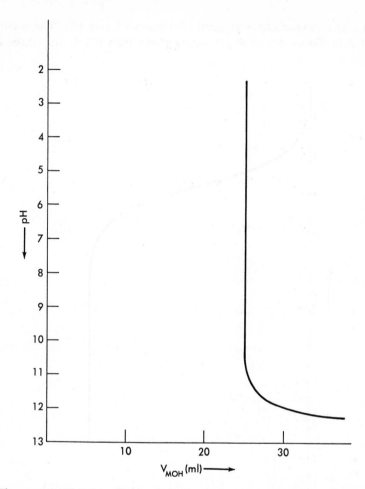

Figure 4.2. Titration Curve of Acetic Acid Calculated from Approximate Equation (4.23).

K_{HA}' can be disregarded with respect to K_{HA}' $(H^+)^2$. After these terms have been stricken, and the equation has been divided by (H^+), there remains

$$(H^+)^2 + \{[M] + K_{HA}'\}(H^+) + K_{HA}'\{[M] - [A]\} = 0 \qquad (4.25)$$

This is now a quadratic equation, and in contrast to the initial cubic equation can be readily solved in explicit form. The quadratic formula gives directly an equation for (H^+).

In terms of volumes of original solution and of added titrant, Equation (4.25) is

$$V_{MOH} = -V_{HA}\left\{\frac{(H^+)^2 + K_{HA}'(H^+) - K_{HA}'M_{HA}}{(H^+)^2 + \{M_{MOH} + K_{HA}'\}(H^+) + K_{HA}'M_{MOH}}\right\} \qquad (4.26)$$

Calculations were made using Equation (4.26) for the titration of acetic acid under the conditions assumed for Figures 4.1 and 4.2. The results are plotted in Figure 4.3. For pH values *greater* than pH 4, only three terms

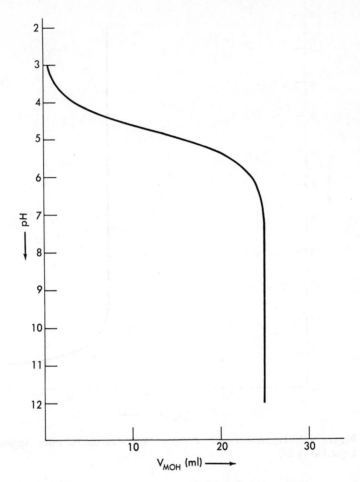

Figure 4.3. Titration Curve of Acetic Acid Calculated from Approximate Equation (4.26).

in the equation make contributions, and so for this particular case, between pH 4 and almost 7, a valid approximate equation for the curve is

$$V_{\text{MOH}} = \frac{V_{\text{HA}} M_{\text{HA}} K_{\text{HA}}'}{(\text{H}^+)\{M_{\text{MOH}} + K_{\text{HA}}'\} + K_{\text{HA}}' M_{\text{MOH}}} \qquad (4.27)$$

Since the numerical value of the apparent equilibrium constant K_{HA}' is much less than M_{MOH} for this special case, it is possible to simplify (4.27) still further. After rearrangement, there results

$$(\text{H}^+) = K_{\text{HA}}' \left\{ \frac{V_{\text{HA}} M_{\text{HA}}}{V_{\text{MOH}} M_{\text{MOH}}} - 1 \right\} \qquad (4.28)$$

An examination of the conditions under which (4.28) is valid is found in problem (4.14).

Figures 4.1, 4.2, and 4.3 collectively are supposed to tell several tales. There are two distinct regions in this titration curve, and the predominant chemical processes are qualitatively different in the two regions. The two regions are individually characterized by two different equilibrium constants. From pH 3 to pH 7, the strong base-weak acid $NaOH-CH_3-COOH$ couple dominates the equilibria, and the most important net process is the removal of a proton from each of the individual acetic acid molecules. When almost 25.00 ml of NaOH solution has been added, the stage is set for a dramatic qualitative change. A drop of titrant, and the solute properties of the solution are no longer those of a particular acid, acetic acid, but rather those of a completely ionized sodium salt, the anion unspecified. The titration curve at higher values of pH is characterized not by K_{HA}' but rather by K_w', and it is the $NaOH-H_2O$ couple which here dominates the equilibria. The three graphs show that the approximate equations give results essentially indistinguishable from the exact equation within certain pH regions, but that outside the regions of validity the approximate equations give numbers which have little chemical meaning, and are absurd. It is important to know exactly what the limitations are for each approximate equation.

Equivalence Point. Analytical determination of the quantity of acid in a solution is commonly made by titrating the solution with a strong base, MOH, of known concentration. The necessary experimental data required for calculation of the acid concentration are the respective volumes of acid and of base needed to bring the solution to the equivalence point. The equivalence point is reached when the number of moles of base added equals the number of moles of the monoprotic acid originally present. If the original solution contained HA as the only solute, and if the titration is performed by addition of a solution containing only MOH and water, then the equivalence point is by definition reached when

$$[M] = [A] \qquad (4.29)$$

An equation will now be derived for the hydrogen-ion concentration at the equivalence point, $(H^+)_e$.

Introduction of the criterion for equivalence and elimination of [M] in Equation (4.8) are readily accomplished by using (4.29), giving

$$(H^+)_e^3 + \{[A] + K_{HA}'\}(H^+)_e^2 = K_w'(H^+)_e + K_w'K_{HA}' \qquad (4.30)$$

or

$$(H^+)_e^2\{(H^+)_e + K_{HA}'\} + [A](H^+)_e^2 = K_w'\{(H^+)_e + K_{HA}'\} \qquad (4.31)$$

Dividing by $\{(H^+)_e + K_{HA}'\}$ and rearranging, there results

$$(H^+)_e^2 = K_w'\left\{\frac{(H^+)_e + K_{HA}'}{(H^+)_e + K_{HA}' + [A]}\right\} \qquad (4.32)$$

Equation (4.32) is still a cubic equation, and it is usually not easy to solve a cubic equation. It is straightforward, however, to obtain solutions of Equation (4.32) for some special cases. The equation simplifies when K_{HA}' is large. It also simplifies when [A] becomes very small. These results can be expressed by equations derived from (4.32), and they are given below:

$$\left. \begin{array}{l} K_{HA}' \gg [A] \\ K_{HA}' \gg (H^+)_e \end{array} \right| \qquad (H^+)_e^2 = K_w' \qquad\qquad (4.33)$$

$$\left. K_{HA}' \gg (H^+)_e \; \right| \qquad (H^+)_e^2 = \frac{K_w' K_{HA}'}{K_{HA}' + [A]} \qquad (4.34)$$

$$\left. \begin{array}{l} [A] \ll K_{HA}' \\ [A] \ll (H^+)_e \end{array} \right| \qquad (H^+)_e^2 = K_w' \qquad\qquad (4.35)$$

For strong acids, Equation (4.33) is a good approximation. For many weak acids (and for all strong acids, too), Equation (4.34) gives good values for $(H^+)_e$. For all acids, Equation (4.35) gives the limiting value of $(H^+)_e$ as [A] approaches zero.

Equation (4.32) can be solved for $(H^+)_e$ by the method of successive approximations for a particular set of K_{HA}' and [A] values. Make a good guess for the value of $(H^+)_e$, substitute this value into the right member of the equation, and then calculate the left member. If the calculated value of $(H^+)_e$ agrees with the first guess, then the problem is solved. If not, a second guess is made, and the procedure is repeated. With judicious choices of successive trial values for $(H^+)_e$, convergence should be rapid. With the aid of a desk calculator, Equation (4.32) can be solved in a few minutes. A reasonable first guess can be made on the basis of Equations (4.33) through (4.35).

The concentration dependence of $(H^+)_e$ can be examined by rewriting Equation (4.30) in the form

$$[A] = \frac{K_w'}{(H^+)_e} + \frac{K_w' K_{HA}'}{(H^+)_e^2} - (H^+)_e - K_{HA}' \qquad (4.36)$$

Equation (4.36) is plotted in Figure 4.4 for four values of K_{HA}'. It is clear that in general $(H^+)_e^2$ is less than K_w' when a weak acid is titrated with a strong base, and that only in the limiting cases represented by Equations (4.33) and (4.35) is the equivalence point the same as the neutrality point. Knowledge of the value of $(H^+)_e$ for the conditions of a particular titration is important when the endpoint indicator is selected for that titration. The theory of such indicators will be discussed later.

A solution of HA titrated to the equivalence point with MOH is identical to a solution of pure MA of the same molarity. Hence Equations (4.30) through (4.36) give the value of (H^+) for certain salt solutions without

added acid or base. Interpreted in this way, Figure 4.4 shows graphically
why it is that the salt of a weak acid and a strong base produces a basic
solution when dissolved in water.

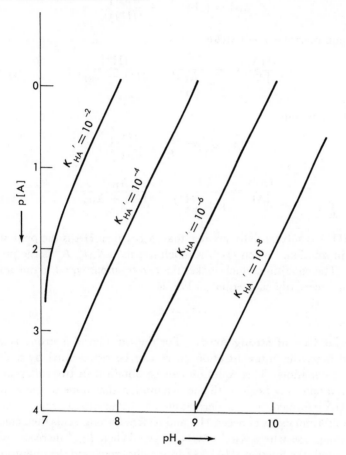

Figure 4.4. Hydrogen-Ion Concentration at the Equivalence Point.

Distribution Fractions. One of the best ways to understand what is
happening in a solution as it is being titrated is to find out how the relative
proportions of the various chemical species are changing. In the case of the
titration of HA with MOH, this means seeing how (H^+) is related to the
two distribution fractions

$$\frac{(HA)}{[A]} \quad \text{and} \quad \frac{(A^-)}{[A]}$$

which together show quantitatively how A is distributed between the two
species HA and A^- in a particular solution. Note that $(HA)/[A]$ is the
fraction of all A containing species present in the solution as HA, and that

$(A^-)/[A]$ is the fraction present as A^-. Equations (4.2) and (4.3) can be readily combined to give

$$[A] = (HA) \left\{ 1 + \frac{K_{HA}'}{(H^+)} \right\} \tag{4.37}$$

whereupon rearrangement yields

$$\frac{(HA)}{[A]} = \frac{1}{1 + \dfrac{K_{HA}'}{(H^+)}} = \frac{(H^+)}{(H^+) + K_{HA}'} \tag{4.38}$$

In the same manner,

$$[A] = (A^-) \left\{ 1 + \frac{(H^+)}{K_{HA}'} \right\} \tag{4.39}$$

$$\frac{(A^-)}{[A]} = \frac{1}{1 + \dfrac{(H^+)}{K_{HA}'}} = \frac{K_{HA}'}{(H^+) + K_{HA}'} \tag{4.40}$$

When (H^+) is substantially greater than K_{HA}', then HA is the predominant species in solution. When (H^+) is much less than K_{HA}', A^- is the principal species. The condition which makes the two fractions equal to one another, and thus necessarily each equal to $1/2$, is

$$(H^+) = K_{HA}'$$

Special Case of Strong Acids. For the titration of a strong acid with a strong base, the entire titration curve can be represented by a simpler, quadratic equation. This equation can be obtained in two different ways. The derivation may begin with the assumption that none of the associated species HA is formed. Or the derivation may begin with a general statement that equilibrium exists between HA and its ions; strong acids then constitute the limiting case where K_{HA}' is very large. When K_{HA}' increases without upper bound, the fraction $(HA)/[A]$ approaches zero, and the quantity (HA) becomes insignificantly small compared to (A^-).

First consider a titration in which the only reaction is

$$H_2O \rightleftarrows H^+ + OH^- \tag{4.41}$$

The equilibrium constant expression, the two conservation equations, and the electroneutrality equation are

$$K_w' = (H^+)(OH^-) \tag{4.42}$$

$$[A] = (A^-) \tag{4.43}$$

$$[M] = (M^+) \tag{4.44}$$

$$(H^+) + (M^+) = (A^-) + (OH^-) \tag{4.45}$$

Equations (4.42), (4.43), and (4.44) can be substituted into Equation (4.45) to give

$$(H^+)^2 + \{[M] - [A]\}(H^+) - K_w' = 0 \qquad (4.46)$$

An identical equation is obtained by examining Equation (4.8) in the limit where K_{HA}' increases without upper bound. To do this, each term in Equation (4.8) is divided by K_{HA}', giving

$$\frac{(H^+)^3}{K_{HA}'} + \left\{\frac{[M]}{K_{HA}'} + 1\right\}(H^+)^2 + \left\{[M] - [A] - \frac{K_w'}{K_{HA}'}\right\}(H^+) - K_w' = 0$$

$$(4.47)$$

As the value of K_{HA}' is increased, $1/K_{HA}'$ becomes smaller, certain terms become insignificantly small compared to others to which they are added, and there results an equation for the entire titration curve,

$$\lim_{K_{HA}' \to \infty} \Big| \quad (H^+)^2 + \{[M] - [A]\}(H^+) - K_w' = 0 \qquad (4.48)$$

It is instructive to examine just how large K_{HA}' must be in order that all terms containing K_{HA}' disappear. The following inequalities are sufficient:

$$\frac{(H^+)^3}{K_{HA}'} \ll (H^+)^2 \qquad (4.49)$$

$$\frac{[M]}{K_{HA}'} \ll 1 \qquad (4.50$$

$$\frac{K_w'(H^+)}{K_{HA}'} \ll K_w' \qquad (4.51)$$

Inequalities (4.49) and (4.51) are equivalent, and can be replaced by

$$(H^+) \ll K_{HA}' \qquad (4.52)$$

An acid will behave in a titration like a strong acid if the two concentrations (H^+) and $[M]$ are always much less than K_{HA}'. This condition can be met in two ways: the concentrations can be low, or the apparent equilibrium constant can be high. For a particular acid, only the concentrations are under the control of the chemist.

Our definition of strong acid requires essentially complete dissociation of the species HA into ions. This can be accomplished at all concentrations if K_{HA}' is sufficiently large. It can also be accomplished for smaller values of the dissociation constant (that is to say, for those acids which have dissociation constants which have smaller values) if concentrations are maintained at a low value. It is an important chemical fact that in water K_{HA}' for some compounds is so low that even at the lowest concentrations these compounds do not behave as strong acids. As an extreme example, CH_4 is not an acid in water simply because no base in water is strong enough to remove one of the covalently-bound protons from carbon, and no amount of dilution can alter this fact. The mathematical equations show this, for it is not possible to decrease both [M] and (H^+) to arbitrarily low values simultaneously. For a particular value of [M], K_w' sets the value of (H^+).

Further simplification is possible for certain pH ranges. In acidic solutions in which $(H^+)^2$ is large compared to K_w', one obtains

$$(H^+)^2 + \{[M] - [A]\}(H^+) = 0 \tag{4.53}$$

or

$$(H^+) = [A] - [M] \tag{4.54}$$

At the equivalence point, $[M] = [A]$, and there results from (4.46) or (4.48)

$$(H^+)_e^2 = K_w' \tag{4.55}$$

In basic solutions in which $(H^+)^2$ is small compared to K_w', Equations (4.19) through (4.23) result.

Equation (4.48) can be solved for (H^+) by means of the quadratic formula to give

$$(H^+) = \frac{[A] - [M]}{2} + \left\{ \frac{\{[M] - [A]\}^2}{4} + K_w' \right\}^{1/2} \tag{4.56}$$

The usual $\pm$ sign is replaced in this case with a $+$ sign, since only positive values of (H^+) are chemically allowed solutions to the equation. This form is particularly useful for making calculations if a desk calculator with automatic square root extraction is available.

Change of variables can be made in the usual way to yield an equation in terms of titrant volume,

$$V_{MOH} = -V_{HA} \left\{ \frac{(H^+)^2 - M_{HA}(H^+) - K_w'}{(H^+)^2 + M_{MOH}(H^+) - K_w'} \right\} \tag{4.57}$$

Determination of K_{HA}' from Titration Data. The numerical value of an equilibrium constant, at a specific set of temperature, pressure, and ionic composition conditions, is known if someone has previously performed appropriate quantitative experiments and then made some appropriate calculations. We are going to look for some reasonably direct ways of determining the value of K_{HA}' from titration data.

Equation (4.11) can be readily solved for K_{HA}', giving

$$K_{HA}' = \frac{-(H^+)^2 - \dfrac{V_{MOH}M_{MOH}(H^+)}{V_{HA} + V_{MOH}} + K_w'}{(H^+) + \dfrac{M_{MOH}V_{MOH} - M_{HA}V_{HA}}{V_{HA} + V_{MOH}} - \dfrac{K_w'}{(H^+)}} \tag{4.58}$$

An approximate value of K_w' can be obtained from other types of measurements, and the remaining quantities appearing on the right side of Equation (4.58) are experimentally known quantities obtained directly from the titration experiment. It would seem that Equation (4.58) permits the direct evaluation of K_{HA}' from a single measurement of pH. Indeed it does, sometimes. But there are some pitfalls which must be recognized.

Experimental values of V_{MOH}, V_{HA}, M_{MOH}, M_{HA}, and particularly (H^+) each have associated experimental uncertainties, and consequently each of the quantities in Equation (4.58) should include the appropriate uncertainty. In the limiting case where K_{HA}' increases without upper bound, the denominator of Equation (4.58) approaches zero; that this must be so can be seen by referring to Equation (4.48). Experimentally the denominator approaches zero within experimental error. Now if the errors involved in the measurements are not considered, the number computed for the denominator may be positive, zero, or negative, and thereby strange and chemically unmeaningful values of the equilibrium constant may be obtained. Division by zero is not allowed, in any event, and hence for large values of the equilibrium constant Equation (4.58) is of no use.

It was shown earlier that in the high pH region titration curves are identical for all monoprotic acids if inequalities (4.15) and (4.16) are satisfied, and if the value of K_w' is reasonably independent of the specific ions in solution. Since the basic portions of the titration curves are essentially independent of K_{HA}', it is to be expected that Equation (4.58) will be indeterminate at sufficiently high values of pH. Equation (4.58) does become indeterminate, because again the denominator becomes experimentally indistinguishable from zero. Let us demonstrate this fact.

Inequality (4.15) permits the term (H^+) to be neglected with respect to $K_w'/(H^+)$, leaving the denominator as

$$\frac{M_{MOH}V_{MOH} - M_{HA}V_{HA}}{V_{HA} + V_{MOH}} - \frac{K_w'}{(H^+)} \qquad (4.59)$$

However, in sufficiently basic solutions, the expression in (4.59) is zero as can be seen by rearranging Equation (4.22). The conclusion is therefore that, within the limits of experimental uncertainty, the denominator of Equation (4.58) is zero if the pH is high enough. If the denominator is zero, the value of K_{HA}' is clearly indeterminate.

Equation (4.58) can be used to determine K_{HA}' from a single measurement of pH if the pH region is properly chosen, if the numerical value of K_{HA}' is not too large, and if the chemical model describing HA as a monoprotic acid and both MOH and MA as completely dissociated species is a valid model. Rather than using just a single measurement, better accuracy and greater confidence can be achieved by utilizing several experimental measurements taken over a range of pH values. This is facilitated by taking advantage of graphical methods. For instance, Equation (4.58) can be written as

$$\alpha K_{HA}' + \beta = 0 \qquad (4.60)$$

where

$$\alpha = (H^+) + \frac{M_{MOH}V_{MOH} - M_{HA}V_{HA}}{V_{HA} + V_{MOH}} - \frac{K_w'}{(H^+)} \qquad (4.61)$$

$$\beta = (H^+)^2 + \frac{M_{MOH}V_{MOH}(H^+)}{V_{HA} + V_{MOH}} - K_w' \qquad (4.62)$$

At each value of V_{MOH}, the value of pH is measured and the corresponding value of (H$^+$) is computed. Using the defining relations (4.61) and (4.62), a value of α and a paired value of β are calculated. A series of experimental measurements of V_{MOH} and of the corresponding pH values thus generates a set of ordered pairs [α,β]. A plot of α vs β should yield a straight line with intercept at the origin and slope equal to K_{HA}'. Even though experimental points are evenly spaced according to volumes of titrant added, or according to pH intervals, the points on this plot will not be evenly spaced, and hence certain experimental points will tend to be given greater weight than others when the line is drawn. The points given the greatest weight may or may not be the most reliable ones.

Another way of plotting the data involves the equation

$$\log_{10}|\alpha| = \log_{10}|\beta| - \log_{10}K_{\text{HA}}' \tag{4.63}$$

which is obtained by taking the logarithm of each side of Equation (4.58).

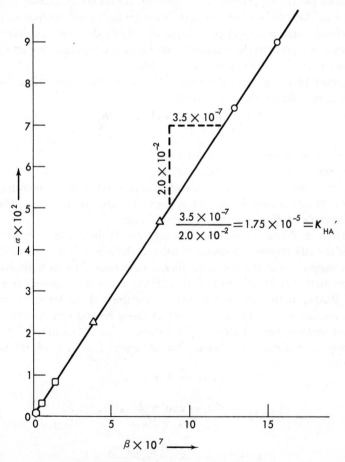

Figure 4.5. Evaluation of K_{HA}' Using Equation (4.60).

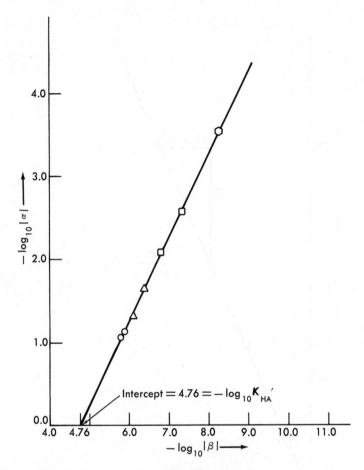

Figure 4.6. Evaluation of K_{HA}' Using Equation (4.63).

The quantities α and β are still defined by Equations (4.61) and (4.62). A plot of $\log_{10}|\alpha|$ vs $\log_{10}|\beta|$ should give a straight line of slope equal to unity and intercept equal to pK_{HA}'. This plot will also weight the various points unevenly, but the weighting will be different than was the case with Equation (4.60).

A third method of plotting the data makes use of the reciprocal equation

$$(1/\alpha)(1/K_{HA}') + 1/\beta = 0 \qquad (4.64)$$

which is the equation for a straight line with $1/\alpha$ plotted versus $1/\beta$. The intercept is zero and the slope is $1/K_{HA}'$. Equations (4.60), (4.63), and (4.64) have been used to plot a set of hypothetical experimental points in Figures 4.5, 4.6, and 4.7. A particular pair $[\alpha,\beta]$ is represented by the same symbol in all three graphs. Compare the manner in which the various points are weighted by the three different graphical methods.

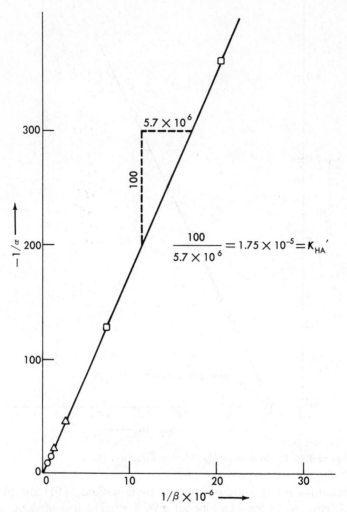

Figure 4.7. Evaluation of K_{HA}' Using Equation (4.64).

The defining equation for the apparent equilibrium constant can be cast in logarithmic form as

$$\log_{10} K_{HA}' - \log_{10}(H^+) = \log_{10}\{(A^-)/(HA)\} \qquad (4.65)$$

The operational definition of (H^+) and the mathematical definition of the operator p transform Equation (4.65) into

$$-pK_{HA}' + pH = \log_{10}\{(A^-)/(HA)\} \qquad (4.66)$$

During the titration of a monoprotic acid, the pH value of the solution will be equal numerically to the pK_{HA}' of the acid when the concentrations of associated acid and dissociated anion are equal. The criterion of equal concentrations of these two species is the *microscopic definition of half-equivalence point*. A *macroscopic half-equivalence point* is often defined as the point at which a volume of base has been added which is equal to half that volume required for reaching the equivalence point.

Microscopic and macroscopic half-equivalence points are not necessarily identical. Insofar as they are the same within the limits of experimental error, the pH value at the macroscopic half-equivalence point provides the datum for a convenient determination of K_{HA}'. Let us examine Equation (4.11) for the case in which $K_{HA}' = (H^+)$, or $pK_{HA}' = pH$. This is the microscopic half-equivalence point. There results

$$\{K_{HA}'\}^3 + \{K_{HA}'\}^2 \left\{ \frac{V_{MOH}M_{MOH}}{V_{MOH} + V_{HA}} + K_{HA}' \right\}$$

$$+ K_{HA}' \left\{ K_{HA}' \left[\frac{V_{MOH}M_{MOH} - V_{HA}M_{HA}}{V_{MOH} + V_{HA}} \right] - K_w' \right\}$$

$$- K_{HA}'K_w' = 0 \qquad (4.67)$$

or

$$V_{MOH}M_{MOH} = \tfrac{1}{2} V_{HA}M_{HA} + \left\{ \frac{K_w' - \{K_{HA}'\}^2}{K_{HA}'} \right\} \{V_{MOH} + V_{HA}\} \qquad (4.68)$$

or

$$\frac{V_{MOH}M_{MOH}}{V_{MOH} + V_{HA}} = \frac{\tfrac{1}{2}V_{HA}M_{HA}}{V_{MOH} + V_{HA}} + \frac{K_w' - \{K_{HA}'\}^2}{K_{HA}'} \qquad (4.69)$$

For the special instance in which $pK_{HA}' = \tfrac{1}{2}pK_w'$, the microscopic and macroscopic definitions are equivalent, since Equation (4.69) then becomes

$$\frac{V_{MOH}M_{MOH}}{V_{MOH} + V_{HA}} = \frac{\tfrac{1}{2}V_{HA}M_{HA}}{V_{MOH} + V_{HA}} = [M] = \frac{1}{2}[A] \qquad (4.70)$$

In this instance, the half equivalence method may be used without approximation.

It is of interest to examine how much error is introduced when the half equivalence method is used for determinations of equilibrium constants not equal to $\{K_w'\}^{1/2}$. Rearrangement of Equation (4.69) gives

$$\frac{V_{MOH}M_{MOH} - \tfrac{1}{2}V_{HA}M_{HA}}{V_{MOH} + V_{HA}} = \frac{K_w' - \{K_{HA}'\}^2}{K_{HA}'} \qquad (4.71)$$

and the right hand member of this equation gives the concentration difference between the macroscopic and microscopic half equivalence points in moles per liter. In general, $pK_{HA}' = pH$ at a value of $\{V_{MOH}M_{MOH}\}/\{V_{MOH} + V_{HA}\}$ which differs from the macroscopic half-equivalence point value by the amount $[K_w' - \{K_{HA}'\}^2]/K_{HA}'$. The experimenter need not be concerned if this error is smaller than the experimental error in determining the macroscopic half-equivalence point. As a rough rule of thumb, the half-equivalence method is useful in the range of pK_{HA}' from 4 to 10 if concentrations of acid and base are of the order of 10^{-1} molar. Although absolute error is independent of solute concentration, the relative error is inversely proportional to solute concentration. Since it is the relative error in the concentration of the macroscopic half-equivalence point which determines the uncertainty in K_{HA}', the method becomes less accurate at lower concentrations.

Buffer Effect. During the course of a titration, a pH range may be encountered in which pH changes very slowly as MOH solution is added. This is then a range of high *buffer capacity*, and the solution is said to be a good buffer in this range. Such a solution effectively resists changes in pH when small quantities of either acid or base are added. Near the equiv-

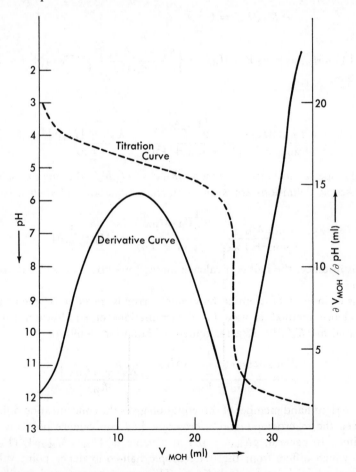

Figure 4.8. Buffer Effect in an Acetic Acid Titration.

alence point, a large change in pH may occur as the result of but a small addition of MOH; buffering is then poor and the buffer capacity is low.

The rate of change of (H^+) as a function of V_{MOH} may be found by differentiating an appropriate function with respect to (H^+). The case of a monoprotic acid being titrated with a strong base can be examined by differentiating Equation (4.12), with the result

$$-\left(\frac{\partial V_{MOH}}{\partial (H^+)}\right)_{V_{HA}, M's}$$

$$= \frac{3(H^+)^2\{V_{MOH} + V_{HA}\} + 2(H^+)\{V_{MOH}[K_{HA}' + M_{MOH}] + V_{HA}K_{HA}'\} + V_{MOH}M_{MOH}K_{HA}' - V_{HA}M_{HA}K_{HA}' - V_{MOH}K_w' - V_{HA}K_w'}{(H^+)^3 + (H^+)^2\{K_{HA}' + M_{MOH}\} + (H^+)\{K_{HA}'M_{MOH} - K_w'\} - K_w'K_{HA}'}$$

$$(4.72)$$

The subscripts following the partial derivative indicate the variables held constant during differentiation. Equation (4.72) is not very manageable, and it is best to use it to perform numerical calculations, plot the results, and look at the graph. Such a graph is presented in Figure 4.8. Some explanation is needed of the process of getting from Equation (4.72) to Figure 4.8.

The quantities V_{MOH} and (H^+) in Equation (4.72) are not independent, and it is necessary to use the appropriate pair of (H^+) and V_{MOH} values for each calculation of the derivative. These pairs can be read directly from the titration curve, and so the first task is to calculate a titration curve, in this case for the titration of 0.100 molar acetic acid with 0.100 molar sodium hydroxide. Each pair $[(H^+), V_{MOH}]$ yields a value for $\partial V_{MOH}/\partial(H^+)$, and the calculated values range from 10^3 to over 10^{13}. Since these numbers cannot be readily plotted on a piece of graph paper of reasonable size, it is convenient to use the relationships

$$\frac{d\ln x}{dy} = \frac{1}{x}\frac{dx}{dy}$$

$$\ln x = 2.303 \log_{10}x$$

to give

$$2.303(H^+)\frac{\partial V_{MOH}}{\partial(H^+)} = -\frac{\partial V_{MOH}}{\partial pH} \qquad (4.73)$$

The new derivative $\partial V_{MOH}/\partial pH$ takes on values between zero and 20 throughout most of the titration curve, and this is the function plotted in Figure 4.8.

Is $\partial V_{MOH}/\partial pH$ the quantity which should be called "buffer capacity?" It has at least some of the desired properties. This derivative function has a sharp minimum at the equivalence point where buffer capacity must pass through a minimum. It has a maximum in the intermediate region of the titration where substantial fractions of total A are present both as HA and as A⁻, and where addition of a few drops of NaOH solution does not cause significant qualitative changes in the composition of the resulting solution. Furthermore, the derivative has a low value at the beginning of the titration where small additions of NaOH convert an essentially undissociated HA solution into a mixture of HA and A⁻, and thus where buffering might be expected to be poor. At high values of V_{MOH} the derivative gets quite large, and in fact increases without upper bound as V_{MOH} gets larger and larger. Chemically, this fact correctly means that a drop of NaOH solution added to many liters of an identical NaOH solution will have no measurable effect on the pH of the solution. The buffer capacity of a solution is dependent on its total volume.

This definition of buffer capacity suffers from the fact that, although it is supposed to be a property of a particular solution, it is so defined as to depend also on the concentration of the solution being added to it. And, although it may seem reasonable that the effect of adding 0.100 molar HCl to the solution would be described by the same derivative with sign changed, we have not included this possibility in the derivation.

In spite of some legitimate objections, we shall use the above derivative as the definition of buffer capacity. It should be realized when reading in the chemical literature that other definitions are sometimes used. Another quantity, less closely related to the experimental titration curve, but free of the dependence on the concentration of added acid or base, is the *buffer index*.

Buffer Index. A more general case of buffer effect will now be considered. The derivation will not be restricted to a titration, and the equations will in fact be simpler because explicit reference to the manner in which the solution is prepared will be eliminated. The pH range will be extended by permitting the addition of either strong acid or strong base, in this case either HCl or NaOH.

The model for this derivation includes the species HA, A⁻, H⁺, OH⁻, Na⁺, Cl⁻, and H_2O, and the conservation equations, equilibria, equilibrium constants, and electroneutrality equation as follows:

$$[A] = (A^-) + (HA) \tag{4.74}$$

$$[Na] = (Na^+) \tag{4.75}$$

$$[Cl] = (Cl^-) \tag{4.76}$$

$$HA \rightleftarrows H^+ + A^- \qquad K_{HA}' = \frac{(H^+)(A^-)}{(HA)} \tag{4.77}$$

$$H_2O \rightleftarrows H^+ + OH^- \qquad K_w' = (H^+)(OH^-) \tag{4.78}$$

$$(Na^+) + (H^+) = (Cl^-) + (A^-) + (OH^-) \tag{4.79}$$

Combination of Equations (4.74) through (4.79) gives

$$[Na] - [Cl] = \frac{K_w'}{(H^+)} - (H^+) + \frac{K_{HA}'[A]}{K_{HA}' + (H^+)} \tag{4.80}$$

Since the solution can be prepared by mixing HCl, HA, and NaOH (as well as NaCl and NaA if desired), then [Na], [Cl], and [A] are independent variables. It is legitimate to take the partial derivative of one of the quantities in [ ]'s while holding the other two constant. Differentiation gives

$$\left(\frac{\partial[Na]}{\partial(H^+)}\right)_{[Cl],[A]} = -\left(\frac{\partial[Cl]}{\partial(H^+)}\right)_{[Na],[A]} = -\frac{K_w'}{(H^+)^2} - 1 - \frac{[A]K_{HA}'}{\{K_{HA}' + (H^+)\}^2} \tag{4.81}$$

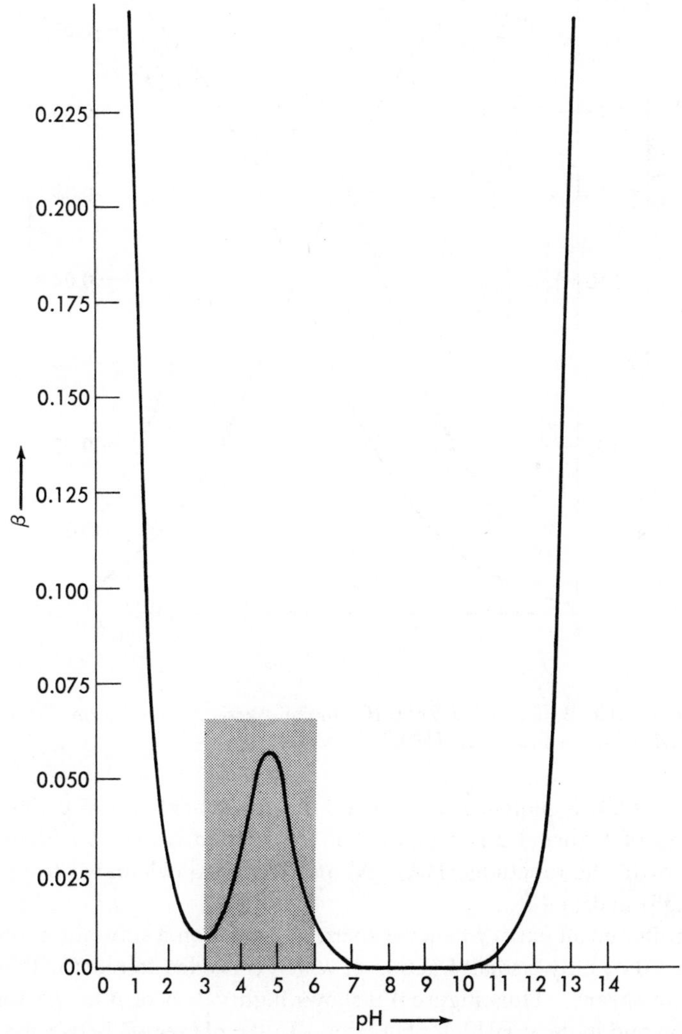

Figure 4.9. Buffer Index β of 0.100 molar Acetic Acid Solution with Added Hydrochloric Acid and Sodium Hydroxide.

Recalling the procedure which gave Equation (4.73), we get

$$-2.303(\text{H}^+)\left(\frac{\partial[\text{Na}]}{\partial(\text{H}^+)}\right)_{[\text{Cl}],[\text{A}]} = \left(\frac{\partial[\text{Na}]}{\partial\text{pH}}\right)_{[\text{Cl}],[\text{A}]} = \beta \qquad (4.82)$$

and this newly-defined β is called the buffer index of the solution. Equations (4.81) and (4.82) together yield

$$\beta = 2.303\left\{\frac{K_w'}{(\text{H}^+)} + (\text{H}^+) + \frac{(\text{H}^+)[\text{A}]K_{\text{HA}}'}{\{K_{\text{HA}}' + (\text{H}^+)\}^2}\right\} \qquad (4.83)$$

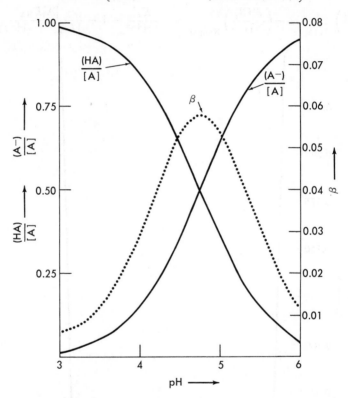

Figure 4.10. Buffer Index β of 0.100 molar Acetic Acid Solution Plotted With the Distribution Fractions (HA)/[A] and (A⁻)/[A].

Equation (4.83) is plotted in Figure 4.9 for acetic acid, [A] = 0.100 molar. A portion of Figure 4.9 is replotted on an expanded scale in Figure 4.10 together with the functions (HA)/[A] and (A⁻)/[A] calculated from Equations (4.38) and (4.40).

The buffer effect exists whenever there is in solution a substantial reservoir of H⁺ or OH⁻, only a small fraction of which is needed to react with a small amount of titrant. Thus Figure 4.9 shows high values of β in the very low pH region and in the very high pH region. In the pH region between 3 and 6, buffering occurs because the reservoir of free protons is supplemented by the bound but potentially available protons on the undissociated HA molecules. In this region, a small increase in pH results in liberation of a significant number of protons. Buffering by HA and A⁻ is best when approximately equal amounts of both species are present. This qualitative discussion can be made quantitative by recalling Equations (4.38), (4.40), and (4.78), and rewriting Equation (4.83) as

$$\beta = 2.303 \left\{ (OH^-) + (H^+) + \frac{(HA)\,(A^-)}{[A]} \right\} \qquad (4.84)$$

For the buffer index to be high, there must be a significant concentration of H⁺, or of OH⁻, or of both HA and A⁻ simultaneously. Conditions assumed for constructing Figure 4.9 were such as to separate almost completely the central peak, due to HA and A⁻ interconversion, from the strong-acid and the strong-base regions. Other values of [A] and K_{HA}' could have been chosen so as to merge this region with one of the extreme-pH regions. Buffer capacity due to HA and A⁻ is concentration dependent, with better buffering occurring at higher concentrations.

Buffer solutions are often used to maintain a constant pH value for a reaction in which important rates or equilibria are appreciably dependent on (H⁺). In choosing a buffer component, it is important to remember that no solute is strictly inert, and that a buffer constituent may enter into the principal reaction under consideration. A buffer solution can be prepared by adding to water weighed amounts of the acid and its corresponding alkali salt. Such a procedure requires prior calculation of the required amounts of acid and salt. Another method involves addition of acid to water, followed by titration of the solution to the desired pH value with the aid of a pH meter. Regardless of how the buffer solution is prepared, it is good laboratory practice to measure the pH of the resulting solution and to make such additions of acid or base as are necessary for a final exact adjustment of pH.

Detection of the Equivalence Point. The ideal condition for a successful analytical titration would be met if the equivalence point were identical to the endpoint. Some method of detecting the pH of equivalence is needed, and the rapid change of pH associated with low buffer capacity near the equivalence point is often utilized. Either a pH meter or an acid-base indicator can be used conveniently. If titration conditions are such as to produce a sharp endpoint in a region of very low buffer capacity near the equivalence point, the chemist's task may be quite simple. The endpoint is then detected by a rapid change in indicator color, or by a dramatic needle deflection on a pH meter, when but a fraction of a drop of titrant is added.

It is evident that, according to Figure 4.8, the equivalence point occurs in a region of extremely low buffer capacity and very near an inflection point in the titration curve, at least for 0.100 molar acetic acid being titrated with 0.100 molar sodium hydroxide. Since detection of the equivalence point in a titration is a critical operation in quantitative volumetric analysis, it is important to investigate the conditions, if any, under which the equivalence point coincides with this inflection point.

We will examine the case of a strong acid being titrated with a strong base, and differentiate Equation (4.57). Equation (4.57) can be rearranged to give

$$V_{\text{MOH}}\{(\text{H}^+)^2 + M_{\text{MOH}}(\text{H}^+) - K_w'\}$$
$$= -V_{\text{HA}}\{(\text{H}^+)^2 - M_{\text{HA}}(\text{H}^+) - K_w'\} \qquad (4.85)$$

Differentiation with respect to (H^+) at constant V_{HA} and M's gives directly

$$\left(\frac{\partial V_{\text{MOH}}}{\partial(\text{H}^+)}\right)_{V_{\text{HA}}, M'\text{s}}\{(\text{H}^+)^2 + M_{\text{MOH}}(\text{H}^+) - K_w'\} + V_{\text{MOH}}\{2(\text{H}^+) + M_{\text{MOH}}\}$$
$$= -V_{\text{HA}}\{2(\text{H}^+) - M_{\text{HA}}\}$$

or

$$\left(\frac{\partial V_{\text{MOH}}}{\partial(\text{H}^+)}\right)_{V_{\text{HA}}, M'\text{s}}\{(\text{H}^+)^2 + M_{\text{MOH}}(\text{H}^+) - K_w'\}$$
$$= -2(\text{H}^+)\{V_{\text{MOH}} + V_{\text{HA}}\} + V_{\text{HA}}M_{\text{HA}} - V_{\text{MOH}}M_{\text{MOH}} \qquad (4.86)$$

The derivative will be a minimum at the inflection point under consideration, and this minimum can be located by taking the second derivative and equating it to zero. We need to find an expression for the second derivative.

Differentiation of Equation (4.86) yields

$$\left(\frac{\partial^2 V_{\text{MOH}}}{\partial(\text{H}^+)^2}\right)_{V_{\text{HA}}, M'\text{s}}\{(\text{H}^+)^2 + M_{\text{MOH}}(\text{H}^+) - K_w'\}$$
$$+ \left(\frac{\partial V_{\text{MOH}}}{\partial(\text{H}^+)}\right)_{V_{\text{HA}}, M'\text{s}}\{2(\text{H}^+) + M_{\text{MOH}}\} = 2\{V_{\text{MOH}} + V_{\text{HA}}\} \qquad (4.87)$$

Equation (4.86) can then be used to eliminate the first derivative, leaving after rearrangement

$$\left(\frac{\partial^2 V_{\text{MOH}}}{\partial(\text{H}^+)^2}\right)_{V_{\text{HA}}, M'\text{s}} = \frac{(\text{H}^+)^2 + (\text{H}^+)\left\{\dfrac{V_{\text{MOH}}M_{\text{MOH}} - V_{\text{HA}}M_{\text{HA}}}{V_{\text{HA}} + V_{\text{MOH}}}\right\} + \dfrac{M_{\text{MOH}}}{2}\left\{\dfrac{V_{\text{MOH}}M_{\text{MOH}} - V_{\text{HA}}M_{\text{HA}}}{V_{\text{HA}} + V_{\text{MOH}}}\right\} + K_w'}{2\{V_{\text{HA}} + V_{\text{MOH}}\}\{(\text{H}^+)^2 + M_{\text{MOH}}(\text{H}^+) - K_w'\}^2}$$
$$(4.88)$$

The position of the inflection point can be found by setting the second derivative equal to zero. This is equivalent to equating to zero the numerator of the right member of Equation (4.88), which gives

$$(\text{H}^+)^2 + (\text{H}^+)\left\{\frac{V_{\text{MOH}}M_{\text{MOH}} - V_{\text{HA}}M_{\text{HA}}}{V_{\text{HA}} + V_{\text{MOH}}}\right\}$$
$$+ \frac{M_{\text{MOH}}}{2}\left\{\frac{V_{\text{MOH}}M_{\text{MOH}} - V_{\text{HA}}M_{\text{HA}}}{V_{\text{HA}} + V_{\text{MOH}}}\right\} + K_w' = 0 \qquad (4.89)$$

The real, positive roots of Equation (4.89) give the concentration of H^+ at the inflection points of the titration curve.

Under what conditions does the equivalence point coincide with an inflection point? At the equivalence point, $[M] = [A]$, and so

$$V_{MOH}M_{MOH} - V_{HA}M_{HA} = 0$$

At the equivalence point, Equation (4.89) must therefore be

$$(H^+)^2 + K_w' = 0 \qquad (4.90)$$

Only real, positive values of (H^+) have chemical meaning, and there are no real, positive roots to Equation (4.90). The conclusion must be that *the equivalence point and the inflection point cannot coincide.*

Equivalence point and inflection point, while not coincident, are experimentally indistinguishable for a strong acid — strong base titration at ordinary concentrations. For experiments in which $M_{MOH} = M_{HA} = M$, straightforward calculation can be made of the quantity $[M]/[A]$ at the inflection point when $(H^+) = (H^+)_e = \{K_w\}^{1/2}$, using Equations (4.89), (4.9), (4.10) and (4.55). Since $[M] = [A]$ at equivalence, $[M]/[A] = 1$ at the inflection point if there is to be coincidence of inflection and equivalence points. This ratio is 0.998 at $M = 10^{-5}$ moles per liter, and is closer to unity at higher concentrations. However, at $M = 6.00 \times 10^{-7}$ moles per liter, $[M]/[A] = 0.500$, meaning that the inflection point in this very dilute solution will occur at the macroscopic half-equivalence point, not at the desired equivalence point. In general, the inflection point in such a titration precedes the equivalence point.[1]

If an inflection in the titration curve can be used to locate the equivalence point within an acceptable range of uncertainty, then endpoint detection is the detection of an inflection point. If the endpoint is sharp, visual inspection of a plot of V_{MOH} vs pH suffices to pinpoint the endpoint near the inflection point. If the endpoint is not very sharp, then it is helpful to estimate the slope of the titration curve at several points on each side of the equivalence point, and then to plot slope (that is, derivative) versus V_{MOH}. The endpoint is more easily recognized in the derivative plot.

Point-by-point plotting of many titration curves, let alone plotting of the derivative curves, is not a task which the typical chemist would like to do for many routine analytical titrations for the sole purpose of endpoint detection. Happily, he does not ordinarily need to. Automatic titrators are available which can be equipped with recorder to plot the titration curve directly on graph paper. As a further refinement, electronic differentiation of the signal from the pH electrodes can be used to plot the first derivative of the titration curve on graph paper, and to stop the titration automatically at an inflection point.

[1]The relationship between equivalence point and inflection point is examined in detail for both strong acid–strong base titrations and for the more complicated case of weak acid–strong base titrations by L. Meites and J. A. Goldman, *Anal. Chim. Acta* **29,** 472 (1963).

For a great many titrations it is a simple matter to select a weak acid endpoint indicator which changes color in the vicinity of the inflection point and thus gives the chemist a visual signal of the approach to and the attainment of the endpoint pH. If an acid HI is to be used in solution as an acid-base indicator, HI and I^- must be of distinctly different colors, and at least one of the colors must be intense enough so that very small quantities of the indicator can be used effectively. Then if a small amount of HI is added to the solution being titrated, a color change will occur as HI is converted to I^-, according to

$$HI \rightleftarrows H^+ + I^- \qquad K_{HI}' = \frac{(H^+)(I^-)}{(HI)} \tag{4.91}$$

Equation (4.91) requires that when $(I^-) = (HI)$, $(H^+) = K_{HI}'$. If the respective colors of HI and of I^- in solution appear about equally intense to the chemist's eye, a color change will be observed when (H^+) changes from more than K_{HI}' to less than K_{HI}'. An indicator will be suitable for a given titration if K_{HI}' is approximately equal to the value of (H^+) at the inflection point.

The observed color change will begin before $(H^+) = K_{HI}'$ and will continue afterwards. It is an accepted rule of thumb that most indicators take a range of almost two pH units for complete color change. The width of the effective transition range depends on the colors involved, the concentration of indicator, the illumination conditions under which the titration is being performed, and most variable of all, the sensitivity of the eye of the observer. When the actual range of transition is critical, this range should be determined by the chemist who will be performing the titration. Table 4.1 presents some common colored compounds which can be used as acid-base indicators and gives approximate pH values which bracket the transition region for each indicator.

A titration which uses a colored indicator for endpoint detection yields only two numbers: the quantity of acid and the volume of standardized base which together produced a solution having the characteristics of the endpoint. For many a routine and well understood analysis performed under standardized conditions, these two numbers are sufficient data, and indeed additional information would not only be unneeded but also probably unwanted. When the reaction is less well controlled, when conditions have been changed, or when a variety of ill defined variables are involved, an analysis of a plotted titration curve is desirable.

Phillips[2] points out that endpoint detection methods involving perception of odor and of taste have been investigated for some titrations. He reports an ingenious endpoint method based on the slipperiness of sodium hydroxide solutions, and suggests an "explosometric endpoint," which might be detected either by sound or by the occasional destruction of the titration vessel.

A variety of sources of experimental error must be considered in evaluation

[2]J. P. Phillips, *J. Chem. Ed.* **35**, 35 (1958).

Table 4.1. TRANSITION RANGES OF SOME COMMON ACID-BASE INDICATORS

Indicator	Visual transition range
Cresol red	pH 0.2 (red) to pH 1.8 (yellow) pH 7.2 (yellow) to pH 8.8 (red)
Methyl violet	pH 0.2 (colorless) to pH 1.8 (blue) pH 2.0 (blue) to pH 3.2 (violet)
Metacresol purple	pH 1.2 (red) to pH 2.8 (yellow) pH 7.6 (yellow) to pH 9.2 (purple)
Thymol blue	pH 1.2 (red) to pH 2.8 (yellow) pH 8.0 (yellow) to pH 9.6 (blue)
Bromphenol blue	pH 3.0 (yellow) to pH 4.6 (blue)
Bromcresol green	pH 3.8 (yellow) to pH 5.4 (blue)
Methyl red	pH 4.4 (red) to pH 6.0 (yellow)
Methyl purple	pH 4.8 (purple) to pH 5.4 (green)
Bromcresol purple	pH 5.2 (yellow) to pH 6.8 (purple)
Chlorphenol red	pH 5.2 (yellow) to pH 6.8 (red)
Bromthymol blue	pH 6.0 (yellow) to pH 7.6 (blue)
Phenol red	pH 6.8 (yellow) to pH 8.4 (red)
o-Cresolphthalein	pH 8.2 (colorless) to pH 9.8 (red)
Phenolphthalein	pH 8.6 (colorless) to pH 10.2 (red)
Alizarin yellow GG	pH 10.1 (yellow) to pH 12.1 (lilac)
Sulfo orange	pH 11.0 (yellow) to pH 12.6 (orange)

Reprinted from the *Fisher Chemical Index 64-C* with permission of the copyright holder, Fisher Scientific Company.

of titration results. The differences among equivalence, inflection point, and endpoint may be significant in numerical terms. If the endpoint is not sharp, uncertainty in locating the endpoint signal results. Addition of a weak acid HI as an indicator means that both HI and HA are being titrated, although at the endpoint not all of HI need necessarily have been converted to I^-. If the value of [I] needed to produce an adequate color change is significant compared to [A], then a correction must be made, most easily by performing a blank titration or control titration in which the amount of titrant needed to produce a color change is determined in the absence of HA. Other sources of error include uncertainties in reading the burette, error in the concentration of MOH, and sampling errors involving the amount of HA originally added.

Water as a Leveling Solvent. If the value of K_{HA}' is very large, or if it is very small, then the titration curve which is experimentally observed is insensitive to the actual numerical value of the equilibrium constant. This effect is called the *leveling effect of water*. Thus very strong acids and very weak acids lose their individual distinctive characteristics in water and become simply strong acids and inert solutes, at least insofar as titration behavior is concerned. The leveling effect is a consequence of the participation of water in these proton transfer equilibria, establishing lower limits to both (H^+) and (OH^-) in aqueous solution. These lower limits are set by the value of K_w' and by the solubilities of acids and bases. In practice, then, the lowest attainable value of (H^+) is set by the highest value of (OH^-) which can be achieved, and the highest value of (OH^-) is set in turn by the solubilities of the available strong bases.

Titration curves of all monoprotic acids lie between two limiting curves, the curves for two extreme cases. These extreme curves are limiting forms of Equation (4.8) when K_{HA}' approaches zero and when K_{HA}' increases without upper bound. The limiting equations are

$$\lim_{K_{HA}' \to \infty} \left| (H^+)^2 + \{[M] - [A]\}(H^+) - K_w' = 0 \right. \tag{4.92}$$

$$\lim_{K_{HA}' \to 0} \left| (H^+)^2 + [M](H^+) - K_w' = 0 \right. \tag{4.93}$$

The apparent dissociation constant of the acid appears in neither equation. Equation (4.92) is the equation for a strong acid. Equation (4.93) differs from the preceding equation only in that $[A] = 0$, and thus the limiting equation for very small K_{HA}' turns out to be the titration curve for water containing either an inert solute, or no solute at all.

Problems

4.1. What is the pH at the equivalence point in a titration of 0.1 molar acetic acid with 0.1 molar sodium hydroxide? Of 0.0001 molar acetic acid with 0.0001 molar sodium hydroxide?

4.2. Derive an equation for the pH at the equivalence point when a weak base is titrated with a strong acid. When a weak base is titrated with a weak acid.

4.3. What is the pH of a solution of 0.1 molar acetic acid? Of 0.1 molar sodium acetate? Of 0.001 molar acetic acid?

4.4. Obtain an equation for the titration curve of a weak base being titrated with a strong acid, and compare the result with the analogous strong base–weak acid equation.

4.5. Calculate the concentrations of all chemical species in a solution prepared by dissolving 0.01 mole of sodium cyanide in enough water to make a liter of solution. There are six species to consider.

4.6. The sharpness of the endpoint in an acid-base titration is markedly dependent on the concentrations of acid and base used. Plot the strong acid–strong base titration curve in the region near equivalence for two appropriate sets of M_{MOH} and M_{HA} values to show graphically how the curve changes shape as concentration is varied.

4.7. Find the approximate form of Equation (4.8) for the case in which both [M] and [A] are large compared to (H^+). Find the approximate form of Equation (4.11) for the case in which both M_{MOH} and M_{HA} are large compared to (H^+). Are the two approximate equations equivalent? For a typical titration, what is the pH range in which the equations are valid?

4.8. Three graphical methods for determining K_{HA}' are shown in Figures 4.5 to 4.7. Critically evaluate these methods. Considering the uncertainties which would be expected in experimental data at the beginning of the titration, near the half equivalence point, and near the endpoint, discuss the type of weighting of points which is most desirable.

4.9. When considering a mixture of two or more acids in the same solution, it is convenient to think of (H^+) as a master variable which converts otherwise independent equations governing the behavior of the separate acids into a single set of simultaneous equations. Thus if a solution is prepared by mixing together benzoic acid, chloroacetic acid, and sodium hydroxide to give a solution with a pH value of 4.00, what is the ratio of concentrations of benzoate ion and of chloroacetate ion? Let total concentration of all benzoate-containing species be 0.1 molar and of all chloroacetate-containing species be 0.2 molar. Assume an apparent dissociation constant for chloroacetic acid equal to 1.35 x 10^{-3}, and an apparent dissociation constant for benzoic acid equal to 6.2 x 10^{-5}.

4.10. How would Equation (4.11) be modified if the original sample were prepared by mixing together HA and MA, and then the solution were titrated with MOH?

4.11. Obtain an equation for the titration curve of a weak base–weak acid titration. What is the value of (H^+) at the equivalence point?

4.12. Examine Equation (4.88). Are there possible conditions under which there could be two inflections? One inflection? No inflection?

4.13. Inequalities (4.50) and (4.52) can be considered to define a strong acid insofar as titration behavior is concerned. The two inequalities are not independent, however, and in fact the value of K_w' places a restriction on the possible values of K_{HA}' which are consistent with strong acid behavior in water. Obtain an expression giving the lower limit of K_{HA}' which permits an acid to behave as a strong acid in an aqueous titration.

4.14. In obtaining Equation (4.54), the assumption is made that (H^+) is large. However, in the same derivation inequality (4.52) places an upper limit on (H^+). A similar situation exists in the derivation of Equation (4.28). Obtain an expression for upper and lower limits on (H^+) under which Equations (4.54) and (4.28) are valid in aqueous solution. Be sure that you made no unnoticed assumptions about values of K_{HA}' or of solute concentrations. What happens if non-aqueous solutions are considered?

4.15. Consider the titration of the acid HA with the strong base MOH, in the presence of the indicator HI. Write down the complete mathematical model for treating the equilibria. What are the algebraic conditions under which the titration curve (V_{MOH} vs pH) is independent of the presence of HI?

4.16. Consider the titration of a sample of NaCN with the titrant HCl. Write down the algebraic equations which comprise the mathematical model for this titration, including conservation equations in terms of [Na] and [Cl]. HCN is a weak acid, with $pK_{HCN}' = 9.32$. Obtain an equation relating volume of titrant added to the value of (H^+) for this titration. What is the low-pH limiting form of the equation for the titration curve?

Suggestion for Experimental Investigation

In a simple titration, the ionic strength changes from an initially low value when the solute is mostly nonionized HA to a value approximately equal to the molarity of the MOH solution when V_{MOH} has reached a large value. Ideally the ionic strength should not change during an experiment for the determination of K_{HA}', since K_{HA}' is in general a function of ionic strength. For careful measurements, experiments must be designed so that ionic strength is kept constant. Design and carry out such an experiment.

5

Diprotic Acids

A chemist concerned with hydrogen-ion equilibria is soon confronted with acids having more than a single dissociable proton. Sulfuric acid, carbonic acid, phosphoric acid, amino acids, and the many dicarboxylic acids are common. Ion-exchange resins are familiar examples of polyacids and polybases. A biochemist is often working with compounds which have several dissociable protons per molecule. So we will inquire into what happens when a single molecule in solution can exist as any one of several distinct chemical species merely by changing the number of protons chemically associated with it. The principles are the same ones encountered in studying the titration curve of a monoprotic acid. But the existence of two or more dissociation steps will introduce additional aspects of the detailed chemistry of acids and bases.

A diprotic acid, H_2A, will be examined, and an equation will be derived for the hydrogen-ion concentration in a solution which is prepared by mixing together known amounts of water, H_2A, MHA, M_2A, and MOH. It will be assumed that in solution there is no formation of complexes with the metal ions. The procedure is then the one previously followed with monoprotic acids. Three apparent equilibrium constants, two conservation equations, and the electroneutrality equation comprise a system of six simultaneous equations in six unknowns; the algebraic problem is one of obtaining a single equation in a single unknown, (H^+).

Relevant solution equilibria and the corresponding apparent equilibrium constants are

$$H_2A \rightleftarrows HA^- + H^+ \qquad K_{H_2A}' = \frac{(HA^-)(H^+)}{(H_2A)} \qquad (5.1)$$

$$HA^- \rightleftarrows A^{--} + H^+ \qquad K_{HA}{}' = \frac{(A^{--})(H^+)}{(HA^-)} \qquad (5.2)$$

$$H_2O \rightleftarrows H^+ + OH^- \qquad K_w{}' = (H^+)(OH^-) \qquad (5.3)$$

Conservation equations required are

$$[A] = (H_2A) + (HA^-) + (A^{--}) \qquad (5.4)$$

$$[M] = (M^+) \qquad (5.5)$$

The electroneutrality condition requires equal numbers of moles of positive and negative charges in solution, and thus a coefficient greater than unity is needed for concentrations of polyvalent ions. Electroneutrality requires a coefficient equal to the net charge on the ion, and hence the term $2(A^{--})$ appears in the electroneutrality equation,

$$(M^+) + (H^+) = (OH^-) + (HA^-) + 2(A^{--}) \qquad (5.6)$$

Equations (5.2), (5.3), (5.5), and (5.6) can be combined to give

$$[M] + (H^+) - \frac{K_w{}'}{(H^+)} = (HA^-)\left\{1 + \frac{2K_{HA}{}'}{(H^+)}\right\} \qquad (5.7)$$

From Equations (5.1), (5.2), and (5.4) comes

$$[A] = (HA^-)\left\{\frac{(H^+)}{K_{H_2A}{}'} + 1 + \frac{K_{HA}{}'}{(H^+)}\right\} \qquad (5.8)$$

The quantity (HA^-) is then eliminated between Equations (5.7) and (5.8), yielding

$$\begin{aligned}
(H^+)^4 &+ (H^+)^3\{[M] + K_{H_2A}{}'\} \\
&+ (H^+)^2\{K_{H_2A}{}'[M] - K_{H_2A}{}'[A] + K_{H_2A}{}'K_{HA}{}' - K_w{}'\} \\
&+ (H^+)K_{H_2A}{}'\{K_{HA}{}'[M] - 2K_{HA}{}'[A] - K_w{}'\} - K_w{}'K_{HA}{}'K_{H_2A}{}' = 0
\end{aligned}$$
$$(5.9)$$

By changing variables, Equation (5.9) can be written in forms more suited for plotting a titration curve. In the usual way, [M] and [A] are related to volume variables by

$$[A] = \frac{V_{H_2A}M_{H_2A}}{V_{H_2A} + V_{MOH}} \qquad (5.10)$$

$$[M] = \frac{V_{MOH}M_{MOH}}{V_{H_2A} + V_{MOH}} \qquad (5.11)$$

where M_{H_2A} is the molarity of the H_2A solution, M_{MOH} is the molarity of the MOH solution, and V_{H_2A} and V_{MOH} are the respective volumes of H_2A

and MOH solutions which have been mixed together. Substitution of Equations (5.10) and (5.11) into Equation (5.9) yields

$$(H^+)^4 + (H^+)^3 \left\{ \frac{V_{MOH}M_{MOH}}{V_{H_2A} + V_{MOH}} + K_{H_2A}' \right\}$$

$$+ (H^+)^2 \left\{ \frac{K_{H_2A}'M_{MOH}V_{MOH} - K_{H_2A}'M_{H_2A}V_{H_2A}}{V_{H_2A} + V_{MOH}} + K_{H_2A}'K_{HA}-' - K_w' \right\}$$

$$+ (H^+)K_{H_2A}' \left\{ \frac{K_{HA}-'M_{MOH}V_{MOH} - 2K_{HA}-'M_{H_2A}V_{H_2A}}{V_{H_2A} + V_{MOH}} - K_w' \right\}$$

$$- K_w'K_{HA}-'K_{H_2A}' = 0 \qquad (5.12)$$

or

$$V_{MOH} = -V_{H_2A} \begin{bmatrix} (H^+)^4 + K_{H_2A}'(H^+)^3 \\ + \{K_{H_2A}'K_{HA}-' - K_{H_2A}'M_{H_2A} - K_w'\}(H^+)^2 \\ + \{-2K_{H_2A}'K_{HA}-'M_{H_2A} - K_w'K_{H_2A}'\}(H^+) \\ \underline{- K_w'K_{HA}-'K_{H_2A}'} \\ (H^+)^4 + \{K_{H_2A}' + M_{MOH}\}(H^+)^3 \\ + \{K_{H_2A}'K_{HA}-' + K_{H_2A}'M_{MOH} - K_w'\}(H^+)^2 \\ + \{K_{H_2A}'K_{HA}-'M_{MOH} - K_w'K_{H_2A}'\}(H^+) \\ - K_w'K_{H_2A}'K_{HA}-' \end{bmatrix} \qquad (5.13)$$

Calculation of a Titration Curve. Direct use of Equation (5.13) for calculation of points on a titration curve is a less formidable undertaking than might at first be imagined. The following numerical values will be assumed for the various parameters needed in order to make an illustrative calculation of the titration curve of succinic acid, the dicarboxylic acid HOOC—CH$_2$—CH$_2$—COOH:

$$K_{H_2A}' = 6.2 \times 10^{-5}$$
$$K_{HA}-' = 2.3 \times 10^{-6}$$
$$K_w' = 1.0 \times 10^{-14}$$
$$M_{MOH} = 0.100 \text{ moles per liter}$$
$$M_{H_2A} = 0.100 \text{ moles per liter}$$
$$V_{H_2A} = 25.00 \text{ ml}$$

Equation (5.13) is of the form

$$V_{MOH} = -V_{H_2A} \left\{ \frac{\alpha}{\beta} \right\} \qquad (5.14)$$

where α and β are the two power series in (H$^+$), defined by Equation (5.13), which become after substitution of the appropriate numerical values

$$\alpha = (H^+)^4 + (6.2 \times 10^{-5})(H^+)^3 - (6.2 \times 10^{-6})(H^+)^2$$
$$- (2.86 \times 10^{-11})(H^+) - (1.43 \times 10^{-24}) \qquad (5.15)$$

$$\beta = (H^+)^4 + (0.100)(H^+)^3 + (6.2 \times 10^{-6})(H^+)^2$$
$$+ (1.43 \times 10^{-11})(H^+) - (1.43 \times 10^{-24}) \qquad (5.16)$$

If integral powers of (H$^+$) are assumed, all multiplications can be performed mentally, and a table can be constructed similar to Tables 5.1, 5.2, and 5.3.

Table 5.1. Calculation of the Titration Curve of Succinic Acid (Numerator)[a].

$(H^+)^4$	$+ (6.2 \times 10^{-5})(H^+)^3$	$- (6.2 \times 10^{-6})(H^+)^2$	$- (2.86 \times 10^{-11})(H^+)$	$- (1.43 \times 10^{-24})$	$= \alpha$
1.00×10^{-8}	$+ 6.2 \times 10^{-11}$	$- 6.2 \times 10^{-10}$	$- 2.86 \times 10^{-13}$	$- 1.43 \times 10^{-24}$	$= +9.4 \times 10^{-9}$
1.00×10^{-12}	$+ 6.2 \times 10^{-14}$	$- 6.2 \times 10^{-12}$	$- 2.86 \times 10^{-14}$	$- 1.43 \times 10^{-24}$	$= -5.17 \times 10^{-12}$
1.00×10^{-16}	$+ 6.2 \times 10^{-17}$	$- 6.2 \times 10^{-14}$	$- 2.86 \times 10^{-15}$	$- 1.43 \times 10^{-24}$	$= -6.49 \times 10^{-14}$
1.00×10^{-20}	$+ 6.2 \times 10^{-20}$	$- 6.2 \times 10^{-16}$	$- 2.86 \times 10^{-16}$	$- 1.43 \times 10^{-24}$	$= -9.06 \times 10^{-16}$
1.00×10^{-24}	$+ 6.2 \times 10^{-23}$	$- 6.2 \times 10^{-18}$	$- 2.86 \times 10^{-17}$	$- 1.43 \times 10^{-24}$	$= -3.48 \times 10^{-17}$
1.00×10^{-28}	$+ 6.2 \times 10^{-26}$	$- 6.2 \times 10^{-20}$	$- 2.86 \times 10^{-18}$	$- 1.43 \times 10^{-24}$	$= -2.92 \times 10^{-18}$
1.00×10^{-32}	$+ 6.2 \times 10^{-29}$	$- 6.2 \times 10^{-22}$	$- 2.86 \times 10^{-19}$	$- 1.43 \times 10^{-24}$	$= -2.86 \times 10^{-19}$
1.00×10^{-36}	$+ 6.2 \times 10^{-32}$	$- 6.2 \times 10^{-24}$	$- 2.86 \times 10^{-20}$	$- 1.43 \times 10^{-24}$	$= -2.86 \times 10^{-20}$
1.00×10^{-40}	$+ 6.2 \times 10^{-35}$	$- 6.2 \times 10^{-26}$	$- 2.86 \times 10^{-21}$	$- 1.43 \times 10^{-24}$	$= -2.86 \times 10^{-21}$
1.00×10^{-44}	$+ 6.2 \times 10^{-38}$	$- 6.2 \times 10^{-28}$	$- 2.86 \times 10^{-22}$	$- 1.43 \times 10^{-24}$	$= -2.87 \times 10^{-22}$
1.00×10^{-48}	$+ 6.2 \times 10^{-41}$	$- 6.2 \times 10^{-30}$	$- 2.86 \times 10^{-23}$	$- 1.43 \times 10^{-24}$	$= -3.00 \times 10^{-23}$
1.00×10^{-52}	$+ 6.2 \times 10^{-44}$	$- 6.2 \times 10^{-32}$	$- 2.86 \times 10^{-24}$	$- 1.43 \times 10^{-24}$	$= -4.29 \times 10^{-24}$

[a] Only the italicized quantities have been included in the addition of terms to give α.

Table 5.2. Calculation of the Titration Curve of Succinic Acid (Denominator)[a].

$$(H^+)^4 \quad + (0.100)(H^+)^3 + (6.2 \times 10^{-6})(H^+)^2 + (1.43 \times 10^{-11})(H^+) - (1.43 \times 10^{-24}) = \beta$$

$(H^+)^4$	$+ (0.100)(H^+)^3$	$+ (6.2 \times 10^{-6})(H^+)^2$	$+ (1.43 \times 10^{-11})(H^+)$	$- (1.43 \times 10^{-24})$	$= \beta$
1.00×10^{-8}	$+ 1.00 \times 10^{-7}$	$+ 6.2 \times 10^{-10}$	$+ 1.43 \times 10^{-13}$	$- 1.43 \times 10^{-24}$	$= +1.10 \times 10^{-7}$
1.00×10^{-12}	$+ 1.00 \times 10^{-10}$	$+ 6.2 \times 10^{-12}$	$+ 1.43 \times 10^{-14}$	$- 1.43 \times 10^{-24}$	$= +1.07 \times 10^{-10}$
1.00×10^{-16}	$+ 1.00 \times 10^{-13}$	$+ 6.2 \times 10^{-14}$	$+ 1.43 \times 10^{-15}$	$- 1.43 \times 10^{-24}$	$= +1.63 \times 10^{-13}$
1.00×10^{-20}	$+ 1.00 \times 10^{-16}$	$+ 6.2 \times 10^{-16}$	$+ 1.43 \times 10^{-16}$	$- 1.43 \times 10^{-24}$	$= +8.63 \times 10^{-16}$
1.00×10^{-24}	$+ 1.00 \times 10^{-19}$	$+ 6.2 \times 10^{-18}$	$+ 1.43 \times 10^{-17}$	$- 1.43 \times 10^{-24}$	$= +2.06 \times 10^{-17}$
1.00×10^{-28}	$+ 1.00 \times 10^{-22}$	$+ 6.2 \times 10^{-20}$	$+ 1.43 \times 10^{-18}$	$- 1.43 \times 10^{-24}$	$= +1.49 \times 10^{-18}$
1.00×10^{-32}	$+ 1.00 \times 10^{-25}$	$+ 6.2 \times 10^{-22}$	$+ 1.43 \times 10^{-19}$	$- 1.43 \times 10^{-24}$	$= +1.43 \times 10^{-19}$
1.00×10^{-36}	$+ 1.00 \times 10^{-28}$	$+ 6.2 \times 10^{-24}$	$+ 1.43 \times 10^{-20}$	$- 1.43 \times 10^{-24}$	$= +1.43 \times 10^{-20}$
1.00×10^{-40}	$+ 1.00 \times 10^{-31}$	$+ 6.2 \times 10^{-26}$	$+ 1.43 \times 10^{-21}$	$- 1.43 \times 10^{-24}$	$= +1.43 \times 10^{-21}$
1.00×10^{-44}	$+ 1.00 \times 10^{-34}$	$+ 6.2 \times 10^{-28}$	$+ 1.43 \times 10^{-22}$	$- 1.43 \times 10^{-24}$	$= +1.42 \times 10^{-22}$
1.00×10^{-48}	$+ 1.00 \times 10^{-37}$	$+ 6.2 \times 10^{-30}$	$+ 1.43 \times 10^{-23}$	$- 1.43 \times 10^{-24}$	$= +1.29 \times 10^{-23}$
1.00×10^{-52}	$+ 1.00 \times 10^{-40}$	$+ 6.2 \times 10^{-32}$	$+ 1.43 \times 10^{-24}$	$- 1.43 \times 10^{-24}$	$= 0$

[a] Only the italicized quantities have been included in the addition of terms to give β.

Table 5.3. CALCULATION OF THE TITRATION CURVE OF
SUCCINIC ACID (V_{MOH} vs pH).

(H$^+$)	pH	α	β	α/β	V_{MOH}(ml)
$10^{-2.00}$	2.00	$+9.4 \times 10^{-9}$	1.10×10^{-7}	$+8.5 \times 10^{-2}$	-2.14
$10^{-3.00}$	3.00	-5.17×10^{-12}	1.07×10^{-10}	-4.83×10^{-2}	$+1.21$
$10^{-4.00}$	4.00	-6.49×10^{-14}	1.63×10^{-13}	-3.98×10^{-1}	$+9.95$
$10^{-5.00}$	5.00	-9.06×10^{-16}	8.63×10^{-16}	-1.050	$+26.25$
$10^{-6.00}$	6.00	-3.48×10^{-17}	2.06×10^{-17}	-1.689	$+42.23$
$10^{-7.00}$	7.00	-2.92×10^{-18}	1.49×10^{-18}	-1.96	$+49.00$
$10^{-8.00}$	8.00	-2.86×10^{-19}	1.43×10^{-19}	-2.00	$+50.00$
$10^{-9.00}$	9.00	-2.86×10^{-20}	1.43×10^{-20}	-2.00	$+50.00$
$10^{-10.00}$	10.00	-2.86×10^{-21}	1.43×10^{-21}	-2.00	$+50.00$
$10^{-11.00}$	11.00	-2.87×10^{-22}	1.42×10^{-22}	-2.02	$+50.53$
$10^{-12.00}$	12.00	-3.00×10^{-23}	1.29×10^{-23}	-2.33	$+58.14$
$10^{-13.00}$	13.00	-4.29×10^{-24}	0	Indeterminate	

This calculated plot of V_{MOH} vs pH is part of Figure 5.3.

It is evident from an inspection of Tables 5.1 and 5.2 that in no pH region are all terms of the equation required, and it follows that approximate equations can be developed for restricted values of pH. It may be surprising to find that there is no inflection point at the volume of titrant corresponding to "titration of the first proton." It may not seem reasonable that K_{H_2A}' and $K_{HA}{}^{-\prime}$ should have different values when the two carboxyl groups are identical. A variety of questions arise for the first time with diprotic acids, and many of these questions will be discussed in this chapter.

By comparing Equations (5.9), (5.12), and (5.13) with the corresponding equations for a monoprotic acid [(4.8), (4.11), and (4.12)], it is possible to make some predictions about the family of equations which would result if similar derivations were carried out for acids with an increasing number of dissociable protons. It appears that no matter how many dissociation equilibria are involved, it will still be possible to write an explicit equation for

$$V_{MOH} = f((H^+)) \tag{5.17}$$

where $f((H^+))$ will be the ratio of two power series in (H^+). Although computation problems may become massive, it will always be possible to calculate a theoretical titration curve of V_{MOH} vs (H^+) if the values of the various equilibrium constants are known. Determination of the individual equilibrium constants from experimental data may become quite difficult. Writing an explicit equation of the form

$$(H^+) = f(V_{MOH}) \tag{5.18}$$

was difficult enough for a monoprotic acid and the task becomes practically impossible for the higher acids. In very basic solutions a simple approximate solution does exist, and we will now look for such a solution.

The High-pH Approximation. If the solution is basic enough so that

$$(H^+)^2 \ll K_w' \tag{5.19}$$

$$(H^+) \ll K_{H_2A}' \tag{5.20}$$

$$(H^+) \ll K_{HA^-}' \tag{5.21}$$

then virtually all the original H_2A and HA^- has been converted to A^{--} and titration behavior of the solution will be essentially independent of the nature of the specific acid used. This can be seen by rewriting Equation (5.9) as

$$(H^+)^4 + (H^+)^3 K_{H_2A}' + (H^+)^2 K_{H_2A}' K_{HA^-}' - (H^+)^2 K_w' - (H^+) K_{H_2A}' K_w'$$
$$= -[M]\{(H^+)^3 + (H^+)^2 K_{H_2A}' + (H^+) K_{H_2A}' K_{HA^-}'\}$$
$$+ [A]\{(H^+)^2 K_{H_2A}' + 2(H^+) K_{H_2A}' K_{HA^-}'\} + K_w' K_{H_2A}' K_{HA^-}' \tag{5.22}$$

Each of the terms of the left member of Equation (5.22) is negligible compared to $K_w' K_{H_2A}' K_{HA^-}'$ by virtue of inequalities (5.19), (5.20), and (5.21). These inequalities also permit elimination of all but one of the terms in each of the brackets. There then is left

$$0 = -[M](H^+) K_{H_2A}' K_{HA^-}' + 2[A](H^+) K_{H_2A}' K_{HA^-}' + K_w' K_{H_2A}' K_{HA^-}' \tag{5.23}$$

or

$$[M] - 2[A] = \frac{K_w'}{(H^+)} = (OH^-) \tag{5.24}$$

When an acid has n dissociable protons, and when

$$(H^+)^2 \ll K_w'$$

$$(H^+) \ll K_{HnA}'$$

$$\cdots$$

$$(H^+) \ll K_{A^{(n-1)-}}'$$

the titration curve is given in general by

$$[M] - n[A] = \frac{K_w'}{(H^+)} \tag{5.25}$$

It should be realized that in aqueous solution it will not always be possible to reduce the value of (H^+) to a value low enough to satisfy these inequalities.

Distribution Functions. Any solution containing H_2A also contains some HA^- and some A^{--}. The relative number of molecules of each of these three species will depend on the pH and on the values of the equilibrium constants. It is conceptually useful to consider the three species as all being —A— molecules, each with two binding sites which can be individually occupied by a proton or unoccupied. Thus —A— with one site occupied is H—A—, and —A— with two sites occupied is H—A—H.

The fractions of all A–containing species present as H_2A, HA^-, and A^{--} will be determined by the particular distribution of available protons on the available sites. Consider a collection of five —A— molecules,

$$—A—\qquad —A—\qquad —A—\qquad —A—\qquad —A—$$

on which five protons are to be distributed. Different distributions are possible, and for each distribution the fractions $(H_2A)/[A]$, $(HA^-)/[A]$, and $(A^{--})/[A]$ will have different values. Three possible distributions, together with the resulting distribution fractions, are

---

$$H—A—\qquad H—A—\qquad H—A—\qquad H—A—\qquad H—A—$$

$$\frac{(H_2A)}{[A]} = \frac{0}{5} = 0; \quad \frac{(HA^-)}{[A]} = \frac{5}{5} = 1; \quad \frac{(A^{--})}{[A]} = \frac{0}{5} = 0$$

$$H—A—H\qquad H—A—H\qquad H—A—\qquad —A—\qquad —A—$$

$$\frac{(H_2A)}{[A]} = \frac{2}{5}; \quad \frac{(HA^-)}{[A]} = \frac{1}{5}; \quad \frac{(A^{--})}{[A]} = \frac{2}{5}$$

$$H—A—H\qquad H—A—\qquad H—A—\qquad H—A—\qquad —A—$$

$$\frac{(H_2A)}{[A]} = \frac{1}{5}; \quad \frac{(HA^-)}{[A]} = \frac{3}{5}; \quad \frac{(A^{--})}{[A]} = \frac{1}{5}$$

During the titration of H_2A, the three species H_2A, HA^-, and A^{--} may each in turn comprise an appreciable fraction of [A]. The functional dependence of these fractions on (H^+) will now be examined.

Equation (5.8) is readily rearranged to give

$$\frac{(HA^-)}{[A]} = \frac{1}{\dfrac{(H^+)}{K_{H_2A}'} + 1 + \dfrac{K_{HA^-}'}{(H^+)}} \tag{5.26}$$

Equations (5.1), (5.2), and (5.4) give

$$\frac{(H_2A)}{[A]} = \frac{1}{1 + \dfrac{K_{H_2A}'}{(H^+)} + \dfrac{K_{H_2A}'K_{HA^-}'}{(H^+)^2}} \tag{5.27}$$

Equations (5.1), (5.2), and (5.4) also give

$$\frac{(A^{--})}{[A]} = \frac{1}{\dfrac{(H^+)^2}{K_{H_2A}'K_{HA^-}'} + \dfrac{(H^+)}{K_{HA^-}'} + 1} \tag{5.28}$$

Equations (5.26), (5.27), and (5.28) are distribution functions. They describe how protons are distributed on binding sites in solution at a particular pH, and they describe how "A" is distributed among three differently-protonated species.

The three distribution functions provide an excellent means for visualizing how the chemical composition of a solution changes as the value of (H^+) is varied over many orders of magnitude. The fraction $(H_2A)/[A]$ is a monotonically increasing function of (H^+) and will reach its highest values at the lowest accessible values of pH. The fraction $(A^{--})/[A]$ is a monotonically decreasing function of (H^+) and will therefore take on its highest values at the highest pH values. Equation (5.26) is more interesting, having a maximum. No fractions depend on $[A]$.

Distribution functions for sulfurous acid are plotted in Figure 5.2, and for succinic acid in Figure 5.4. Similar equations can be derived by the same method for acids with any number of dissociable protons.

Macroscopic and Microscopic Equilibrium Constants. The treatment thus far of the dissociation of H_2A has not been given in complete molecular detail. Following Adams[1], the dissociation of H_2A is formulated diagrammatically as

$$
\begin{array}{ccc}
 & H-A-H & \\
{}^-A-H & & H-A^- \\
 & A^{--} &
\end{array}
\tag{5.29}
$$

Here it is explicitly recognized that the completely ionized A^{--} can be formed by either of two distinct reaction pathways which differ only in the order in which the two protons are removed. The four chemical steps and the associated apparent equilibrium constants are then

$$
H-A-H \rightleftarrows H^+ + {}^-A-H \qquad K_1' = \frac{(H^+)({}^-A-H)}{(H-A-H)}
\tag{5.30}
$$

$$
H-A-H \rightleftarrows H^+ + H-A^- \qquad K_2' = \frac{(H^+)(H-A^-)}{(H-A-H)}
\tag{5.31}
$$

$$
H-A^- \rightleftarrows H^+ + A^{--} \qquad K_3' = \frac{(H^+)(A^{--})}{(H-A^-)}
\tag{5.32}
$$

$$
{}^-A-H \rightleftarrows H^+ + A^{--} \qquad K_4' = \frac{(H^+)(A^{--})}{({}^-A-H)}
\tag{5.33}
$$

These four equilibrium constants are not independent. If the values of any three are known, the value of the fourth can be readily calculated. This can be seen from Equations (5.30) through (5.33) by noting that

$$
\frac{K_1'}{K_2'} = \frac{({}^-A-H)}{(H-A^-)}
\tag{5.34}
$$

$$
\frac{K_3'}{K_4'} = \frac{({}^-A-H)}{(H-A^-)}
\tag{5.35}
$$

[1]E. Q. Adams, *J. Am. Chem. Soc.* **38**, 1503 (1916).

It is therefore apparent that

$$\frac{K_1'}{K_2'} = \frac{K_3'}{K_4'}, \quad K_1' = \frac{K_3'K_2'}{K_4'} \tag{5.36}$$

Parameters K_1', K_2', K_3', and K_4' characterize the molecular mechanism of the dissociation and are called *microscopic equilibrium constants*. The equilibrium constants which are experimentally accessible by observations of the macroscopic properties of a beaker of solution in the laboratory are K_{H_2A}' and K_{HA^-}'; they may be obtained from analysis of a titration curve and are called *macroscopic equilibrium constants*.

In writing Equation (5.1), the symbol (HA$^-$) was used to represent $\{(^-A\text{---}H) + (H\text{---}A^-)\}$. Equations (5.1) and (5.2) can therefore be rewritten as the following equivalent expressions:

$$K_{H_2A}' = \frac{(H^+)\{(^-A\text{---}H) + (H\text{---}A^-)\}}{(H_2A)} \tag{5.37}$$

$$K_{HA^-}' = \frac{(A^{--})(H^+)}{\{(^-A\text{---}H) + (H\text{---}A^-)\}} \tag{5.38}$$

It can be seen by comparison of Equations (5.30) through (5.33) with Equations (5.37) and (5.38) that the microscopic and macroscopic equilibrium constants are related by

$$K_{H_2A}' = K_1' + K_2' \tag{5.39}$$

$$\frac{1}{K_{HA^-}'} = \frac{1}{K_3'} + \frac{1}{K_4'}; \quad K_{HA^-}' = \frac{K_4'K_3'}{K_4' + K_3'} \tag{5.40}$$

Unfortunately, there exist three independent microscopic equilibrium constants but only two observable macroscopic equilibrium constants. It is therefore not possible to evaluate any of the microscopic constants from just a titration curve. Further information is required. This is an important general limitation of equilibrium acid-base titrations. If equilibrium is always maintained throughout the experiment, titration behavior gives no information about distribution of species having the same number of protons. This limitation applies if there is no way to vary the concentration of one species independently of the concentrations of the other isoprotic species. Rate studies and certain other nonequilibrium experiments can sometimes give the needed extra data. We will later look at the titration of amino acids, and with amino acids a plausible theoretical assumption makes possible numerical evaluation of all microscopic equilibrium constants.

Now consider reaction (5.29) for the special case in which

$$K_1' = K_2' = K_3' = K_4' \tag{5.41}$$

Such a situation might well be expected with a long-chain symmetrical dicarboxylic acid. The two carboxyl groups should have identical ionization constants, and if the carboxyl groups are sufficiently far apart, the ionization of one group should not appreciably affect the ionization of the other. Substituting equalities (5.41) into Equations (5.39) and (5.40), one obtains

$$K_{H_2A}' = 2K_1' \qquad (5.42)$$

$$K_{HA^-}' = \frac{\{K_1'\}^2}{2K_1'} = \frac{K_1'}{2} \qquad (5.43)$$

Equations (5.42) and (5.43) yield the surprising result

$$K_{H_2A}' = 4K_{HA^-}' \qquad (5.44)$$

Equation (5.44) requires that the two apparent equilibrium constants determined by titration differ by a factor of four even though the two groups being titrated are identical. It can be shown[1] that if the four microscopic constants are not equal, then

$$\frac{K_{H_2A}'}{K_{HA^-}'} > 4 \qquad (5.45)$$

Here then is a warning: it is not valid in general to identify macroscopic equilibrium constants with the dissociation of specific groups on a polyprotic acid.

The Principle of Microscopic Reversibility. The fact that there exist but three independent equilibrium constants to describe the four equilibria in reaction (5.29) suggests that one of the sets of double arrows is redundant, and that an indistinguishable titration curve would result if one set of arrows were omitted. This suggestion can be checked by examining the consequences of removing an arbitrary set of reaction arrows.

Let us examine a dissociation which proceeds via the diagrammatic scheme

$$\begin{array}{ccc} & \text{H—A—H} & \\ ^-\text{A—H} & & \text{H—A}^- \\ & \text{A}^{--} & \end{array} \qquad (5.46)$$

The three remaining equilibria are individually characterized by Equations (5.30), (5.31), and (5.33), these equations combining to give

$$\frac{K_1'K_4'}{K_2'} = \frac{(\text{H}^+)(\text{A}^{--})}{(\text{H—A}^-)} \qquad (5.47)$$

It is known from Equations (5.32) and (5.36) that for reactions (5.29), the reaction scheme with four sets of reaction arrows,

$$\frac{K_1'K_4'}{K_2'} = K_3' \qquad (5.48)$$

and

$$K_3' = \frac{(\text{H}^+)(\text{A}^{--})}{(\text{H—A}^-)} \qquad (5.49)$$

All the information contained in the missing reaction (5.32) is thus supplied

[1] E. Q. Adams, *J. Am. Chem. Soc.* **38**, 1503 (1916).

by the remaining three reactions. Both (5.29) and (5.46) must yield identical equilibrium titration curves. This is a general result which comes about because the condition of chemical equilibrium for a whole system requires that each individual reaction be in equilibrium. Equilibrium must be established for all pairs of double arrows. It follows that in a cyclic system the position of equilibrium is independent of one of the steps (any one, but only one), and hence a catalyst for any one step cannot shift the position of equilibrium. Step by step application of this principle gives the result that catalysts can have no effect on the ratios of concentrations at equilibrium. This result is a consequence of the *principle of microscopic reversibility*.

The principle of microscopic reversibility requires a priori rejection of the scheme

$$
\begin{array}{ccc}
 & \text{H—A—H} & \\
 \nearrow & & \searrow \\
 {}^{-}\text{A—H} & & \text{H—A}^{-} \\
 \nwarrow & & \swarrow \\
 & \text{A}^{--} &
\end{array}
\qquad (5.50)
$$

as a chemical mechanism for attaining and maintaining equilibrium. Mechanism (5.50) with appropriate rates could yield the same relative concentrations of the four chemical species as do (5.29) and (5.46). Equilibrium in a pairwise sense does not exist between any two species, however. Addition of a catalyst for any one of the steps changes the position of equilibrium. Elimination of any one arrow results in all species save one disappearing. This particular application of microscopic reversibility to the requirement of double arrows for all microscopic chemical steps is called the principle of detailed balancing of chemical reactions. The principle of microscopic reversibility is not a consequence of the laws of thermodynamics, but instead arises instead from more detailed statistical treatments.

For our purposes, the consequences of the principle of microscopic reversibility involve the detailed balancing of chemical reactions, and are threefold: (1) at equilibrium all microscopic chemical reaction steps are in pairwise equilibrium, (2) at equilibrium forward and reverse rates for each path in an overall reaction are equal, and (3) a catalyst affects forward and reverse reaction rates in such a way as to have no effect on the equilibrium concentrations of reacting species.

On Seeing Two Endpoints. Comparison of titration curves for a variety of diprotic acids reveals striking differences. The shape of the titration curve for succinic acid (HOOC—CH$_2$—CH$_2$—COOH, $pK_{H_2A}' = 4.21$, $pK_{HA^-}' = 5.64$)[2] resembles qualitatively the shape of the titration curve for a monoprotic weak acid with a single endpoint inflection at about [M] = 2[A]. For sulfurous acid (H$_2$SO$_3$, $pK_{H_2A}' = 1.76$, $pK_{HA^-}' = 7.21$)[2]

---

[2] These pK' values are approximate. Since the equilibrium constants depend on temperature and ionic strength, it is necessary to specify conditions rather carefully when a precise value of K' is needed. No such conditions have been specified in this discussion. The arguments presented here are based on the orders of magnitude of the equilibrium constant values.

the situation is clearly different, with two sharp endpoint inflections appearing in the titration curve, at least at some concentrations. The inflection points are near [M] = [A] and [M] = 2[A].

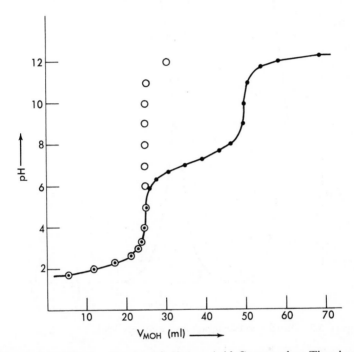

Figure 5.1. Titration Curve of Sulfurous Acid Compared to Titration Curve Calculated from First Dissociation Constant Alone. The points ⊙ and ○ are calculated assuming a monoprotic acid with apparent equilibrium constant equal to the observed first dissociation constant. The points ⊙ and ● are calculated from Equation (5.13) and lie on the titration curve for a diprotic acid.

A plot of $(HA^-)/[A]$ vs pH for succinic acid shows that no more than 75 percent of the [A] can ever be present as HA^-, whereas for sulfurous acid there is a range of one pH unit in which HA^- is virtually the only species present. It makes sense to speak of titrating H_2SO_3 to HSO_3^-, but there is no clear meaning to the statement that $HOOC—CH_2—CH_2—COOH$ has been titrated to $HOOC—CH_2—CH_2—COO^-$. One important criterion for seeing two endpoints is that it be possible to convert essentially all molecules of the acid into the half-ionized form. This criterion is related to the relative magnitudes of the two equilibrium constants.

Sulfurous acid behaves like a monoprotic acid throughout a substantial part of the low-pH region of the titration, and from the lowest pH values up to pH 5 the titration curve is represented equally well by Equation (5.13) and Equation (4.12). With succinic acid, however, Equation (4.12) for a monoprotic acid is not a very good approximation except at the very lowest pH values. We will show that the condition which makes $(HA^-)/[A]$ virtually

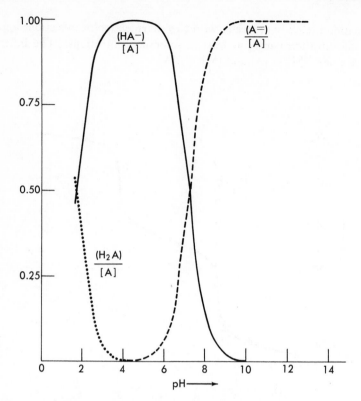

Figure 5.2. Distribution Diagram for Sulfurous Acid.

equal to unity at some pH is closely related to the condition which makes the the equation for a monoprotic acid an excellent approximation to the diprotic acid titration curve from the lowest pH values to the first endpoint for those acids which show a sharp inflection at the half-equivalence point.

During the titration of a diprotic acid, the fraction of all A-containing species present as singly-protonated HA^- is given by Equation (5.26), which when differentiated with respect to (H^+) gives

$$\frac{d\{(HA^-)/[A]\}}{d(H^+)} = \left\{ \frac{K_{HA}{'}}{(H^+)^2} - \frac{1}{K_{H_2A}{'}} \right\} \left\{ \frac{(HA^-)}{[A]} \right\}^2 \qquad (5.51)$$

The value of (H^+) at which $(HA^-)/[A]$ is a maximum is found by setting the derivative in Equation (5.51) equal to zero. This gives

$$(H^+)^2{}_{\max(HA^-)/[A]} = K_{H_2A}{'}K_{HA}{'} \qquad (5.52)$$

By combining Equations (5.26) and (5.52) there is found an equation for maximum attainable value of the $(HA^-)/[A]$ ratio,

$$\left\{ \frac{(HA^-)}{[A]} \right\}_{\max} = \frac{1}{2\left\{ \dfrac{K_{HA}{'}}{K_{H_2A}{'}} \right\}^{1/2} + 1} \qquad (5.53)$$

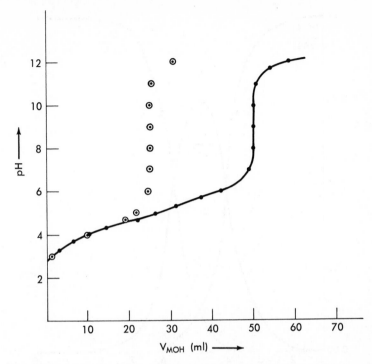

Figure 5.3. Titration Curve of Succinic Acid Compared to Titration Curve Calculated from First Dissociation Constant Alone. The points ⊙ and ○ are calculated assuming a monoprotic acid with apparent equilibrium constant equal to the observed first dissociation constant. The points ⊙ and ● are calculated from Equation (5.13), and lie on the titration curve for a diprotic acid.

The maximum $(HA^-)/[A]$ ratio is an explicit function only of the ratio of the two equilibrium constants and thus of the difference between the two pK' values. Some calculated values are presented in Table 5.4. The maximum

Table 5.4. MAXIMUM ATTAINABLE VALUES OF $(HA^-)/[A]$.

$\dfrac{K_{HA^-}'}{K_{H_2A}'}$	$\left\{\dfrac{(HA^-)}{[A]}\right\}_{max}$
1/4	0.50
1/9	0.60
1/16	0.67
1/25	0.71
1/36	0.75
1/100	0.83
$1/10^3$	0.94
$1/10^4$	0.98
$1/10^6$	0.998

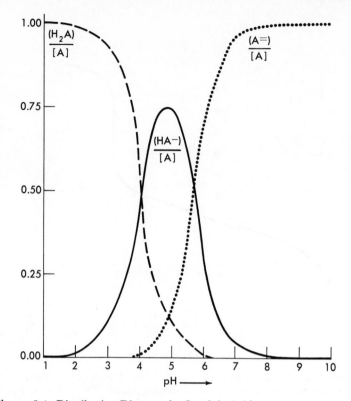

Figure 5.4. Distribution Diagram for Succinic Acid.

$(HA^-)/[A]$ ratio will not be within experimental reach if $(H^+)_{\max(HA^-)/[A]}$ lies outside the range permitted in aqueous solution with available acids and bases. Inspection of Table 5.4 reveals that in order to come within two percent of having all A species present as HA^-, it is necessary to have K's in the ratio of at least 10^4. Figures 5.1 and 5.3 show that when M_{MOH} and M_{H_2A} are 0.100, a ratio of K's of 1:30 is not small enough to yield two end-points, whereas a ratio of $1:10^5$ is adequate.

It will be remembered that for a diprotic acid with identical, noninteracting groups, the two macroscopic equilibrium constants stand in the ratio of 1:4. For such an acid, at most only half of the molecules can exist as HA^-, and then a fourth are H_2A and the remaining fourth are A^{--}. This is just the distribution which would be expected statistically when an attempt is made to arrange n protons on $2n$ equally-probable binding sites. Four equally-probably microscopic species result, H—A—H, H—A$^-$, $^-$A—H, and A^{--}. Increasing the number of available protons converts H—A$^-$ to H—A—H, $^-$A—H to H—A—H, and A^{--} to either H—A$^-$ or $^-$A—H. This process results in a net decrease in the fraction present as H—A$^-$ and $^-$A—H. In a similar manner, a decrease of available protons also reduces the fraction present as half-protonated species.

The only way to alter this statistical distribution is to have nonidentical binding sites which have different intrinsic bonding energies, or to permit interaction between the two sites so that removal of the first proton changes the bonding energy between the second site and a proton. Site interaction is certainly the only factor which makes the $K_{H_2A}'/K_{HA}-'$ ratio larger than four for succinic acid, and it may be the only factor involved for sulfurous acid.

Since Equation (5.13) has about twice as many terms as does Equation (5.9), it will be simpler to examine the latter expression in an attempt to find conditions which will reduce this equation for a diprotic acid to the corresponding monoprotic equation. It is necessary to eliminate four terms, and this can be done if there is imposed the inequality

$$(H^+) \gg K_{HA}-' \tag{5.54}$$

Then

$$(H^+)^3 K_{H_2A}' \quad \gg (H^+)^2 K_{HA}-' K_{H_2A}'$$
$$(H^+)^2 K_{H_2A}'[M] \gg (H^+) K_{H_2A}' K_{HA}-'[M] \tag{5.55}$$
$$(H^+)^2 K_{H_2A}'[A] \gg 2(H^+) K_{H_2A}' K_{HA}-'[A]$$
$$(H^+) K_{H_2A}' K_w' \gg K_{HA}-' K_{H_2A}' K_w'$$

which are the inequalities required. The problem then becomes one of finding the circumstances under which (H^+) is sufficiently large compared to the second dissociation constant from the beginning of the titration until the first of the two endpoints is reached.

The first endpoint is reached when the ratio $(HA^-)/[A]$ reaches unity, or if this condition cannot be achieved (and of course it never quite can) at some value of pH higher than the pH at which $(HA^-)/[A]$ reaches its maximum value. Recalling Equation (5.52), it is evident that the first endpoint must occur at some pH value such that

$$pH_{endpoint} \geq \frac{pK_{HA}-' + pK_{H_2A}'}{2} \tag{5.56}$$

It is also required by inequality (5.54) that

$$pH_{endpoint} \ll pK_{HA}-' \tag{5.57}$$

It follows that $pK_{HA}-' \gg pK_{H_2A}'$.

Titration Curve When All Microscopic Equilibrium Constants are Equal. Equation (5.9), the equation for the titration curve of a diprotic acid H_2A, assumes an unexpected form in the special circumstances when all microscopic equilibrium constants are equal. Then, according to Equations (5.42) and (5.43),

$$K_{H_2A}' = 2K_1'$$

$$K_{HA}-' = \frac{K_1'}{2}$$

Equation (5.9), written now in terms of K_1', becomes

$$(H^+)^4 + (H^+)^3\{[M] + 2K_1'\}$$
$$+ (H^+)^2\{2K_1'[M] - 2K_1'[A] + (K_1')^2 - K_w'\} \qquad (5.58)$$
$$+ (H^+)\{(K_1')^2[M] - 2(K_1')^2[A] - 2K_1'K_w'\}$$
$$- (K_1')^2K_w' = 0$$

Close inspection of Equation (5.58) reveals that it can be factored to give

$$\{(H^+) + K_1'\}[(H^+)^3 + (H^+)^2\{[M] + K_1'\}$$
$$+ (H^+)\{K_1'[M] - 2K_1'[A] - K_w'\} - K_1'K_w'] = 0 \qquad (5.59)$$

Since $\{(H^+) + K_1'\}$ can never be zero, both sides of the equation can be divided by this factor, and there then results

$$(H^+)^3 + (H^+)^2 \{[M] + \{K_1'\}\} + (H^+)\{K_1'[M] - 2K_1'[A] - K_w'\} - K_1'K_w' = 0 \qquad (5.60)$$

which is the equation for the titration curve for a *monoprotic* acid in which the total concentration of all acid species is 2[A].

There would thus be no difference between the observed titration curve of a monoprotic acid with apparent dissociation constant K_1' and the observed titration curve of a diprotic acid with apparent dissociation constants $2K_1'$ and $K_1'/2$ if the total concentration of acid species is expressed in each case in terms of moles of proton-binding sites. In the absence of knowledge of molecular structure of the particular acid, the observed titration curves could be *equally well* described in terms a monoprotic chemical model with one equilibrium constant or a diprotic chemical model with two equilibrium constants.

Amino Acids. The distinction between microscopic and macroscopic equilibrium constants is an important feature of a treatment of the acid-base behavior of amino acids. Amino acids are compounds having the structure

$$\underset{\displaystyle H}{\overset{\displaystyle R}{H_2N-\overset{|}{\underset{|}{C}}-COOH}}$$

where R is some organic group. In the simple amino acids to be discussed here, R contains no dissociable hydrogens. Four distinct chemical species must be considered, namely

$$\underset{\displaystyle \underset{A^\circ}{H}}{\overset{\displaystyle R}{H_2N-\overset{|}{\underset{|}{C}}-COOH}} \qquad\qquad \underset{\displaystyle \underset{A^+}{H}}{\overset{\displaystyle R}{^+H_3N-\overset{|}{\underset{|}{C}}-COOH}}$$

$$\underset{\displaystyle \underset{A^\pm}{H}}{\overset{\displaystyle R}{^+H_3N-\overset{|}{\underset{|}{C}}-COO^-}} \qquad\qquad \underset{\displaystyle \underset{A^-}{H}}{\overset{\displaystyle R}{H_2N-\overset{|}{\underset{|}{C}}-COO^-}}$$

Equilibria and corresponding microscopic apparent equilibrium constants are

$$A^+ \rightleftarrows H^+ + A^\pm \qquad K_1' = \frac{(H^+)(A^\pm)}{(A^+)} \qquad (5.61)$$

$$A^+ \rightleftarrows H^+ + A^\circ \qquad K_2' = \frac{(H^+)(A^\circ)}{(A^+)} \qquad (5.62)$$

$$A^\pm \rightleftarrows H^+ + A^- \qquad K_3' = \frac{(H^+)(A^-)}{(A^\pm)} \qquad (5.63)$$

$$A^\circ \rightleftarrows H^+ + A^- \qquad K_4' = \frac{(H^+)(A^-)}{(A^\circ)} \qquad (5.64)$$

$$A^\circ \rightleftarrows A^\pm \qquad K_5' = \frac{(A^\pm)}{(A^\circ)} \qquad (5.65)$$

Only three of the microscopic equilibrium constants are independent by virtue of the relationships

$$\frac{K_1'}{K_2'} = \frac{K_4'}{K_3'} = K_5' \qquad (5.66)$$

which can be verified by combination of Equations (5.61) through (5.65)

According to Equation (5.65), the ratio of concentrations of uncharged A° to zwitterion $A^\pm$ is independent of pH. This happens because both species have the same number of dissociable protons. In a titration experiment it is not possible to distinguish between these two species, and consequently the sum of concentrations $\{(A^\pm) + (A^\circ)\}$ is the experimentally-meaningful quantity in a titration. The two observable macroscopic apparent equilibrium constants are

$$K_A' = \frac{(H^+)\{(A^\pm) + (A^\circ)\}}{(A^+)} \qquad (5.67)$$

$$K_B' = \frac{(H^+)(A^-)}{\{(A^\pm) + (A^\circ)\}} \qquad (5.68)$$

Equations (5.67) and (5.68) can be combined with Equations (5.61) through (5.65) to give relations between microscopic and macroscopic apparent equilibrium constants as follows:

$$K_A' = K_1' + K_2' \qquad (5.69)$$

$$K_B' = \frac{K_3' K_4'}{K_4' + K_3'} \qquad (5.70)$$

Since there are three independent microscopic constants and but two macroscopic constants, the microscopic equilibrium constants are indeterminate if only titration data are available. However, chemical intuition and judgment can lead to a reasonable assumption about the value of one of the microscopic equilibrium constants. If it is assumed that K_2' for an amino acid, say alanine, is equal to the dissociation constant K_{HA}' of the alanine ester (which can have no carboxyl ionization), then K_1' can be directly calculated from Equation (5.69). When this is done, the ratio K_1'/K_2' is found to have the value $10^{5.4}$, and this is then strong experimental evidence for asserting that the zwitterionic form of alanine predominates overwhelmingly over the uncharged form in aqueous solution.[3]

Once it is known that experimentally for alanine the ratio K_1'/K_2' (and therefore according to Equation (5.66) the ratio K_4'/K_3') is very large compared to unity, it is possible to simplify Equations (5.69) and (5.70). Since K_1' is much larger than K_2', Equation (5.69) becomes

$$K_A' = K_1' \tag{5.71}$$

Equation (5.70) can be written without approximation as

$$K_B' = \frac{K_3'}{1 + \frac{K_3'}{K_4'}} \tag{5.72}$$

Since K_3'/K_4' is so small that it can be neglected with respect to unity, Equation (5.72) becomes, for alanine,

$$K_B' = K_3' \tag{5.73}$$

In this special case it is possible to identify both K_A' and K_B' individually with single microscopic steps. In general, however, this procedure is not possible.

Isoelectric and Isoionic Solutions. An isoelectric solution of a polyprotic acid is a solution in which the average net charge of all polyelectrolyte species is zero. There can be no isoelectric solution of a polycarboxylic acid, since the average net charge is always negative. However, for an amino acid the condition is simply satisfied. The net charge of $A^\pm$ and of A° is in each case zero, and only A^+ and A^- need be considered in the averaging. Since the charges on these species are equal and opposite, the isoelectric condition of the simple amino acid is

$$(A^+) = (A^-) \tag{5.74}$$

Solving the appropriate equilibrium-constant expressions for (A^+) and (A^-) permits use of Equation (5.74) to give

$$\{(A^\pm) + (A^\circ)\}\left\{\frac{(H^+)}{K_A'}\right\} = \{(A^\pm) + (A^\circ)\}\left\{\frac{K_B'}{(H^+)}\right\} \tag{5.75}$$

Division of both sides by the common factor and the slight rearrangement yields

$$(H^+)^2 = K_A'K_B' \tag{5.76}$$

[3] J. T. Edsall, "Dipolar Ions and Acid-Base Equilibria," Chapter 4 in E. J. Cohn and J. T. Edsall, *Proteins, Amino Acids and Peptides* (American Chemical Society Monograph No. 90). New York: Reinhold Publishing Corp., 1943.

The isoelectric pH is thus

$$pH_{isoelectric} = \frac{pK_A' + pK_B'}{2} \qquad (5.77)$$

Insofar as the apparent equilibrium constants are independent of concentration, the isoelectric pH is independent of concentration.

Electrophoresis is a convenient experimental technique for determining the isoelectric pH of a polyelectrolyte solution, and is often used for biological macromolecules. If equilibrium is rapidly established between the various ionic species, there will be no directional migration of ions when an isoelectric solution is subjected to an electric field. In an electrophoresis experiment, a solution is placed between two electrodes and some method, often optical, is employed to detect concentration changes and thus bulk migration of ions. If the average net charge is positive, migration toward the negative pole will occur. Migration toward the positive pole will be observed if the average net charge is negative, and no migration will occur for an isoelectric solution.

An *isoionic solution* of an acid in water is a solution in which the only ions present are the various forms of the acid and the two species, H^+ and OH^-, derived from the solvent water. The isoionic pH is a function of the concentration of the acid and in general has a value which is different from the isoelectric pH. Experimental determination of the isoionic pH is easily made by measuring the pH of a solution prepared by dissolving some pure acid in water. For a simple amino acid the isoionic condition can be stated by the electroneutrality equation

$$(A^+) + (H^+) = (A^-) + (OH^-) \qquad (5.78)$$

A conservation equation can be written as

$$[A] = (A^+) + (A^\pm) + (A^\circ) + (A^-) \qquad (5.79)$$

The ion product of water and Equations (5.67) and (5.68) can be combined with Equation (5.78) to give

$$(A^+) = \frac{\dfrac{K_w'}{(H^+)} - (H^+)}{1 - \dfrac{K_A'K_B'}{(H^+)^2}} \qquad (5.80)$$

Equations (5.67), (5.68), and (5.78) yield

$$[A] = (A^+)\left\{ 1 + \frac{K_A'}{(H^+)} + \frac{K_A'K_B'}{(H^+)^2} \right\} \qquad (5.81)$$

The concentration of A^+ can then be eliminated between Equations (5.80) and (5.81) to give the results

$$[A]\left\{ 1 - \frac{K_B'K_A'}{(H^+)^2} \right\} = \left\{ \frac{K_w'}{(H^+)} - (H^+) \right\}\left\{ 1 + \frac{K_A'}{(H^+)} + \frac{K_A'K_B'}{(H^+)^2} \right\} \qquad (5.82)$$

$$\left\{ 1 - \frac{K_B'K_A'}{(H^+)^2} \right\} = \frac{1}{[A]}\left\{ \frac{K_w'}{(H^+)} - (H^+) \right\}\left\{ 1 + \frac{K_A'}{(H^+)} + \frac{K_A'K_B'}{(H^+)^2} \right\} \qquad (5.83)$$

Equations (5.82) and (5.83) turn out to be some more of the ubiquitous fourth-degree equations. A value of (H^+) can be picked, substituted into either equation, and a value of [A] thus obtained. If the resulting value of [A] is positive and no greater than the solubility of A, then the calculation has given the (H^+) value for an isoionic solution of concentration [A]. This method of calculation proceeds smoothly when a desk calculator is available.

Two limiting cases are informative. In the limit of infinite dilution, [A] approaches zero and both sides of Equation (5.82) must likewise approach zero. If the right side is to be zero, then the factor

$$\frac{K_w'}{(H^+)} - (H^+)$$

must be zero. There thus results the limiting relation

$$\lim_{[A] \to 0} \left| (H^+)_{\text{isoionic}} = \{K_w'\}^{1/2} \right. \tag{5.84}$$

In like manner, when $1/[A]$ approaches zero and [A] increases without upper bound, Equation (5.83) shows that

$$1 - \frac{K_B' K_A'}{(H^+)^2}$$

must approach zero. This results in the mathematical statement

$$\lim_{[A] \to \infty} \left| (H^+)_{\text{isoionic}} = \{K_B' K_A'\}^{1/2} \right. \tag{5.85}$$

Equation (5.85) should be compared with Equation (5.76). This comparison reveals that the isoelectric pH and the isoionic pH approach the same value at high values of amino acid concentration. In experimental terms, however, this statement may not necessarily be very meaningful, since [A] cannot be increased to values greater than the solubility of the amino acid.

For the amino acid alanine at $25°C.$, numerical values for the isoionic hydrogen ion concentration differ by less than a factor of ten for the two limiting cases of low [A] and high [A]. The quantity $\{K_B' K_A'\}^{\frac{1}{2}}$ has the value $10^{-6.1}$, and thus the pH of any isoionic aqueous alanine solution at room temperature must have a value between 6.1 and 7.0.

Determination of Equilibrium Constants from Titration Data. When experimental methods such as absorption spectrophotometry permit direct determination of a curve of $(HA^-)/[A]$ vs (H^+), such a curve yields information about the values of the equilibrium constants. Differentiation of Equation (5.26), and setting the derivative equal to zero gives Equation (5.52)

$$(H^+)^2_{\max(HA^-)/[A]} = K_{H_2A}' K_{HA^-}'$$

If either equilibrium constant is known from other experiments, the second can be calculated from a knowledge of the (H^+) value at which $(HA^-)/[A]$ is a maximum.

A more general method of calculating the two apparent equilibrium constants from experimental titration data involves a rearrangement of Equation (5.12) into a form in which the equilibrium constants are grouped as multiplicative factors, as

$$\alpha = K_{H_2A}'K_{HA-}'\beta + K_{H_2A}' \tag{5.86}$$

where

$$\alpha = \frac{(H^+)^3 + (H^+)^2\left[\dfrac{V_{MOH}M_{MOH}}{V_{H_2A} + V_{MOH}}\right] - (H^+)K_w'}{(H^+)^2 + (H^+)\left[\dfrac{V_{MOH}M_{MOH} - V_{H_2A}M_{H_2A}}{V_{H_2A} + V_{MOH}}\right] - K_w'} \tag{5.87}$$

$$\beta = \frac{(H^+)^2 + (H^+)\left[\dfrac{V_{MOH}M_{MOH} - 2V_{H_2A}M_{H_2A}}{V_{H_2A} + V_{MOH}}\right] - K_w'}{(H^+)^3 + (H^+)^2\left[\dfrac{V_{MOH}M_{MOH} - V_{H_2A}M_{H_2A}}{V_{H_2A} + V_{MOH}}\right] - K_w'(H^+)} \tag{5.88}$$

A plot of α vs β gives the product $K_{H_2A}'K_{HA-}'$ as slope and K_{H_2A}' as intercept. Slope divided by intercept is K_{HA-}', and thus this graphical method gives a value for each equilibrium constant.

When graphing experimental points it is important to use data from regions of the titration curve in which the shape of the curve is strongly dependent on the values of the equilibrium constants. Equation (5.24) shows that the shape of the titration curve is the same for all diprotic acids if the solution is sufficiently basic, and thus it is not possible to obtain information about the two equilibrium constants in solutions of such high pH.

When n is Large. It should be manifestly clear at this point that detailed information about the individual dissociation steps of an n-protic acid is not easily or simply obtained from experimental titration curves when n is very large. And yet chemists studying macromolecules such as nucleic acids, proteins, and synthetic polyelectrolytes are interested in obtaining as much information as possible from the titration curves of these substances, principally because some of the most distinctive properties of these materials derive from their polyprotic nature.

When n is large, concentrations of the separate species are usually not individually determinable. A more meaningful experimental quantity is the average number of protons associated with each molecule of the acid at a given set of conditions of pH, temperature, pressure, ionic strength, etc. This average number of protons is termed $\bar{v}$.

The quantity $\bar{v}$ gives no information about the chemical state of any specific molecule. Being an average of the protonation states of many molecules, $\bar{v}$ gives information about the system as a whole. In order to characterize the system, a chemist would like to find out how the many molecular species are distributed about this average, and what fraction of the molecules exist with a specified number of protons. Since there are many combining sites for protons on a polyprotic acid, the most detailed description would give information about how these protons are arranged on the individual molecules. It should be pointed out that a description in such complete detail was not possible for amino acids using titration data alone. For poly-acids with many combining sites the problem is much more complicated, and a variety of simplified models are used to gain at least a qualitative understanding of the processes involved. One approach to this problem is examined in Chapter 9.

Problems

5.1. For the triprotic acid, H_3A, derive an expression for the fraction $(H_2A^-)/[A]$ as a function of (H^+) and three equilibrium constants. Find the limiting values of the fraction for the special cases of very low (H^+) and very high (H^+).

5.2. Plot a graph of ionic strength versus V_{NaOH} in a titration of 0.1 molar H_2SO_3 with 0.1 molar NaOH.

5.3. Figure 5.4 is a plot of three distribution curves for succinic acid. Some chemists prefer another type of distribution diagram, in which the functions plotted are

$$\frac{(H_2A)}{[A]} \text{ vs pH}$$

$$\frac{\{(H_2A) + (HA^-)\}}{[A]} \text{ vs pH}$$

For succinic acid, plot these two functions on the same set of coordinate axes, and then discuss the significance of the various areas of this distribution diagram.

5.4. Consider a solution prepared by mixing together one mole oxalic acid, some NaOH, some HCl, and enough water to make a total volume of one liter. Calculate the concentrations of H_2Ox, HOx^-, and $Ox^=$ in the solution for the cases when the pH is 2.00, 4.00, 6.00, and 8.00. Make use of distribution fractions, noting that

$$(H_2Ox) = \frac{(H_2Ox)}{[Ox]} [Ox]$$

$$(HOx^-) = \frac{(HOx^-)}{[Ox]} [Ox]$$

and so forth. For oxalic acid, $pK_{HOx^-}' = 4.0$, $pK_{H_2Ox}' = 1.0$.

Suggestions for Further Study

1. It was shown on page 93 that in the limiting case in which all four microscopic equilibrium constants for a dicarboxylic acid are equal, the

first and second macroscopic dissociation constants differ for statistical reasons by a factor of four. Since both carboxyl groups are "intrinsically identical," an observed ratio of dissociation constants different from four might well be interpreted in terms of electrostatic interactions. Some representative papers dealing with quantitative aspects of this problem include:

J. G. Kirkwood and F. H. Westheimer, *J. Chem. Phys.* **6**, 506, 513 (1938); *Trans. Faraday Soc.* **43**, 77 (1947).

√ C. Tanford, *J. Am. Chem. Soc.* **79**, 5348 (1957).

√ M. J. S. Dewar and P. J. Grisdale, *J. Am. Chem. Soc.* **84**, 3539, 3541, 3546, 3548 (1962).

2. Equilibria involved in the titration of tyrosine involves twelve microscopic equilibrium constants, and all twelve have been evaluated experimentally. Details are given in R. B. Martin, J. T. Edsall, D. B. Wetlaufer, and B. R. Hollingworth, *J. Biol. Chem.* **233**, 1429 (1958).

3. Titration of a carbon dioxide solution with strong base can be followed with a pH meter, and the experimental titration curve shows an inflection point about midway in the titration with however no clear indication of the equivalence point at which $2[M] = [CO_2]$. An elegant spectrophotometric titration method has been described [A. L. Underwood and L. H. Howe III, *Anal. Chem.* **34**, 692 (1962)]. It is found experimentally that a plot of optical absorbance, A, vs volume of titrant is linear throughout a substantial portion of the titration, and that an accurate equivalence point can be located by extrapolation of the linear portion of the curve. Absorbance is determined in the ultraviolet at a wavelength of 235 mμ. The absorbance at 235 mμ of a solution containing various carbonate species can be reasonably well approximated by

$$A = \epsilon(CO_3^{--})$$

where ϵ is the molar extinction coefficient of CO_3^{--}.

Critically examine this titration. Does a calculated plot of titrant volume versus absorbance turn out to have a linear portion? Why should a linear extrapolation yield the equivalence point?

6

Acid-Base Titrations
in Nonaqueous Solvents

Man is inescapably involved in the chemistry of aqueous media. In vivo biochemistry is aqueous chemistry, food preparation is aqueous chemistry, and agriculture is aqueous chemistry. It is no evolutionary and ecological accident that a prospering water-based biological community such as ours exists in the midst of a plentiful supply of water, and in a temperature range between the boiling point and the freezing point of aqueous solutions. Chemists work in laboratories in which hot, cold, and distilled water, steam, and ice are available as general utilities. Because of toxicity, flammability, cost, and legal restrictions, solvents other than water are often treated as special reagents. Many nonaqueous solvents must be kept away from oxygen, light, flames, and water. Temperatures colder than or hotter than room temperature are frequently needed, if the reactions are to be carried out in the liquid phases. It is foolish, albeit easy, to ignore the many advantages of solvents other than distilled water for specific reactions.

Only a chemist who works mostly with aqueous solutions really finds it meaningful to divide all acid-base chemistry into aqueous chemistry and nonaqueous chemistry. Each solvent has its own advantages and disadvantages, its own characteristics, and its own peculiarities. If quantitative experiments are to be interpreted in a solvent other than water, the solvent must be considered as its own special case. Bearing these important considerations in mind, a few generalizations will be made, and then the particular case of acetic acid as a solvent will be examined.

If acid-base reactions are defined as the chemical reactions involving proton transfer, then solvents can be divided into two groups for a particular acid-base reaction. In some solvents the reaction may proceed by molecular collision of the acid and the base, with resulting direct proton transfer. In other solvents the same reaction may proceed by both acid and base transferring protons with solvent, the solvent providing a pool of protons available for reaction. This basis for classification involves a distinction in terms of kinetic mechanism, an important distinction when rates of reaction are interpreted, but often a meaningless distinction when equilibrium properties are being considered.

When transfer of protons involves a pool of solvent protons, then the solvent exerts a leveling effect on acid and base strength. If the solvent does not contribute a pool of protons, then each acid-base couple can be treated independently of the solvent, and no leveling effect need be considered. From the point of view of equilibrium calculations, both protic and aprotic solvents can be considered on a continuum, with some equilibrium constant functioning as K_w' does for water having widely different values. It is to be expected that dissociation constants will be different in different solvents.

Solvents differ widely in physical properties such as melting point, boiling point, vapor pressure, surface tension, viscosity, toxicity, and reactivity with air. Some solvents are particularly suited for use with a glass burette, since they yield very small drops and have no noticeable meniscus at the solvent-glass interface. Use of a Teflon stopcock eliminates the messy problem of stopcock grease dissolving in the titrant. There is often no necessity for a reaction to be performed on a desk top in an open beaker at room temperature, although such experiments are convenient. If low temperature thermostats are employed, and if the solutions can be contained in a closed atmosphere which excludes the experimenter, the range of accessible experiments can be extended significantly. It is vital that temperature and pressure be so controlled so that solvent does not evaporate from standardized solutions.

Simple glass electrodes, calomel electrodes, and metal electrodes respond surprisingly well in a variety of nonaqueous media, with a few pecularities. Glass electrodes change properties drastically when dehydrated, and so when glass electrodes are used in dehydrating media, complications are to be expected. Dehydration does not necessarily preclude use of glass electrodes, but special conditioning procedures may be required. Some amazing effects on behavior of glass electrodes due to traces of K^+ have been reported.[1] Electrodes containing aqueous filling solutions must be used within a restricted temperature range which can extend as low as $-5\,°C$ and as high as $+110\,°C$, but which often is from $+5$ to $+50\,°C$.[2] Reference electrodes having a liquid-liquid junction between an aqueous filling solution and the nonaqueous sample present special problems. In some cases rate processes across this boundary may be very slow and equilibrium behavior may be

[1]G. A. Harlow, *Anal. Chem.*, **34,** 149 (1962).
[2]Modified calomel and glass electrodes useful to temperatures as low as $-30\,°C$ have been described by L. v. D. Berg, *Anal. Chem.* **32,** 628 (1960).

difficult to attain. The precise nature of electron-transfer reactions at the various metal electrodes is not understood, but the reactions are certainly different in different solvents, and an empirical approach to electrode performance is often required. It is worthwhile to consult the chemical literature for collective experience of other chemists before undertaking measurements in an unfamiliar solvent.

Throughout this book a dual approach is taken toward the role of solvents. The solvent is considered as a supporting medium which permits preparation of arbitrarily dilute solutions in which chemical species under consideration can be separated by a region of solvent. Somehow the solvent interacts with solute, but the details of how this interaction occurs are not considered, and the effect of all interactions is summarized in the numerical values of the various equilibrium constants. A second role of solvent in acid-base reactions involves the ability of many solvents to supply a pool of solvated protons, and this ability is interpreted usually as an autoionization reaction characterized by an equilibrium constant such as K_w' for water. An alternative coordination model is discussed lucidly by Drago and Purcell.[3]

Titration in Glacial Acetic Acid. Glacial acetic acid is said to be a differentiating solvent for acids, since $HClO_4$, H_2SO_4, and HCl which act as strong acids in water have observably different strengths in glacial acetic acid. The strongest acid, $HClO_4$, is a common titrant, and equations will be developed below for the titration of the base pyridine with $HClO_4$ in glacial acetic acid. The symbols Py and PyH^+ will be used to represent pyridine and pyridine with a protonated nitrogen.

The chemical model for this system includes the chemical species Py, PyH^+, $HClO_4$, ClO_4^-, CH_3—$COOH$, CH_3—COO^-, and H^+. The symbol H^+ is as usual representing a solvated proton, and just as in water the actual species are a series beginning with H_3O^+, in glacial acetic acid the actual species are CH_3—$COOH_2^+$ and perhaps larger aggregates. Three equilibria will be considered:

$$PyH^+ \rightleftarrows Py + H^+ \qquad K_{PyH^+}' = \frac{(Py)(H^+)}{(PyH^+)} \qquad (6.1)$$

$$HClO_4 \rightleftarrows H^+ + ClO_4^- \qquad K_{HClO_4}' = \frac{(H^+)(ClO_4^-)}{(HClO_4)} \qquad (6.2)$$

$$CH_3-COOH \rightleftarrows H^+ + CH_3-COO^- \quad K_{CH_3-COOH}' = (H^+)(CH_3-COO^-) \qquad (6.3)$$

As is conventional, the activity of the solvent is taken as unity in the pure solvent, and the activity coefficient is incorporated in the apparent equilibrium constant in Equation (6.3). The two conservation equations are

$$[Py] = (Py) + PyH^+) \qquad (6.4)$$

$$[ClO_4] = (HClO_4) + (ClO_4^-) \qquad (6.5)$$

[3]R. S. Drago and K. F. Purcell, *Prog. Inorg. Chem.*, **6**, 271 (1964).

Electroneutrality requirement is

$$(PyH^+) + (H^+) = (ClO_4^-) + (CH_3\text{---}COO^-) \tag{6.6}$$

Substitution into Equation (6.6) of results obtained by combination of Equations (6.1) through (6.5) yields

$$\frac{[Py]}{\dfrac{K_{PyH^+}'}{(H^+)} + 1} + (H^+) = \frac{[ClO_4]}{\dfrac{(H^+)}{K_{HClO_4}'} + 1} + \frac{K_{CH_3COOH}'}{(H^+)} \tag{6.7}$$

Rearrangement leads to

$$
\begin{aligned}
&(H^+)^4 + (H^+)^3\{[Py] + K_{PyH^+}' + K_{HClO_4}'\} \\
&+ (H^+)^2\{[Py]K_{HClO_4}' + K_{PyH^+}'K_{HClO_4}' - [ClO_4]K_{HClO_4}' - K_{CH_3\text{---}COOH}'\} \\
&+ (H^+)\{ -[ClO_4]K_{HClO_4}'K_{PyH^+}' - K_{CH_3\text{---}COOH}'K_{PyH^+}' - K_{HClO_4}'K_{CH_3\text{---}COOH}'\} \\
&- K_{CH_3\text{---}COOH}'K_{PyH^+}'K_{HClO_4}' = 0 \tag{6.8}
\end{aligned}
$$

Equation (6.8) is very nearly the same as the result found in problem (4.11) for the titration of a weak acid with a weak base in water. Transformation to volume variables is made by use of

$$[ClO_4] = \frac{V_{HClO_4}M_{HClO_4}}{V_{HClO_4} + V_{Py}} \tag{6.9}$$

$$[Py] = \frac{V_{Py}M_{Py}}{V_{HClO_4} + V_{Py}} \tag{6.10}$$

Introduction of Equations (6.9) and (6.10) into Equation (6.8) gives, after rearrangement,

$$
V_{HClO_4} = -V_{Py}\left\{
\frac{
\begin{aligned}
&(H^+)^4 + (H^+)^3[M_{Py} + K_{PyH^+}' + K_{HClO_4}'] \\
&+ (H^+)^2[M_{Py}K_{HClO_4}' + K_{PyH^+}'K_{HClO_4}' - K_{CH_3\text{---}COOH}'] \\
&+ (H^+)[-K_{CH_3\text{---}COOH}'K_{PyH^+}' - K_{CH_3\text{---}COOH}'K_{HClO_4}'] \\
&- K_{CH_3\text{---}COOH}'K_{PyH^+}'K_{HClO_4}'
\end{aligned}
}{
\begin{aligned}
&(H^+)^4 + (H^+)^3[K_{PyH^+}' + K_{HClO_4}'] \\
&+ (H^+)^2[K_{PyH^+}'K_{HClO_4}' - K_{CH_3\text{---}COOH}' - K_{HClO_4}'M_{HClO_4}] \\
&+ (H^+)[-K_{HClO_4}'K_{PyH^+}'M_{HClO_4} - K_{CH_3\text{---}COOH}'K_{PyH^+}' \\
&\qquad - K_{CH_3\text{---}COOH}'K_{HClO_4}'] \\
&- K_{CH_3\text{---}COOH}'K_{PyH^+}'K_{HClO_4}'
\end{aligned}
}
\right\} \tag{6.11}
$$

Equation (6.11) is plotted in Figure (6.1), using the following set of numerical values for the various equilibrium constants, concentrations, and sample volume:

$$K_{CH_3\text{---}COOH}' = 3.6 \times 10^{-14}$$

$$K_{HClO_4}' = 1.34 \times 10^{-5}$$

$$K_{PyH^+}' = 4.5 \times 10^{-9}$$

$$M_{HClO_4} = 0.100 \text{ moles per liter}$$

$$M_{Py} = 0.100 \text{ moles per liter}$$

$$V_{Py} = 25.00 \text{ ml}$$

The equation is then

$$V_{HClO_4} = -V_{Py} \left\{ \frac{\begin{array}{c}(H^+)^4 + 0.100(H^+)^3 + (1.34 \times 10^{-6})(H^+)^2 \\ - (4.8 \times 10^{-20})(H^+) - 2.17 \times 10^{-28}\end{array}}{\begin{array}{c}(H^+)^4 + (1.34 \times 10^{-5})(H^+)^3 - (1.34 \times 10^{-6})(H^+)^2 \\ - (6.0 \times 10^{-15})(H^+) - 2.17 \times 10^{-28}\end{array}} \right\} \tag{6.12}$$

The titration curve in Figure 6.1 shows an inflection point very near the equivalence point. If a suitable electrode combination can be found, poten-

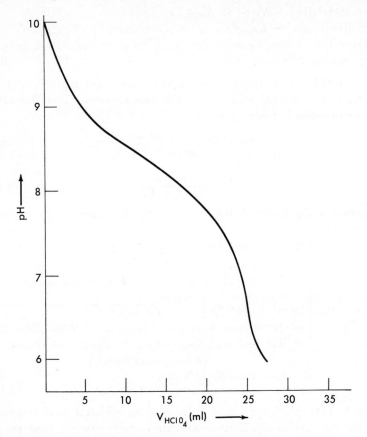

Figure 6.1. Titration Curve of Pyridine with Perchloric Acid in Glacial Acetic Acid.

tiometric detection of an endpoint should be possible. The glass electrode functions well in glacial acetic acid, but some calomel electrode assemblies which utilize a fiber junction between internal filling solution and sample do not come to stable equilibrium in glacial acetic acid. A silver–silver chloride electrode makes a good reference electrode, as does a simple silver metal electrode.

The symbol "(H^+)" refers in aqueous solution to a proton surrounded by a water molecule, but in acetic acid it refers to a proton surrounded by acetic acid molecules. There is no a priori reason to expect a simple correspondence between glass electrode response in the two systems, and so if pH is to be operationally defined in the acetic acid system, it must be realized that acetic acid pH and water pH are two different quantities. In order to avoid confusion, nonaqueous titration curves are often reported in either "arbitrary pH units" or more simply merely in terms of millivolts.

If K_{CH_3-COOH}' Were Zero. If K_{CH_3-COOH}' had the value zero, then a limiting form of Equation (6.11) could be obtained in which several terms disappear. When numerical values given above are substituted, there results an equation analogous to Equation (6.12), namely

$$V_{HClO_4} = -V_{Py}\left\{ \frac{(H^+)^3 + 0.100(H^+)^2 + (1.34 \times 10^{-6})(H^+)}{(H^+)^3 + (1.34 \times 10^{-5})(H^+) - (1.34 \times 10^{-6})(H^+)} \atop \qquad\qquad\qquad - 6.0 \times 10^{-15} \right\}$$

$$(6.13)$$

Within the range of pH and V_{HClO_4} plotted in Figure 6.1, the two equations (6.13) and (6.12) give identical calculated values of V_{HClO_4} as a function of (H^+).

For many solvents autoionization does not occur. If autoionization does not occur, then there will probably not be a pool of protons available from the solvent, and consequently the value of (H^+), whatever is meant by the symbol in this aprotic solvent, will be zero. It is therefore misleading to perform a derivation in terms of (H^+) for equilibria in an aprotic solvent. A more meaningful derivation considers a chemical model which includes the species PyH^+, Py, $HClO_4$, and ClO_4^- reacting according to the chemical equation

$$PyH^+ + ClO_4^- \rightleftarrows Py + HClO_4 \qquad (6.14)$$

All reference to the proton and to the solvent is eliminated, and the solvent is reduced to the role of a supporting medium. The solvent is inert in terms of the formulation of equilibria, and all chemical interactions between solvent and solute, important as they may be in certain cases, enter the mathematical discussion only by way of the numerical values of the parameter K', the apparent equilibrium constant for reaction (6.14).

In protic solvents equilibrium is established among the reacting acid-base couples, the endpoint indicator, and the indicating pH electrode assembly by means of the pool of solvent protons, and thus there is great flexibility in the possible combinations of endpoint indicators, electrodes, and acid-base couples themselves. If autoionization does not occur, then equilibrium must be established by direct proton exchange between reactant molecules. For a variety of kinetic and mechanistic reasons, such chemical reactions may be extremely slow and quite specific.

In the absence of the equilibrating species H^+, there is the important question of what variable is to be plotted versus volume in the titration curve. An appropriate variable can be defined in terms of the equilibrium constant for (6.14) written as

$$K' = \frac{(Py)(HClO_4)}{(PyH^+)(ClO_4^-)} \tag{6.15}$$

$$K'\frac{(PyH^+)}{(Py)} = \frac{(HClO_4)}{(ClO_4^-)} = \varphi \tag{6.16}$$

where φ is the acid-base quotient, a quantity which changes monotonically throughout a titration and which changes especially rapidly in the vicinity of a sharp endpoint inflection. The quantity φ is convenient for describing endpoint indicators. If the reaction

$$ClO_4^- + HI \rightleftarrows I^- + HClO_4 \qquad K_I' = \frac{(I^-)(HClO_4)}{(HI)(ClO_4^-)} \tag{6.17}$$

occurs involving the indicator species I^- and HI, then combination of Equations (6.16) and (6.17) gives

$$\frac{(HClO_4)}{(ClO_4^-)} = K_I'\frac{(HI)}{(I^-)} = \varphi \tag{6.18}$$

If one knows how φ changes during a titration, it is a simple matter to calculate how the ratio $(HI)/(I^-)$ changes if the indicator equilibrium constant is known.

Problems

6.1. Show that under certain limiting conditions Equation (6.11) reduces to the equation of a strong acid-strong base titration, and of a strong base-weak acid titration. What are these limiting conditions?

6.2. Consider a titration in an aprotic solvent. Include in the chemical model reactions (6.14) and (6.17). Obtain an equation for the fraction $(HI)/(I^-)$ as a function of titrant volume added.

6.3. Critically examine Equations (6.8) and (6.11) for the conditions of concentration and values of equilibrium constants which combine to give a sharp inflection in the titration curve near equivalence.

6.4. Formulate the chemical and mathematical models for a titration in anhydrous ammonia [W. C. Fernelius and G. B. Bowman, *Chem. Rev.* **26**, 3 (1940): C. A. Kraus, *Chem. Rev.* **26**, 95 (1940)]. In sulfur dioxide [N. N. Lichtin, *Prog. Phys. Org. Chem.* **1**, 75 (1963)]. In tertiary butyl alcohol [L. W. Marple and J. S. Fritz, *Anal. Chem.* **35**, 1223, 1431 (1963)].

6.5. In the discussion of Equation (6.13), it is asserted that Equations (6.13) and (6.12) give identical results within a limited range of pH and V_{HClO_4} values. Under what conditions does a nonzero value of K_{CH_4-COOH}' affect the shape of the titration curve? Be quantitative.

Suggestions for Experimental Investigations

1. The titration curve of sodium formate in water shows no detectable inflection point at the equivalence point when aqueous hydrochloric acid is used as titrant. A sharp endpoint is observed when the titration is performed in glacial acetic acid using perchloric acid as titrant. Determine such a titration curve. Standardization of the perchloric acid can be made by titration of potassium acid phthalate in glacial acetic acid. This standardization titration cannot be performed in water so as to yield a detectable endpoint, but the endpoint is quite sharp in acetic acid. From the shapes of the titration curves, estimate if possible one or more of the relevant apparent equilibrium constants. It may be necessary to employ a mixed equilibrium constant for analysis of the titration curves, considering (H^+) defined by pH given by the pH meter.

2. Consult the chemical literature and find a method of titrating phenols. Evaluate one of the procedures by performing a titration, following the titration perhaps with both indicator and an indicating electrode assembly. A few research papers which may give some guidance are:

Ethylenediamine solvent: M. L. Moss, J. H. Elliott, and R. T. Hall, *Anal. Chem.* **20,** 784 (1948).

Dimethylformamide solvent: J. P. Butler and T. P. Czepiel, *Anal. Chem.* **28,** 1468 (1956).

Tetrabutylammonium hydroxide titrant: G. A. Harlow, C. M. Noble, and G. E. A. Wyld, *Anal. Chem.* **28,** 787 (1956).

3. When no solvent seems to have the appropriate properties for an analytical application, a mixed-solvent system can be considered. Fritz discusses some mixed solvent titrations [J. S. Fritz, *Anal. Chem.* **24,** 306 (1952)] for analysis of organic nitrogen salts. Repeat one of these titrations, and then observe the effect if any of altering the ratios of solvent constituents.

Bibliographical Note

An excellent monograph on theory and methodology of nonaqueous titrations is J. Kucharský and L. Šafařík, *Titrations in Non-Aqueous Solvents*, trans. by K. Šumbera, Amsterdam: Elsevier Publishing Company, 1965. Other general references are:

A. H. Beckett and E. H. Tinley, *Titrations in Non-Aqueous Solvents*, 2d ed. Poole, England: British Drug Houses Ltd., 1957.

J. S. Fritz, *Acid-Base Titrations in Nonaqueous Solvents*, Columbus, Ohio: G. Frederick Smith Chemical Company, 1952.

S. R. Palit, M. N. Das, and G. R. Somayajulu, *Non-Aqueous Titration*, Calcutta: Indian Association for the Cultivation of Science, 1954.

I. M. Kolthoff and S. Bruckenstein, "Acid-Base Equilibria in Nonaqueous

Solutions," Chap. 13, part I, sect. B of I. M. Kolthoff and P. J. Elving, eds., *Treatise on Analytical Chemistry*, New York: Interscience Publishers, Inc., 1959.

Two good general books on chemistry in nonaqueous solvents are H. H. Sisler, *Chemistry in Non-Aqueous Solvents*, New York: Reinhold Publishing Corporation, 1961, and L. F. Audrieth and J. Kleinberg, *Non-Aqueous Solvents*, New York: John Wiley & Sons, 1953.

7

Complex-ion Equilibria

Many interesting chemical species are conveniently classified together as complex ions. A complex ion is a chemical species containing a central ion, usually a metal ion, to which is attached one or more ligands. A ligand may be a monatomic ion such as chloride, a solvent molecule, an organic entity such as ethylenediamine, or just about anything else which will form one or more chemical bonds with the central ion, the nuclear ion of the complex.

Chemistry of complex ions which contain transition-metal ions as nuclei has been intensively studied and this is an active area of theoretical and experimental research. Use of complex formation as an analytical tool has provided simple titration methods for determination of trace amounts of many polyvalent cations. There has been considerable investigation of equilibria involving reactions of metal ions with molecules of particular biochemical interest. Complex formation involving ore-forming metals has been recognized as important in geochemical ore deposition.

Titration of a cation with a reagent which forms a one-one complex in solution results in a rather simple titration curve. The only reaction which needs to be considered is

$$B + X \rightleftarrows BX \qquad (7.1)$$

where B is some metal ion, X a ligand species, and BX the complex ion. Indicated charges have been omitted from the ions for the sake of generality and simplicity, and because the electroneutrality equation will not be needed. The apparent equilibrium constant, written as a formation constant, is

$$K' = \frac{(BX)}{(B)(X)} \qquad (7.2)$$

117

Two conservation equations are needed:

$$[B] = (B) + (BX) \tag{7.3}$$

$$[X] = (X) + (BX) \tag{7.4}$$

No harm is done in writing down an electroneutrality equation, but it gives no additional information. Equations (7.2), (7.3), and (7.4) can be combined to eliminate both (X) and (BX), yielding

$$(B)^2 + (B)\left\{[X] - [B] + \frac{1}{K'}\right\} - \frac{[B]}{K'} = 0 \tag{7.5}$$

Alternatively, (B) and (BX) can be eliminated to give

$$(X)^2 + (X)\left\{[B] - [X] + \frac{1}{K'}\right\} - \frac{[X]}{K'} = 0 \tag{7.6}$$

Any distinction between central ion and ligand is arbitrary for a one-one complex, and the equations developed make no such distinction. The arbitrary choice of the metal as central ion is of course made in anticipation of additional binding of ligands about a single metal ion. Polynuclear complexes are, however, more common than sometimes suspected.

Suppose the titrant MX is being dispensed from a buret into a flask containing BY in solution, the cation M and the anion Y so chosen that they participate in no complex formation reactions. Then the burette readings give V_{MX} directly, and the familiar type of variable change is

$$[X] = \frac{V_{MX}M_{MX}}{V_{MX} + V_{BY}} \tag{7.7}$$

$$[B] = \frac{V_{BY}M_{BY}}{V_{MX} + V_{BY}} \tag{7.8}$$

Equations (7.5), (7.7), and (7.8) combine to give

$$V_{MX} = V_{BY}\left[\frac{-(B)^2 + (B)\left\{M_{BY} - \frac{1}{K'}\right\} + \frac{M_{BY}}{K'}}{(B)^2 + (B)\left\{M_{MX} + \frac{1}{K'}\right\}}\right] \tag{7.9}$$

At the equivalence point, $[X] = [B]$, and Equation (7.5) becomes

$$(B)_e = \frac{-1 + \sqrt{1 + 4[B]K'}}{2K'} \tag{7.10}$$

where $(B)_e$ is the concentration of B at equivalence. Equation (7.10) gives the physically-required result

$$\lim_{[B]\to 0}\left|(B)_e = 0\right. \tag{7.11}$$

Equation (7.11) is correct, but it misses an important chemical consideration. Using the binomial expansion[1] for the square root, Equation (7.10) becomes

$$(B)_e = \frac{2[B]K' - 2[B]^2 K'^2 + \cdots}{2K'} \tag{7.12}$$

for the case in which $4[B]K'$ is less than unity. If $4[B]K'$ is small enough, then

$$2[B]K' \gg 2[B]^2 K'^2$$

The limiting result can be stated as

$$\lim_{[B] \ll 1/4K'} \Big| (B)_e = [B] = [X] \tag{7.13}$$

If the concentrations are small compared to $1/K'$, then no significant complexation will occur at the equivalence point. In fact, this condition applied to Equations (7.5) and (7.6) requires that throughout the titration $[B] = (B)$ and $[X] = (X)$.

An appreciation of how the magnitude of the formation constant affects the shape of the titration curve can be gained by examination of Figures 7.1 and 7.2 Each of the curves is plotted from Equation (7.9) with $M_{BY} = M_{MX} = 0.100$ moles per liter and $V_{BY} = 25.00$ ml, but the value of K' is taken to be 1, 10, 10,000, and 10,000,000,000. For each of the titrations represented in Figure 7.1, a substantial fraction of $[B]$ is present as B at the equivalence point. This fact demands that the properties of the solution will be very much the same just before and just after the equivalence point; there is not opportunity for a dramatic concentration change, because all relevant concentrations are comparable in magnitude to concentrations in the titrant. The situation is qualitatively different in the titration shown in Figure 7.2. When 24.95 ml of titrant have been added, only 0.1 percent of $[B]$ remains uncomplexed. Less than 0.10 ml of titrant then converts the solution from the case in which $(B) \gg (X)$ to the case in which $(B) \ll (X)$.

For large enough values of K', the titration curve from beginning to the equivalence point is independent of the value of K'. Equation (7.9) becomes

$$V_{MX} = V_{BY} \left\{ \frac{-(B)^2 + M_{BY}(B)}{(B)^2 + M_{MX}(B)} \right\} \tag{7.14}$$

and this expression stays the same no matter how much larger K' becomes. The region following equivalence is given by

$$V_{MX} = V_{BY} \frac{M_{BY}}{M_{MX}} \left\{ \frac{(B) + \dfrac{1}{K'}}{(B)} \right\} \tag{7.15}$$

---

[1]If x^2 is less than unity, then the binomial expression $(1 + x)^n$ can be written as an infinite series. The first few terms in the expansion are

$$(1 + x)^n = 1 + nx + \frac{(n - 1)nx^2}{2!} + \frac{(n - 2)(n - 1)nx^3}{3!} + \cdots$$

The quantities 2! and 3! are factorials. Thus $2! = (1)(2)$, and $3! = (1)(2)(3)$.

and the shape of the titration curve is determined in part by the value of K'. The greater the value of K', the greater the change of (B) at the equivalence point.

The principal difference between the titration of an acid by a base in water, and the titration of a metal by a ligand in water, is that there is a nonzero lower limit to (H$^+$) in water, but there is nothing to prevent (B) from becoming arbitrarily close to zero except the values of K', [B], and [X].

Multiple-Ligand Complexes. To characterize the equilibria in a chemical system containing metal ions, ligands, and the resulting complexes, a chemist seeks answers to several types of questions: What is the stoichiometric composition of each of the complexes? When several mole-

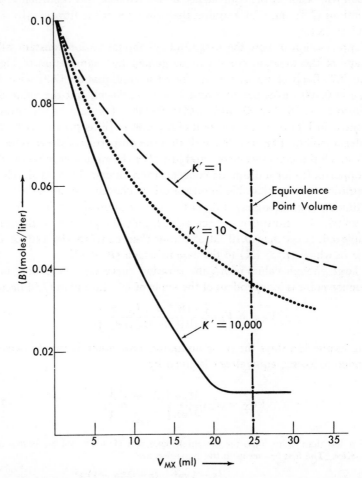

Figure 7.1. Titration Curves for One-One Complex Plotted for Three Values of the Equilibrium Constant. $M_{MX} = M_{BY} = 0.100$ moles per liter, $V_{BY} = 25.00$ ml.

cules of the ligand are combined with a single metal ion, what are the step-wise equilibrium constants for successive attachment of ligands? What is the effect of competitive equilibria, such as acid-base equilibria, on the reactions being studied?

Search for answers to questions such as these may begin by postulation of a certain set of chemical reactions which in turn yields a mathematical model, analysis of the mathematical model to make predictions about the macroscopic properties of the system, and then comparison of these predictions with the properties which are observed experimentally. Algebraic procedures are much the same as those used in working with other equilibria; all relevant equilibrium constant expressions and conservation equations are written down, and then these are combined and pondered.

The following discussion will be limited to mononuclear complexes, com-

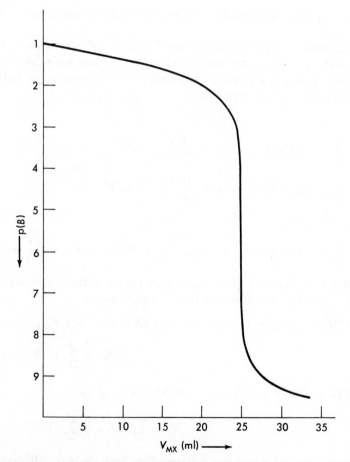

Figure 7.2. Titration Curve for One-One Complex Plotted for $K' = 10^{10}$. $M_{MX} = M_{BY} = 0.100$ moles per liter, $V_{BY} = 25.00$ ml.

plexes whose formation in solution can be described by a set of chemical equations such as

$$B + X \rightleftarrows BX_1 \qquad K_1' = \frac{(BX_1)}{(B)(X)}$$

$$BX_1 + X \rightleftarrows BX_2 \qquad K_2' = \frac{(BX_2)}{(BX_1)(X)}$$

$$\cdots \qquad\qquad \cdots \qquad\qquad (7.16)$$

$$BX_{i-1} + X \rightleftarrows BX_i \qquad K_i' = \frac{(BX_i)}{(BX_{i-1})(X)}$$

$$\cdots \qquad\qquad \cdots$$

$$BX_{n-1} + X \rightleftarrows BX_n \qquad K_n' = \frac{(BX_n)}{(BX_{n-1})(X)}$$

A maximum of n ligand molecules can react with a single B ion in this reaction scheme.

The apparent equilibrium constants K_1', K_2', $\cdots$, K_n' are stepwise equilibrium constants. These stepwise equilibrium constants are related to a set of β's, the overall equilibrium constants for the formation of individual chemical species, by the equations

$$\beta_0 = 1$$

$$B + X \rightleftarrows BX_1 \qquad \beta_1 = \frac{(BX_1)}{(B)(X)} = K_1'$$

$$B + 2X \rightleftarrows BX_2 \qquad \beta_2 = \frac{(BX_2)}{(B)(X)^2} = K_1'K_2' \qquad (7.17)$$

$$\cdots \qquad\qquad \cdots$$

$$B + iX \rightleftarrows BX_i \qquad \beta_i = \frac{(BX_i)}{(B)(X)^i} = K_1'K_2'\cdots K_i' = \prod_{j=1}^{i} K_j'$$

The capital Greek pi indicates a multiplication of the i different factors K_1', K_2', $\cdots$, K_i. The two conservation equations are

$$[X] = (X) + (BX_1) + 2(BX_2) + \cdots + i(BX_i) + \cdots + n(BX_n)$$

$$= (X) + \sum_{i=1}^{n} i(BX_i) \qquad (7.18)$$

$$[B] = (B) + (BX_1) + (BX_2) + \cdots + (BX_i) + \cdots + (BX_n)$$

$$= (B) + \sum_{i=1}^{n} (BX_i) = \sum_{i=0}^{n} (BX_i) \qquad (7.19)$$

Note that in the more compact notation of the indicated sum, (B) is replaced by the equivalent but unconventional symbol (BX_0).

Distribution of Species. A set of equations will now be derived to relate the fractions $(B)/[B]$, $(BX_1)/[B]$, $\cdots$, $(BX_n)/[B]$ to the β's and thus to the K's. To find the equation

$$\frac{(B)}{[B]} = f(\beta\text{'s})$$

Equations (7.17) and (7.19) are combined to give

$$[B] = (B)\beta_0 + (B)(X)\beta_1 + (B)(X)^2\beta_2 + \cdots + (B)(X)^n\beta_n = (B) \sum_{i=0}^{n} \beta_i(X)^i$$
(7.20)

Equation (7.20) yields directly

$$\frac{(B)}{[B]} = \frac{1}{\sum_{i=0}^{n} \beta_i(X)^i}$$
(7.21)

Note that the fraction $(B)/[B]$ is equal to unity when (X) is zero, and is a monotonically decreasing function of (X).

To get a similar expression for $(BX_1)/[B]$, Equations (7.17) are transformed by dividing each equation by β_1. This gives

$$\frac{\beta_0}{\beta_1} = \frac{(B)(X)}{(BX_1)}$$

$$\frac{\beta_1}{\beta_1} = 1$$
(7.22)

$$\frac{\beta_2}{\beta_1} = \frac{(BX_2)}{(BX_1)(X)}$$

$$\cdots$$

$$\frac{\beta_i}{\beta_1} = \frac{(BX_i)}{(BX_1)(X)^{i-1}}$$

Equations (7.19) and (7.22) together yield

$$[B] = \frac{\beta_0}{\beta_1}\frac{(BX_1)}{(X)} + \frac{\beta_1}{\beta_1}(BX_1) + \frac{\beta_2}{\beta_1}(BX_1)(X) + \cdots + \frac{\beta_n}{\beta_1}(BX_1)(X)^{n-1}$$

$$= (BX_1) \sum_{i=0}^{n} \frac{\beta_i}{\beta_1}(X)^{i-1} \qquad (7.23)$$

which rearranges to

$$\frac{(BX_1)}{[B]} = \frac{1}{\sum_{i=0}^{n} \frac{\beta_i}{\beta_1}(X)^{i-1}}$$
(7.24)

The fraction $(BX_1)/[B]$ is zero for (X) equal to zero. It increases and passes through a maximum as (X) increases, and finally approaches zero asymptotically if (X) gets very large, provided that n is two or greater.

The fraction of all B containing species present as the fully-complexed species BX_n is found in the same manner to be

$$\frac{(BX_n)}{[B]} = \frac{1}{\sum\limits_{i=0}^{n} \frac{\beta_i}{\beta_n} (X)^{i-n}} \tag{7.25}$$

If n is greater than zero, this fraction is a monotonically increasing function of (X), approaching the limit of unity as (X) gets large. It is not chemically meaningful to speak of the limit as (X) increases without upper bound, since solubility considerations always limit (X) to some finite value.

In general, there exists the equation for the fraction of all B-containing species present as BX_j,

$$\frac{(BX_j)}{[B]} = \frac{1}{\sum\limits_{i=0}^{n} \frac{\beta_i}{\beta_j} (X)^{i-j}}, \quad 0 \leq j \leq n \tag{7.26}$$

For some chemical systems, the quantity $(BX_j)/[B]$ is an experimentally measurable quantity. In such cases, equations such as (7.21), (7.24), (7.25) and (7.26) may be used for direct calculation of the β's and then in turn the apparent stepwise formation constants.

Microscopic Equilibrium Constants and the Statistical Factor. In Chapter 5 it was shown that for statistical reasons the two macroscopic dissociation constants must differ by a factor of four, even though all microscopic equilibrium constants be equal, for a diprotic carboxylic acid with two identical, noninteracting carboxyl groups. Later in Chapter 9 the same considerations will be applied to a polyprotic acid which will be described as a polymer skeleton to which are attached many identical, distinguishable combining sites for protons. For this case, as for the diprotic acid, a simple relationship between macroscopic and microscopic equilibrium constants can be obtained on the basis of statistical distribution of protons on these sites.

There are fundamental differences between linear polyprotic acids and complex ions which must be recognized. The number and the position of binding "sites" on a metal ion depends on the particular ligand, and site rearrangement may occur as ligands successively replace coordinated solvent molecules. There is a serious problem in deciding whether sites are distinguishable. Evaluation of the statistical factors for complex-ion formation requires arguments based on the mechanism of the reaction.

We will consider the formation of a complex with $n = 4$, and with the central ion and all four ligands lying in the same plane. If all B—X bonds are identical and equivalent, this complex is a *square-planar complex*. The formation reactions will be described as proceeding via the displacement of a solvent molecule from a coordination position by a ligand. In order to discuss stepwise formation, it is necessary to specify the arrangement of coordinated solvent molecules. It will be shown that a different statistical factor results for two cases: an initial square-planar arrangement of four solvent molecules, and an initial arrangement of six solvent molecules at the vertices of a regular octahedron, an *octahedral complex.*

There is but one geometric isomer and thus but one square-planar distinguishable species corresponding to each of the formulas B, BX_1, BX_3, and BX_4. However, BX_2 can exist in both cis and trans forms. The quantity (BX_2) is thus the sum of the concentrations $(cisBX_2)$ and $(transBX_2)$. Microscopic equilibrium constants and corresponding equilibria are

$$B + X \rightleftarrows BX_1 \qquad K_a' = \frac{(BX_1)}{(B)(X)}$$

$$BX_1 + X \rightleftarrows cisBX_2 \qquad K_b' = \frac{(cisBX_2)}{(BX_1)(X)}$$

$$BX_1 + X \rightleftarrows transBX_2 \qquad K_c' = \frac{(transBX_2)}{(BX_1)(X)} \qquad (7.27)$$

$$cisBX_2 + X \rightleftarrows BX_3 \qquad K_d' = \frac{(BX_3)}{(cisBX_2)(X)}$$

$$transBX_2 + X \rightleftarrows BX_3 \qquad K_e' = \frac{(BX_3)}{(transBX_2)(X)}$$

$$BX_3 + X \rightleftarrows BX_4 \qquad K_f' = \frac{(BX_4)}{(BX_3)(X)}$$

Equations (7.16) and (7.27) can be combined to yield

$$K_1' = K_a', \quad K_2' = K_b' + K_c', \quad K_3' = \frac{K_d' K_e'}{K_d' + K_e'}, \quad K_4' = K_f' \quad (7.28)$$

Equations (7.28) give as much information as can be obtained without introduction of extrathermodynamic assumptions. A reasonable kinetic assumption for identical, noninteracting sites is that the rate of addition of X will be proportional to the number of available sites, and that the rate of removal of X will be proportional to the number of bound X. This assumption applied successively to individual species permits evaluation of equilibrium constant ratios for a particular detailed chemical model for complex formation.

If the completely solvated metal ion is an octahedral solvent-metal complex, then discussion of successive addition of ligands to yield a square-planar complex must take into account the fact that at least two ligand molecules are required, together with the central ion, to define a plane. There are thus six equivalent sites available for addition of X to B to give BX_1. There is only one way to dissociate the single X from a BX_1 ion. The equilibrium constant K_a' is thus proportional to $6/1$. The proportionality constant K' will be set equal to K_d', since K_d' must be proportional to $2/2$.

The plane of the complex is defined in the species $cis\text{BX}_2$, BX_3, and BX_4, but not in $trans\text{BX}_2$ in which the two ligands and the central ion are colinear. This model does not permit the formation of the species $cis\text{BX}_3$ in which no trans pair of ligands exists; incorporation of such a pathway into the model

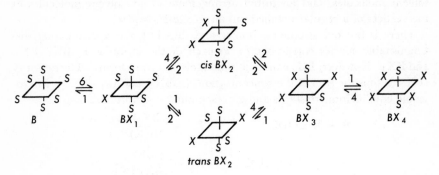

Figure 7.3. Formation of Square-Planar Ligand-Metal Complex from Octahedral Solvent-Metal Complex.

would change the derived statistical factor. Using Figure 7.3, all microscopic equilibrium constants can be evaluated:

$$K_a' = 6K', \; K_b' = 2K', \; K_c' = (\tfrac{1}{2})K', \; K_d' = K', \; K_e' = 4K', \; K_f' = (\tfrac{1}{4})K' \tag{7.29}$$

The macroscopic constants are then

$$K_1' = 6K', \; K_2' = (\tfrac{5}{2})K', \; K_3' = (\tfrac{4}{5})K', \; K_4' = (\tfrac{1}{4})K' \tag{7.30}$$

If a square planar solvent-metal complex is converted in a stepwise fashion into a square planar ligand-metal complex, a possible mechanism is one in which the plane of the complex is defined by the coordinated solvent molecules, as shown in Figure 7.4. The microscopic equilibrium constants are

$$K_a' = 4K', \; K_b' = K', \; K_c' = (\tfrac{1}{2})K', \; K_d' = K', \; K_e' = 2K', \; K_f' = (\tfrac{1}{4})K' \tag{7.31}$$

This gives the set of macroscopic formation constants

$$K_1' = 4K', \; K_2' = (\tfrac{3}{2})K', \; K_3' = (\tfrac{2}{3})K', \; K_4' = (\tfrac{1}{4})K' \tag{7.32}$$

The important point to be made is that (7.30) and (7.32) are different; the relative magnitudes of the macroscopic equilibrium constants are dependent on mechanism even when all microscopic formation constants are statistically determined.

Bjerrum Formation Function. The Danish physical chemists, Niels Bjerrum and his son Jannik Bjerrum, introduced and developed an important quantity, the average number of ligands bound to the central group, to which they gave the symbol $\bar{n}$. The algebraic definition is

$$\bar{n} = \frac{[\text{X}] - (\text{X})}{[\text{B}]} \tag{7.33}$$

Introduction of Equations (7.17), (7.18), and (7.19) into (7.33) yields

$$\bar{n} = \frac{\sum_{i=1}^{n} i(BX_i)}{\sum_{i=0}^{n} (BX_i)} = \frac{(B)\sum_{i=1}^{n} i\beta_i(X)^i}{(B)\sum_{i=0}^{n} \beta_i(X)^i} = \frac{\sum_{i=1}^{n} i\beta_i(X)^i}{\sum_{i=0}^{n} \beta_i(X)^i} \tag{7.34}$$

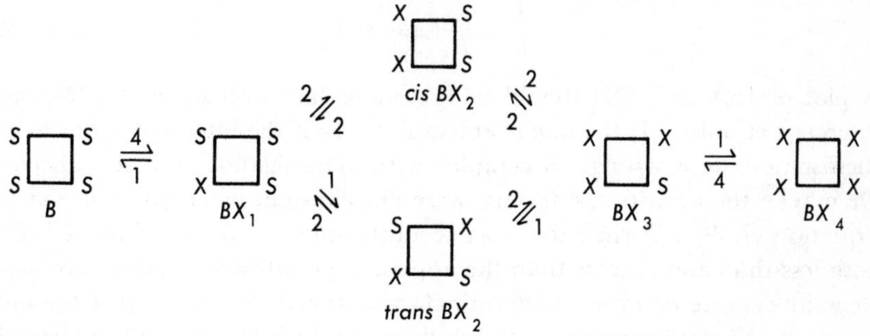

Figure 7.4. Formation of Square-Planar Ligand-Metal Complex from Square-Planar Solvent-Metal Complex.

If accurate measurements of $\bar{n}$ can be made at a series of known values of (X), then calculation of the equilibrium constants is reasonably straight-forward. The fundamental experimental problem is the determination of (X), the concentration of free, uncomplexed ligand. The Bjerrums called Equation (7.34) the *formation function* of the system.

Equation (7.34) gives $\bar{n}$ as a function of but one variable, (X). In particular $\bar{n}$ is not a function of (B) or of [B]. Experiments should always be performed to check for a dependence of $\bar{n}$ on [B]. Presence of such a dependence is strong evidence for polynuclear complexes. Independence of $\bar{n}$ on [B] does not exclude the possibility of certain types of polynuclear complexes.

The simplest situation is encountered when only one ligand can be bound to a single central ion. When n is unity, Equations (7.21), (7.24), and (7.34) reduce to

$$\frac{(B)}{[B]} = \frac{1}{1 + K_1'(X)} \tag{7.35}$$

$$\frac{(BX)}{[B]} = \frac{K_1'(X)}{1 + K_1'(X)} \tag{7.36}$$

$$\bar{n} = \frac{K_1'(X)}{1 + K_1'(X)} \tag{7.37}$$

Note that

$$\bar{n} = \frac{(BX)}{[B]} = 1 - \frac{(B)}{[B]} \tag{7.38}$$

Equations (7.35), (7.36), and (7.37) can each be solved directly for K_1' and in principle the determination of (X)/[B], (BX)/[B], or $\bar{n}$ at a single value of

(X) is sufficient to find the numerical value of K_1'. It is better experimental practice to make measurements at several values of (X) so as to utilize many points in evaluating the equilibrium constant. Graphical methods are often used.

Equation (7.37) for a monoligand complex can be converted into a convenient form for plotting by taking the reciprocal of each side, giving

$$\frac{1}{\bar{n}} = \frac{1}{K_1'(X)} + 1 \tag{7.39}$$

A plot of $1/\bar{n}$ vs $1/(X)$ should be a straight line with slope of $1/K_1'$ and intercept of unity. If the line is not straight, or if the intercept is not unity, then something is wrong. A complex with more ligands may be suspected. Or maybe the activity coefficients were not constant when (X) was varied. Equation (7.39) will yield the most accurate values of K_1' if values of $1/(X)$ both less than and greater than the apparent equilibrium constant are used. Very inaccurate or even indeterminate results will be obtained if the only values of (X) used correspond to solutions in which virtually all or virtually none of the B is complexed as BX. Equation (7.37) can also be written as

$$\bar{n}[1 + K_1'(X)] = K_1'(X)$$

$$\bar{n} = K_1'(X)[1 - \bar{n}]$$

$$\frac{\bar{n}}{1 - \bar{n}} = K_1'(X) \tag{7.40}$$

Thus a plot of $\bar{n}/(1 - \bar{n})$ vs (X) should be a straight line with slope equal to K_1' and intercept of zero. This method will be inaccurate if n has a value near unity for most of the measurements, thus making the quantity $(1 - \bar{n})$ subject to large uncertainty.

When n is two, and as many as two ligands can be bound to a single central group, Equation (7.34) becomes

$$\bar{n} = \frac{\beta_1(X) + 2\beta_2(X)^2}{1 + \beta_1(X) + \beta_2(X)^2} \tag{7.41}$$

For evaluation of the two overall equilibrium constants, it is desirable to rearrange Equation (7.41) so that some function of $\bar{n}$ and (X) can be plotted versus another function of $\bar{n}$ and (X) to give a straight line. Equations (7.42) and (7.43) are two such rearrangements.

$$\frac{\bar{n}}{(\bar{n} - 1)(X)} = \beta_2 \frac{(\bar{n} - 2)(X)}{1 - \bar{n}} - \beta_1 \tag{7.42}$$

$$\frac{(2 - \bar{n})(X)^2}{\bar{n}} = \frac{\beta_1}{\beta_2} \frac{(\bar{n} - 1)}{\bar{n}}(X) + \frac{1}{\beta_2} \tag{7.43}$$

In both cases a knowledge of the slope and intercept is sufficient to determine both β_1 and β_2. Problems appear when using (7.42) near $\bar{n} = 1$, since at this point two denominators become zero.

These equations for formation of BX_2 will give no information regarding formation of the BX_2 complex and no value of β_2 if all measurements are made on solutions in which (X) is so low that much more BX is present than BX_2. In such cases, the data may fit equations such as (7.39) or (7.40). The algebraic reason for this can be seen by noting that the condition for (BX) being substantially greater than (BX_2) is that

$$\frac{(BX_2)}{(BX)} \ll 1 \qquad (7.44)$$

From Equations (7.17) comes the relation

$$\frac{(BX_2)}{(BX)} = \frac{\beta_2}{\beta_1}(X) \qquad (7.45)$$

Inequality (7.45) and Equation (7.44) combine to give

$$\beta_2(X) \ll \beta_1 \qquad (7.46)$$

If Equation (7.41) is restricted by condition (7.46), $\bar{n}$ is given by

$$\bar{n} = \frac{\beta_1(X)}{1 + \beta_1(X)} \qquad (7.47)$$

which is of course Equation (7.37), since $\beta_1 = K_1'$.

A variety of techniques have been developed for dealing with the successively more difficult problems of determining successively more apparent equilibrium constants from a single set of experimental measurements. Most recent innovation has been the use of high-speed electronic computers to fit numerical data to theoretical equations by approximation methods. All stepwise equilibrium constants have been determined for formation of complexes with as many as six ligands. Experimental problems are greatest when equilibrium constants are very nearly equal, for then quite accurate data are necessary.

Spectrophotometric Determination of K_1' When $n = 1$. The optical absorbance of a solution containing only B, X, and BX is given by the equation

$$A = l\epsilon_B(B) + l\epsilon_X(X) + l\epsilon_{BX}(BX) + \text{const} \qquad (7.48)$$

where A is the absorbance determined at some wavelength with a spectrophotometer, ϵ_B, ϵ_X, and ϵ_{BX} the molar extinction coefficients of species B, X, and BX, and the constant a number, dependent on the absorbance of the solvent and the spectrophotometer cell, which can be eliminated from experimental measurements by means of a reference cell containing only solvent, or by use of a base line determined with solvent alone. The quantity l is the optical pathlength of the cell. For measurements taken with a cell of unit length, with the absorbance of cell and solvent subtracted, a quantity A' is obtained which is related to the solute concentrations by

$$A' = \epsilon_B(B) + \epsilon_X(X) + \epsilon_{BX}(BX) \qquad (7.49)$$

No mention has been made of such species as Na^+ and ClO_4^- without which the solutions cannot be prepared. There is a wide and useful wavelength range from the near infrared through the visible and far into the ultraviolet in which these species in aqueous solution are transparent and thus make no contribution to the measured absorbance.

A special case will be examined in which measurements are made on solutions in which $[X] \gg [B]$, so that (BX) can always be neglected with respect to (X) in an indicated sum. Thus the conservation equation for X,

$$[X] = (BX) + (X)$$

can be approximated by

$$[X] = (X) \tag{7.50}$$

It will also be assumed that it is possible to find some wavelength at which the absorbance due to X is so small that Equation (7.49) can be approximated by

$$A' = \epsilon_B(B) + \epsilon_{BX}(BX) \tag{7.51}$$

The apparent equilibrium constant is

$$K_1' = \frac{(BX)}{(B)(X)} \tag{7.52}$$

and the conservation equation for B is

$$[B] = (B) + (BX) \tag{7.53}$$

Equations (7.50), (7.52), and (7.53) yield

$$K_1'[B][X] = (BX)\{1 + K_1'[X]\} \tag{7.54}$$

Equations (7.51) and (7.53) together give

$$(BX) = \frac{A' - \epsilon_B[B]}{\epsilon_{BX} - \epsilon_B} \tag{7.55}$$

Elimination of (BX) between Equations (7.54) and (7.55) results in

$$K_1'[B][X] = \left\{\frac{A' - \epsilon_B[B]}{\epsilon_{BX} - \epsilon_B}\right\}\{1 + K_1'[X]\} \tag{7.56}$$

The reciprocal is taken of each side of Equation (7.56), both sides are then multiplied by $\{1 + K_1'[X]\}$, and there is obtained

$$\frac{1}{[B]\{\epsilon_{BX} - \epsilon_B\}} + \frac{1}{[B][X]K_1'\{\epsilon_{BX} - \epsilon_B\}} = \frac{1}{A' - \epsilon_B[B]} \tag{7.57}$$

Noting that when $[X] = 0$, $A' = \epsilon_B[B]$, it is seen that at constant [B] and variable [X] the right-hand member of Equation (7.57) can be calculated from observed absorbance readings. A plot of $1/\{A' - \epsilon_B[B]\}$ vs $1/[X]$ at constant [B] should give a straight line with slope and intercept which together suffice for determination of K_1'.

This method has both strengths and weaknesses. Under appropriately-chosen conditions of wavelength and of concentrations, K_1' can be determined from a series of absorbance measurements without knowledge of the value of [B] or of the value of any of the extinction coefficients. In fact, the absorbance values can all be in error by an additive constant or by a multiplicative constant, and the method does not suffer. Since the labelling of ligand and central atom is arbitrary, either reactant can be the one present in large excess. No individual determination of (B), (X), (BX), or [B] need be made. The major limitation is that K_1' must have a value which permits a large excess of one reactant to be present and still allows changes in that reactant concentration to change significantly the ratio (BX)/[B] so that absorbance changes can be observed. And it is necessary that whatever changes are made in [X] affect the absorbance only because of changes in (BX) and (B), not because in changes in the absorbance of X. These two restrictions limit the generality of the method.

A more serious criticism is that this method requires that only a one-one complex be formed, even though analysis of just such absorbance measurements may be the only way to tell the stoichiometry of the complex. The burden of proof usually falls on the chemist who would claim the largest number of coordinated ligands; the accepted procedure is to assume only a one-one complex unless the data demands a more complicated species. There is a circularity to the reasoning which is difficult to avoid.

Spectrophotometric Determination of K_1' and K_2' When $n = 2$. The discussion of the previous section can be extended to the chemical model described by the equilibria

$$B + X \rightleftarrows BX \qquad K_1' = \frac{(BX)}{(B)(X)} \qquad (7.58)$$

$$BX + X \rightleftarrows BX_2 \qquad K_2' = \frac{(BX_2)}{(BX)(X)} \qquad (7.59)$$

for the special conditions in which $[X] \gg [B]$ so that both (BX) and $2(BX_2)$ can be neglected with respect to (X) in the conservation equation for X, and in which it is possible to find a wavelength such that absorbance due to X is so small that the absorbance in a cell of unit pathlength can be written as

$$A' = \epsilon_B(B) + \epsilon_{BX}(BX) + \epsilon_{BX_2}(BX_2) \qquad (7.60)$$

The two conservation equations are

$$[X] = (X) \qquad (7.61)$$

$$[B] = (B) + (BX) + (BX_2) \qquad (7.62)$$

Equations (7.60), (7.61), (7.58), and (7.59) can be combined to eliminate all species concentrations except (B), giving

$$A' = (B)\{\epsilon_B + \epsilon_{BX}K_1'[X] + \epsilon_{BX_2}K_1'K_2'[X]^2\} \qquad (7.63)$$

Equations (7.58), (7.59), (7.61), and (7.62) together yield

$$[B] = (B)\{1 + K_1'[X] + K_1'K_2'[X]^2\} \tag{7.64}$$

The concentration (B) is then eliminated between Equations (7.63) and (7.64), leaving

$$A' = [B]\left\{\frac{\epsilon_B + \epsilon_{BX}K_1'[X] + \epsilon_{BX_2}K_1'K_2'[X]^2}{1 + K_1'[X] + K_1'K_2'[X]^2}\right\} \tag{7.65}$$

We have here an equation relating three experimental quantities, A', [B], and [X], by means of two equilibrium constants which we wish to evaluate, and three extinction coefficients. Further manipulation is required to cast (7.65) in a form useful for converting experimental data into numerical values for K_1' and K_2'.

One rearranged form of (7.65) is

$$\frac{1}{[X]}\left\{\frac{A' - \epsilon_B[B]}{A' - \epsilon_{BX}[B]}\right\} = -K_1' - K_1'K_2'[X]\left\{\frac{A' - \epsilon_{BX_2}[B]}{A' - \epsilon_{BX}[B]}\right\} \tag{7.66}$$

which is an equation of the form

$$\alpha = -K_1' - K_1'K_2'\beta \tag{7.67}$$

In favorable situations, when the species B, BX, and BX_2 have distinctly different absorption spectra, and when the values of the two equilibrium constants are such as to permit preparation of solutions in which the only B containing species are B, or just B and BX, or just BX and BX_2, it is possible to make reliable estimates of the values of the three extinction coefficients. if this is possible, then experiments can be interpreted in which A' is determined for a series of solutions of varying [X] and constant [B], since for each solution the quantities α and β in (7.67) can be calculated and then plotted to obtain what should be a linear graph with slope of $-K_1'K_2'$ and intercept of $-K_1'$.

Problems

7.1. Show why the electroneutrality equation is not required for the derivations of this chapter.

7.2. Can the methods discussed in this chapter be used to distinguish between the possibility of mononuclear complexes of the type BX, BX_2, $\cdots$, BX_n, and of dinuclear complexes of the type B_2X, B_2X_2, $\cdots$, B_2X_n?

Suggestions for Further Study

There is a critical distinction between achieving a good fit between experimental data and an equation like (7.57) or (7.66), and establishing the existence of one or two chemical complexes. A criterion for reliability of formation constants determined spectrophotometrically is given by W. B. Person, *J. Am. Chem. Soc.* **87**, 167 (1965). The student will find that a careful study of this paper and some of the bibliography cited by Person can be instructive and rewarding.

Bibliographical Note

A thorough treatment of the determination of equilibrium constants for complex formation in solution is F. J. C. Rossotti and H. Rossotti, *The Determination of Stability Constants*, New York: McGraw-Hill Book Company, Inc., 1961. One of the first and still among the most important monographs on the general theory of determining stepwise equilibrium constants for complex ions is J. Bjerrum, *Metal Ammine Formation in Aqueous Solution*, E. Christensen, trans., 2d ed., Copenhagen: P. Haase and Son, 1957.

Containing both a discussion of theory and practice, and a compilation of experimental values of equilibrium constants, is K. B. Yatsimirskii and V. P. Vasil'ev, *Instability Constants of Complex Compounds*, D. A. Paterson, trans., London: Pergamon Press, 1960. A complete tabulation of equilibrium constants for complexation reactions in solution is L. G. Sillén and A. E. Martell, *Stability Constants of Metal-Ion Complexes*, London: The Chemical Society, 1964.

An excellent balance between theory and practice in use of complexation reactions in analytical titrations is achieved in G. Schwarzenbach, *Complexometric Titrations*, H. Irving, trans., London: Methuen and Co. Ltd., 1957, a little book which contains detailed instructions for many titration procedures. A more recent theoretical treatment intended as a guide for the critical selection of analytical methods based on complexation reactions is A. Ringbom, *Complexation in Analytical Chemistry*, New York: Interscience Publishers, 1963. Acid-base reactions are discussed by Ringbom as a special case of complex formation, and the treatment differs significantly from the methods discussed in this textbook. The student may find a comparison informative.

8

Oxidation-Reduction Equilibria

There are formal analogies between acid-base equilibria and oxidation-reduction equilibria. In both cases the chemistry involved is the chemistry of coupled reactions — acid-base couples and oxidation-reduction couples. The mechanism of attaining equilibrium in both cases is via transfer reactions — proton transfer and electron transfer. The essential information about any of the reactions is contained in the set of equilibrium constants which characterize the relevant equilibria, provided that the systems are at chemical equilibrium.

There are also significant differences. Most chemists agree that the solvated proton is a chemical species which can exist in many solvents in high concentration, whereas the same chemists argue that an electron is not an ordinary chemical species in solution. Although there are vast differences in rates of proton transfer reactions, it is nevertheless usually safe to assume that an acid-base reaction has reached equilibrium as soon as reactants have been mixed. It is seldom safe to assume that rates in an oxidation-reduction reaction are as fast; time for reaching equilibrium is often long compared to times in which chemical manipulations ordinarily are performed.

The emphasis in this chapter is on the equilibrium properties of solutions, even though many of these reactions present fascinating problems in chemical kinetics and in determination of mechanism.[1] Discussion of a simple titration is presented in general equilibrium terms. But since specific kinetic factors

[1]J. O. Edwards, *Inorganic Reaction Mechanisms: An Introduction.* New York: W. A. Benjamin, Inc., 1964, chap. 7.

134

are so much a part of oxidation-reduction reactions, it is important to approach each new redox reaction as an individual case.

Oxidation-Reduction Titrations. Consider a titration in which a solution of NY is added to MY_2 solution, Y^- being an anion which takes no part in the equilibria except to contribute negative charges for electroneutrality, and M^{++} and N^+ being cations which react according to the equation

$$M^{++} + N^+ \rightleftarrows M^+ + N^{++} \qquad K' = \frac{(M^+)(N^{++})}{(M^{++})(N^+)} \qquad (8.1)$$

Conservation equations which can be written include

$$[M] = (M^{++}) + (M^+) \qquad (8.2)$$

$$[N] = (N^{++}) + (N^+) \qquad (8.3)$$

$$[Y] = (Y^-) \qquad (8.4)$$

$$[Y] = 2[M] + [N] \qquad (8.5)$$

The electroneutrality equation is

$$2(M^{++}) + (M^+) + 2(N^{++}) + (N^+) = (Y^-) \qquad (8.6)$$

The concentration of Y^- can be eliminated by combination of Equations (8.4), (8.5), and (8.6), giving

$$2(M^{++}) + (M^+) + 2(N^{++}) + (N^+) = 2[M] + [N] \qquad (8.7)$$

An equation is sought which relates (M^{++}) to the known total concentrations $[M]$ and $[N]$. Concentrations of M^+ and N^+ will be eliminated first. Equations (8.2), (8.3), and (8.7) combine to yield

$$(M^{++}) + (N^{++}) = [M] \qquad (8.8)$$

Equations (8.1), (8.2), and (8.3) give

$$(N^{++}) = \frac{K'[N]}{\dfrac{[M]}{(M^{++})} - 1 + K'} \qquad (8.9)$$

Elimination of (N^{++}) between Equations (8.8) and (8.9) results in an equation for the titration curve in terms of (M^{++}),

$$(M^{++})^2 + (M^{++}) \frac{2[M] + K'\{[N] - [M]\}}{K' - 1} - \frac{[M]^2}{K' - 1} = 0 \qquad (8.10)$$

We will examine this equation for three cases in which there is no explicit dependence on the value of the equilibrium constant: the case of large K', the case of small K', and the case of K' equal to unity.

There is a singularity in the titration curve equation at $K' = 1$ where two denominators are zero and hence two fractions are indeterminate. If the entire equation is multiplied by $\{K' - 1\}$ and the result examined for the case $K' = 1$, it is found that throughout the entire titration

$$(M^{++}) = \frac{[M]^2}{[M] + [N]} \tag{8.11}$$

When K' is very small compared to unity, and if $[N]$ is not much greater than $[M]$, there results the limiting equation

$$(M^{++})^2 - 2(M^{++})[M] + [M]^2 = 0 \tag{8.12}$$

which factors into

$$\{(M^{++}) - [M]\}^2 = 0 \tag{8.13}$$

and thus is satisfied by

$$(M^{++}) = [M] \tag{8.14}$$

For very large values of K', Equation (8.10) becomes

$$(M^{++})^2 + (M^{++})\{[N] - [M]\} = 0 \tag{8.15}$$

or, under the constraint of nonnegative concentrations,

$$\begin{aligned}(M^{++}) &= [M] - [N], \; [M] \geq [N] \\ (M^{++}) &= 0, \; [M] \leq [N]\end{aligned} \tag{8.16}$$

Equations (8.14) and (8.16) give the chemically expected consequences of very small and very large equilibrium constants. If K' is small enough, no reaction can be observed. If K' is large enough, the reaction yields products and leaves only the one reactant present in excess, the other reactant concentration being reduced essentially to zero.

Redox Quotient. The defining equation for the apparent equilibrium constant can be rewritten as

$$\frac{(N^{++})}{(N^+)} = K' \frac{(M^{++})}{(M^+)} = Q \tag{8.17}$$

to define Q, the redox quotient. The redox quotient is especially useful in plotting an oxidation-reduction titration curve, and in discussing indicator action and simultaneous oxidation-reduction equilibria. We will first of all express the equation for the titration curve in terms of Q.

Equations (8.2) and (8.3) can be written in terms of Q to give

$$(M^+) = \frac{[M]K'}{K' + Q} \qquad 1 = \frac{[M]}{(M^+)} \frac{K'}{K' + Q}$$

$$(N^+) = \frac{[N]}{1 + Q} \qquad 1 = \frac{[N]}{(N^+)} \frac{1}{1 + Q}$$

which can be substituted into Equation (8.7). Equation (8.17) is used to simplify the result, and there is obtained

$$Q^2[N] + QK'\{[N] - [M]\} - K'[M] = 0 \tag{8.18}$$

Introduction of volume variables of the usual form.

$$[M] = \frac{M_M V_M}{V_M + V_N} \qquad [N] = \frac{M_N V_N}{V_M + V_N} \qquad (8.19)$$

results in

$$V_M = \frac{V_M M_N}{M_M K'} \left\{ \frac{Q^2 + QK'}{Q + 1} \right\} \qquad (8.20)$$

Inspection of Equation (8.20) reveals that Q can vary from zero to infinity. Equation (8.17) restricts Q to zero or positive values. A titration curve is plotted in terms of Q in Figure 8.1 for $K' = 10^3$ and for $K' = 10^6$, using in

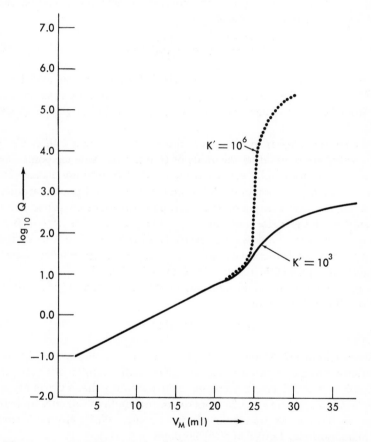

Figure 8.1. Variation of the Redox Quotient Q During a Titration.

each case Equation (8.20). It can be readily seen that if K' is large enough, there is a sharp endpoint inflection in the titration curve, and it would therefore be expected that endpoint detection could be achieved.

Redox Indicators. A general visual redox indicator can undergo a reversible oxidation-reduction transformation, and the oxidized and reduced forms have different colors. An indicator can be incorporated into the model for the titration discussed above by including the simultaneous reaction

$$N^+ + I^{++} \rightleftharpoons N^{++} + I^+ \qquad K_I' = \frac{(N^{++})(I^+)}{(N^+)(I^{++})} \qquad (8.21)$$

where I^+ and I^{++} are the reduced and oxidized forms of the indicator. If the sum of concentrations $\{(I^+) + (I^{++})\}$ is small compared to one or more of the concentrations (M^{++}), (M^+), (N^{++}), and (N^+), then the indicator species can be disregarded when the electroneutrality equation is written. The indicator distribution fractions $(I^+)/[I]$ and $(I^{++})/[I]$ are thus related to V_M only through the equilibrium constant expression, Equation (8.21), which can be written in terms of Q as

$$\frac{(N^{++})}{(N^+)} = K_I' \frac{(I^{++})}{(I^+)} = Q \qquad (8.22)$$

The redox quotient serves as a master variable for the titration, and the value of $(I^{++})/(I^+)$ can be found at any point in the titration by reading a value of Q from Figure 8.1, and then substituting the value of Q into Equation (8.22).

If the color change is to occur near the equivalence point, then K_I' must have a value approximating the value of Q at the equivalence point. Selection of an indicator can be particularly difficult if there is not a sharp inflection in the redox titration curve, because there is an additional variable not present in the previously-discussed acid-base titrations in protic solvents. Not only must the redox indicator have the proper value of K_I', but the indicator must react rapidly and reversibly with either titrant or sample to form an oxidation-reduction couple. The range of possible redox indicators available for a particular titration is often quite limited.

An equivalent result could have been obtained by considering, instead of reaction (8.21), the reaction

$$M^+ + I^{++} \rightleftharpoons M^{++} + I^+$$

Electrochemical Cells. The presence of two electrodes at which oxidation-reduction reactions can take place with transfer of electrons between solution and electrode gives rise to the possibility that a thermodynamic system such as a solution can do work on its surroundings not only by changes in volume but also by transfer of electric charge. When electrical work is thus made possible, Equation (1.6) becomes

$$dE = TdS - PdV + \mathbf{E}dC \qquad (8.23)$$

as a criterion for equilibrium in a closed chemical system which can interact with surroundings by heat exchange, by volume changes, and by exchange of electric charge. The quantity $\mathbf{E}$ is the potential difference between the two electrodes, and C is the electric charge.

The complete differential dE is still given by Equation (1.7), since the state of the system is completely specified by the specification of S, V, and the n's. Since Equation (1.10) necessarily follows from (1.7), and since Equations (8.23) and (1.10) are simultaneously valid for the same system,

$$\sum_j \left(\frac{\partial E}{\partial n_j}\right)_{V,S,n_i \neq n_j} dn_j = \mathbf{E}dC = \sum_j \mu_j dn_j \qquad (8.24)$$

When Equation (8.24) is expanded explicitly for a generalized reaction of the form (1.21), introduction of the degree of advancement gives

$$e\mu_E + f\mu_F + \cdots - x\mu_X - y\mu_Y - \cdots = \mathbf{E}\frac{dC}{d\xi} \qquad (8.25)$$

One mole of electrons corresponds to 96,493 coulombs and is called the Faraday, F. If n is the number of electrons transferred when e molecules of E and f molecules of F react to form x molecules of X and y molecules of Y, then the derivative $dC/d\xi$ becomes nF. Introduction of Equation (1.26) gives

$$nF\mathbf{E} = e\mu_E{}^\circ + f\mu_F{}^\circ + \cdots - x\mu_X{}^\circ - y\mu_Y{}^\circ - \cdots - RT \ln\frac{a_X{}^x a_Y{}^y \cdots}{a_E{}^e a_F{}^f \cdots}$$
$$(8.26)$$

Substitution of Equation (1.28) into Equation (8.26) gives

$$\mathbf{E} = \mathbf{E}^\circ - \frac{RT}{nF} \ln\frac{a_X{}^x a_Y{}^y \cdots}{a_E{}^e a_F{}^f \cdots} \qquad (8.27)$$

where $\mathbf{E}^\circ$ is defined by

$$\mathbf{E}^\circ = \frac{RT}{nF} \ln K \qquad (8.28)$$

Equations (8.27) and (8.28) are used in two important ways. A widely-used method of tabulating equilibrium constants is based on (8.28). Equation (8.27), commonly called the Nernst equation (after Walther Nernst, the pioneer physical chemist, who published a similar equation in terms of concentrations prior to the invention of ionic activities), permits quantitative discussion of the potential developed by various electrochemical cells used to follow concentration changes in solution.

Inspection of Equations (1.28) and (8.28) reveals that without approximation it is possible to write

$$\mathbf{E}_1{}^\circ - \mathbf{E}_2{}^\circ = \mathbf{E}^\circ = \frac{RT}{nF}\{\ln K_1 - \ln K_2\} \qquad (8.29)$$

where $\mathbf{E}_1{}^\circ$ and $\mathbf{E}_2{}^\circ$ are called normal half-cell electrode potentials, corresponding to the equilibrium constants K_1 and K_2 for the two half reactions. Thus reaction (8.1) can be written as two half reactions,

$$M^{++} + e^- \rightleftarrows M^+ \qquad K_1 = \frac{a_{M^+}}{a_{M^{++}}} \qquad (8.30)$$

$$N^{++} + e^- \rightleftarrows N^+ \qquad K_2 = \frac{a_{N^+}}{a_{N^{++}}} \qquad (8.31)$$

The problem of how to enter an activity for the electron, e^-, in the equilibrium constant expressions has been ignored. Whatever quantity is put in must be the same in both (8.30) and (8.31), and it will disappear when the logarithms are subtracted in (8.29). Associated with Equations (8.30) and (8.31) are

$$\mathbf{E}_1{}^\circ = \frac{RT}{nF} \ln K_1 \tag{8.32}$$

$$\mathbf{E}_2{}^\circ = \frac{RT}{nF} \ln K_2 \tag{8.33}$$

A tabulation of relatively few half reactions and associated half-cell electrode potentials gives information about the equilibrium constants for all possible combinations of these half reactions. An actual overall chemical equation is obtained by subtracting two half reactions in such a way that the electrons cancel.

Although the difference of the two half-cell electrode potentials is a measurable, operational quantity for many chemical reactions, the single half-cell electrode potential is never measurable. Since only differences have physical significance, each electrode potential is known only within some arbitrary additive constant. If a consistent procedure is followed, the additive constant will be the same for all electrode potentials, and the constant will always disappear when subtraction is made. The conventional way of handling this problem is to *define* the electrode potential of a standard hydrogen electrode as zero, and tabulate all other electrode potentials as relative electrode potentials, potentials relative in each case to the arbitrary assignment of zero to the standard hydrogen electrode potential.

The standard hydrogen electrode is a platinum electrode surrounded in solution by bubbles of hydrogen gas at a pressure of one atmosphere. The reaction which occurs at the electrode surface is

$$H^+ + e^- \rightleftarrows \tfrac{1}{2}H_2(g) \tag{8.34}$$

When a_{H^+} is unity, the single electrode potential of this electrode is defined as zero. The problem of evaluating a single-ion activity has been discussed in Chapter 3. The conventional meaning of the half reaction

$$M^{++} + e^- \rightleftarrows M^+ \tag{8.35}$$

is really then

$$M^{++} + \tfrac{1}{2}H_2(g) \rightleftarrows H^+ + M^+ \tag{8.36}$$

Equation (8.32) can be written in terms of an apparent equilibrium constant,

$$\mathbf{E}_1{}^\circ = \frac{RT}{nF} \ln K_1' + \frac{RT}{nF} \ln \frac{y_{M^+}}{y_{M^{++}}} \tag{8.37}$$

It is convenient to incorporate the activity coefficient term and the normal potential into a single constant, giving

$$\mathbf{E}_1{}^\circ - \frac{RT}{nF} \ln \frac{y_{M^+}}{y_{M^{++}}} = \frac{RT}{nF} \ln K_1{}' = \mathbf{E}_1{}^{\circ\prime} \tag{8.38}$$

where $\mathbf{E}_1{}^{\circ\prime}$ is called a formal half-cell electrode potential. Discussion of a potentiometric titration curve will be in terms of the formal potentials.

Oxidation-reduction titrations are conveniently followed by observing the change of potential of an electrochemical cell composed of the sample solution and two electrodes. In a well designed experiment the endpoint of the titration is signalled by a sharp change in potential. It is important to realize that the observed value of the potential as well as the shape of a plot of potential versus volume of added titrant is critically dependent on the particular choice of electrodes. Only in a few cases are the electrode processes well understood, and it is often necessary to take a quite empirical point of view toward electrode behavior.

Potentiometric Titration Curve. Again reaction (8.1) will be considered, and a titration will be performed in which a solution of NY is added to a solution of MY_2. The redox quotient changes during the titration according to Equation (8.20).

The separation of variables into sums which resulted in Equations (8.29) through (8.33) can be carried one step further to transform Equation (8.27) into

$$\mathbf{E}_1 - \mathbf{E}_2 = \mathbf{E}_1{}^{\circ\prime} - \mathbf{E}_2{}^{\circ\prime} - \frac{RT}{F} \ln \frac{(M^+)}{(M^{++})} + \frac{RT}{F} \ln \frac{(N^+)}{(N^{++})} \tag{8.39}$$

where the subscript 1 refers to species M^+ and M^{++}, and subscript 2 refers to species N^+ and N^{++}. Since the equation is written in terms of concentrations, the equation is also written in terms of formal potentials. Equation (8.39) can be separated into two equations,

$$\mathbf{E}_1 = \mathbf{E}_1{}^{\circ\prime} - \frac{RT}{F} \ln \frac{(M^+)}{(M^{++})} \tag{8.40}$$

$$\mathbf{E}_2 = \mathbf{E}_2{}^{\circ\prime} - \frac{RT}{F} \ln \frac{(N^+)}{(N^{++})} \tag{8.41}$$

It is assumed that chemical equilibrium is maintained throughout the titration, and at equilibrium Equations (8.27) and (8.28) require

$$\mathbf{E} = 0 \tag{8.42}$$

Therefore throughout the entire titration

$$\mathbf{E}_1 = \mathbf{E}_2 \tag{8.43}$$

The progress of an oxidation-reduction titration is often followed by recording the emf of a cell composed of the sample solution, a reference electrode, and an indicating electrode. A calomel electrode is often used as a reference elctrode, and in a great many cases the change of potential of the calomel electrode during a titration appears to be insignificantly small. When both oxidized and reduced forms are in solution, differing only in the number of electrons, a reversible indicating electrode can be a metal wire made of platinum, silver, gold, or some other "inert" metal. Although the actual mechanism of reaction at the electrode surface may be quite compli-cated, the net reaction is electron transfer between species in solution and the metal wire.

Because of the condition expressed in Equation (8.43), it is only required that the indicating electrode respond to one of the two reactions of the oxidation-reduction couple. However, if the electrode responds reversibly to both reactions, the same emf will result. Equation (8.41) gives the single electrode potential of the indicating electrode. If the reference electrode maintains a constant potential, then changes in the potential difference will be due only to changes in $\mathbf{E}_2$, and these are the changes which will now be investigated.

Utility of the redox quotient becomes apparent when Equations (8.22) and (8.41) are compared. Written in terms of the redox quotient, Equation (8.41) is

$$\mathbf{E}_2 = \mathbf{E}_2{}^{\circ\prime} - \frac{RT}{F} \ln Q \tag{8.44}$$

Since Equation (8.20) permits calculation of plots of Q versus V_M such as in Figure 8.1, combination of Equations (8.20) and (8.44) permits calculation without approximation of the titration curve in terms of emf versus added titrant volume, assuming only adequacy of the chemical model and rever-sibility of the electrodes.

Problems

8.1. Because of the formal analogies between acid-base and oxidation-reduction reactions, it would seem possible to obtain a dilution curve for a water-acid couple in terms of a quantity similar to Q. Can this be done? What is the situation for an acid-base titration in water?

8.2. Plot the indicator fraction $(I^-)/[I]$ vs V_M for the titration of N^+ with M^{++}, the generalized reaction discussed throughout this chapter. Assume $K' = 10^6$, and examine indicators with $K_I' = 10^3$ and $K_I' = 10^4$.

8.3. Obtain an equation similar to (8.20) for a titration involving the re-action.

$$2J^+ + L^{3+} \rightleftarrows 2J^{++} + L^+$$

Suggestion for Experimental Investigation

Smith and Brandt [G. F. Smith and W. W. Brandt, *Anal. Chem.* **21**, 948 (1949)] found that a potentiometric titration curve for the dichromate-iron

(II) couple had a different shape when iron(II) solution was added to dichromate, as compared to the opposite addition of reagents. Repeat the experiment in an attempt to find some way to obtain equilibrium conditions throughout the titration. Does the shape of the curve depend on the speed at which the titrant is added? What happens if a small amount of another substance which can be readily oxidized and reduced is added? Does either curve have the theoretical shape? Is it possible to obtain enough information from this titration curve to evaluate the equilibrium constant for the dichromate-iron(II) couple?

Bibliographical Note

A complete set of tables of both normal and formal oxidation-reduction potentials, giving in each case a reference to the journal article in which experimental details can be found, is G. Charlot, *Oxidation-Reduction Potentials* (Paris: Pergamon Press, 1958), a book prepared under the sponsorship of the Commission on Electrochemical Data of the Section of Analytical Chemistry of the International Union of Pure and Applied Chemistry.

A brief introduction to the many methods of electrochemical analysis is L. L. Leveson, *Introduction to Electroanalysis* (London: Butterworths, 1964). The Preface closes with: "For the inquiring student, this book will prompt more questions than it answers. A bibliography is included as a source of answers to such questions and as an encouragement of the further reading essential for a full understanding of the subject."

Section II

Some Case Studies
in Multiple Equilibria

A research chemist is often concerned with just one set of reactions, but he wants to know as much as possible about these few reactions. He *may* have an interest in general theories which include all possible types of complicated reactions like the ones he is actively investigating, but he *must* be concerned with theories which can give him information about his particular chemical reactions.

The field of multiple equilibria has as its general principles the same fundamental principles already used in the preceding chapters. The art of applying these general principles to specific problems can be learned in part by looking at some case studies. A chemist can learn about multiple equilibria best by trying out the general principles on some of his own problems.

Laboratory experiments and multiple equilibria theory can be fruitfully combined by use of one or more open-ended multiple equilibria experiments with research character in which the student is given freedom to take initiative in experimental design, and has choice in methods of data treatment. A variety of such projects are suggested at the end of chapters; many more can be devised. A student in this way has an opportunity for some insight into the relationships between experiment and theory in quantitative chemistry.

Two types of questions are repeatedly asked. How can experiments be designed to find out what species are in solution, and to find values of the various equilibrium constants? And given the equilibrium constants, how can the various concentrations be calculated, how can the shape of a titration curve be predicted? Section II is concerned with ways these two types of questions have been answered for some specific multiple equilibria in solution.

9

Acid-Base Titration of
a Polyprotic Acid

In Chapter 5 it was shown that a complete description of the acid-base behavior of an amino acid requires three independent microscopic equilibrium constants, although equilibrium titration data provides but two macroscopic equilibrium constants. Thus even with but two dissociable protons on a molecule, all microscopic constants are indeterminate from titration data alone.

When attention is directed toward polyprotic acids with a great many titratable protons per molecule, it becomes necessary to talk about the molecular dissociation equilibria in statistical terms. The quantity of central importance then turns out to be the average number of protons bound per molecule of polymer, this average designated as $\bar{v}$. This average will be approached from two directions: first, a way will be found for calculating $\bar{v}$ from experimental data; and second, an attempt will be made to find a meaningful relationship between $\bar{v}$ and the microscopic equilibrium constants.

Experimental Evaluation of $\bar{v}$. For a solution prepared by mixing together known amounts of the polyacid H_nA, a strong base MOH, and water, there exist two conservation equations

$$[A] = \sum_{i=0}^{n} (H_i A^{-(n-i)}) \tag{9.1}$$

$$[M] = (M^+) \tag{9.2}$$

and an electroneutrality equation

$$(OH^-) + \sum_{i=0}^{n} i(H_{n-i}A^{-i}) = (H^+) + (M^+) \tag{9.3}$$

From Equations (9.1), (9.2), (9.3), and the ion product of water, an expression is sought for $\bar{v}$ in terms of (H^+), $[M]$, and $[A]$. The quantity $\bar{v}$ can be written as

$$\bar{v} = \frac{\text{number of protons bound to sites on A molecules}}{\text{number of molecules of A}} \qquad (9.4)$$

where the symbol "A" denotes any of the variously-protonated species of the polyacid. For greater convenience, Equation (9.4) will be rewritten in the form

$$\bar{v} = n - \frac{\text{number of empty binding sites on A molecules}}{\text{number of molecules of A}} \qquad (9.5)$$

Equations (9.4) and (9.5) can be seen to be equivalent by noting that n is the maximum number of available sites for binding protons to molecules of A. It does not matter what concentration units are used in the fraction, as long as consistency is maintained in numerator and denominator of the same fraction. Thus

$$\bar{v} = n - \frac{\text{moles of empty binding sites per liter of solution}}{\text{moles of A per liter of solution}} \qquad (9.6)$$

$$\bar{v} = n - \frac{\sum_{i=0}^{n} i(H_{n-i}A^{-i})}{[A]} \qquad (9.7)$$

When Equations (9.3) and (9.7) are combined there results

$$\bar{v} = n - \frac{(H^+) + (M^+) - (OH^-)}{[A]} \qquad (9.8)$$

Equations (9.2) and (9.8), with the ion product of water, yield

$$\bar{v} = n - \frac{(H^+) - \dfrac{K_w{}'}{(H^+)} + [M]}{[A]} \qquad (9.9)$$

Titration curves of polyacids are often presented as graphs of $\bar{v}$ vs pH, and Equation (9.9) permits the direct calculation of $\bar{v}$ from experimental quantities (H^+), $[M]$, and $[A]$ if the value of n is known. Sometimes n can be estimated from the titration curve itself. In the case of synthetic macromolecules of known molecular weight, the value of n can be known independently of titration data. Knowledge of structure of some biological macromolecules has progressed to the point where the number and chemical identity of all groups is known without recourse to titration data. However, with at least some biopolymers, and with all synthetic polymers, some heterogeneity exists, and there is a corresponding distribution of values of n about a mean value.

A highly-charged anion will attract the cation M^+ and there may be substantial binding of M^+ to A. Ion binding has not been considered in the derivation of Equation (9.9). It will now be shown that at least in one rather restrictive case, binding of cations makes no difference. For a more general test, see problem (9.2).

The model to be used here allows binding of M^+ only by the completely unprotonated A^{-n}, and allows at most n cations to be bound. The conservation equations become

$$[A] = \sum_{i=0}^{n} (H_{n-i}A^{-i}) + \sum_{j=0}^{n-1} (M_{n-j}A^{-i}) \tag{9.10}$$

$$[M] = (M^+) + \sum_{j=0}^{n-1} (n-j)(M_{n-j}A^{-i}) \tag{9.11}$$

Electroneutrality requires that

$$(OH^-) + \sum_{i=0}^{n} i(H_{n-i}A^{-i}) + \sum_{j=0}^{n-1} j(M_{n-j}A^{-i}) = (H^+) + (M^+) \tag{9.12}$$

An empty binding site will be considered to be any site without a proton, thus converting Equation (9.6) to

$$\bar{v} = n - \frac{\sum_{i=0}^{n} i(H_{n-i}A^{-i}) + \sum_{j=0}^{n-1} n(M_{n-j}A^{-i})}{[A]} \tag{9.13}$$

Introduction of Equation (9.12) gives

$$\bar{v} = n - \frac{(H^+) + (M^+) - (OH^-) - \sum_{j=0}^{n-1} j(M_{n-j}A^{-i}) + \sum_{j=0}^{n-1} n(M_{n-j}A^{-i})}{[A]} \tag{9.14}$$

Equation (9.11) and the ion product of water are next combined with Equation (9.14), and the result is

$$\bar{v} = n - \frac{(H^+) - \frac{K_w}{(H^+)} + [M] - \sum_{j=0}^{n-1} (n-j)(M_{n-j}A^{-i}) + \sum_{j=0}^{n-1} n(M_{n-j}A^{-i}) - \sum_{j=0}^{n-1} j(M_{n-j}A^{-i})}{[A]} \tag{9.15}$$

The three summations in Equation (9.15) require close scrutiny. Each summation, when expanded, is a sum of terms $(M_{n-j}A^{-l})$ with coefficients depending on the value of j. From the three summations arise three terms for each concentration, and when these terms are collected and again summed, there results

$$-\sum_{j=0}^{n-1} (n-j)(M_{n-j}A^{-i}) + \sum_{j=0}^{n-1} n(M_{n-j}A^{-i}) - \sum_{j=0}^{n-1} j(M_{n-j}A^{-i})$$

$$= \sum_{j=0}^{n-1} (-n+j+n-j)(M_{n-j}A^{-i}) = \sum_{j=0}^{n-1} (0)(M_{n-j}A^{-i}) = 0 \tag{9.16}$$

Thus Equation (9.15) becomes identically equal to Equation (9.9).

Equilibrium Constants and $\bar{v}$. Equation (9.9) gives no a priori information about a plot of $\bar{v}$ vs pH. The shape of such a plot depends on the relevant equilibrium constants, and it is necessary to assume some chemical model as the first step in obtaining an equation for $\bar{v}$ as a function of pH. We will initially look at a hypothetical linear polyacid with n identical, independent, noninteracting, distinguishable[1] acidic groups, each group being a binding site for a proton. Later, having examined the consequences of noninteracting sites, this restriction will be relaxed somewhat in an attempt to deal with a real macromolecule in which interactions of at least adjacent groups is important.

Stepwise ionization of the acid H_nA gives this set of reactions and overall dissociation constants:

$$H_nA \rightleftharpoons H_{n-1}A^{-1} + H^+ \qquad \beta_1 = \frac{(H_{n-1}A^{-1})(H^+)}{(H_nA)}$$

$$H_{n-1}A^{-1} \rightleftharpoons H_{n-2}A^{-2} + H^+ \qquad \beta_2 = \frac{(H_{n-2}A^{-2})(H^+)^2}{(H_nA)}$$

. . . .

$$H_{n-i+1}A^{-i+1} \rightleftharpoons H_{n-i}A^{-i} + H^+ \qquad \beta_i = \frac{(H_{n-i}A^{-i})(H^+)^i}{(H_nA)} \qquad (9.17)$$

. . . .

$$HA^{-n+1} \rightleftharpoons A^{-n} + H^+ \qquad \beta_n = \frac{(A^{-n})(H^+)^n}{(H_nA)}$$

There exists only one species of the formula H_nA. However, since any one of the n sites can ionize to yield an $H_{n-1}A^{-1}$ ion, there must be n forms of $H_{n-1}A^{-1}$ which will be designated $H_{n-1}A^{-1}j$, $1 \leq j \leq n$, each species differing from the others solely in that ionization has occurred at a different site. But because the sites are distinguishable, the resulting chemical species are in principle distinguishable. There consequently are n equally probable chemical reactions for the removal of the first proton,

$$H_nA \rightleftharpoons H_{n-1}A^{-1}j + H^+, \, 1 \leq j \leq n \qquad (9.18)$$

and n microscopic equilibrium constants

$$K_{1,j} = \frac{(H_{n-1}A^{-1}j)(H^+)}{(H_nA)}, \, 1 \leq j \leq n \qquad (9.19)$$

Since

$$(H_{n-1}A^{-1}) = \sum_{j=1}^{n} (H_{n-1}A^{-1}j)$$

----

[1] In a solution containing 100 acetic acid molecules, it is necessary to consider these molecules not only identical but also indistinguishable. There is no way to name or number these molecules to keep track of them as they move about apparently randomly in solution. The situation is different for a linear polymer, however, since the monomeric groups are covalently bonded in a specific order, and one can mentally number these groups starting from one end. These numbered groups may be identical, but they are distinguishable, since each has a different number.

it is straightforward to write the macroscopic β_1 in terms of the set of microscopic $K_{1,j}$'s:

$$\beta_1 = (H^+) \frac{\sum\limits_{j=1}^{n} (H_{n-1}A^{-1}j)}{(H_nA)}$$

$$= \sum_{j=1}^{n} \frac{(H_{n-1}A^{-1}j)(H^+)}{(H_nA)} \tag{9.20}$$

$$= \sum_{j=1}^{n} K_{1,j}$$

It has already been assumed that all these sites are identical, and it necessarily and conveniently follows that

$$K_{1,1} = K_{1,2} = \cdots = K_{1,j} = \cdots = K_{1,n} \tag{9.21}$$

$$\sum_{j=1}^{n} K_{1,j} = nK_{1,j} \tag{9.22}$$

Equations (9.20) and (9.22) together yield

$$\beta_1 = nK_{1,j} \tag{9.23}$$

(To keep the nomenclature from becoming overly cumbersome, the primes have been omitted from all the apparent equilibrium constants in this chapter.)

Removal of a second proton can proceed according to any of the reactions

$$H_{n-1}A^{-1}j \rightleftarrows H_{n-2}A^{-2}k + H^+ \qquad K_{j,k} = \frac{(H_{n-2}A^{-2}k)(H^+)}{(H_{n-1}A^{-1}j)} \tag{9.24}$$

$$1 \leq j \leq n, 1 \leq k \leq \frac{n(n-1)}{2}$$

There are $n(n-1)/2$ different forms of $H_{n-2}A^{-2}$ because there are $n(n-1)/2$ ways in which $(n-2)$ protons can be arranged on n distinguishable sites. This is also the number of ways in which two vacancies can be distributed among n distinguishable sites. The various ways of distributing the protons for the $n = 4$ series $(H_4A, \cdots, A^{-4})$ are shown in Figure 9.1. Absence of interaction between identical sites imposes equality upon all the $K_{j,k}$'s and requires that $K_{j,k} = K_{1,j}$. Hence

$$K_{1,j}K_{j,k} = \frac{(H_{n-2}A^{-2}k)(H^+)}{(H_nA)} = K_{1,j}{}^2 \tag{9.25}$$

The relationship between macroscopic and microscopic equilibrium constants is established by noting that

$$(H_{n-2}A^{-2}) = \sum_{k=1}^{n(n-1)/2} (H_{n-2}A^{-2}k) \tag{9.26}$$

Substitution into the defining equation for β_2, using Equation (9.25), gives

$$\beta_2 = \frac{n(n-1)}{2} K_{1,j}{}^2 \qquad (9.27)$$

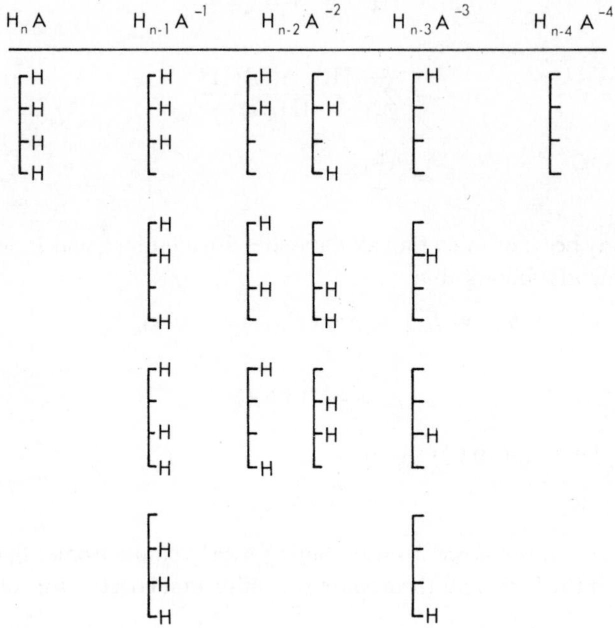

Figure 9.1. Distinct Species in the Stepwise Removal of Protons from H_4A.

In general, the number of different forms of $H_{n-i}A^{-i}$ is

$$\frac{\prod\limits_{j=0}^{i-1}(n-j)}{i!}$$

The indicated product

$$\prod\limits_{j=0}^{i-1}(n-j)$$

is simply $n!$ without the first factors from unity to $(n-i)$. Thus

$$\prod\limits_{j=0}^{i-1}(n-j) = \frac{n!}{(n-i)!} \qquad (9.28)$$

So there are $n!/(n-i)!i!$ different forms of $H_{n-i}A^{-i}$. And this means that in general

$$\beta_i = \frac{n!}{i!(n-i)!} K_{1,j}{}^i \qquad (9.29)$$

The next step is to combine this relationship, a relationship between the individual macroscopic overall equilibrium constants and the microscopic equilibrium constant $K_{1,j}$, with the definition of $\bar{v}$.

The definition to be used for $\bar{v}$ is Equation (9.7). Rewritten in terms of concentrations of all species, this equation becomes

$$\bar{v} = n - \frac{\sum\limits_{i=0}^{n} i(H_{n-i}A^{-i})}{\sum\limits_{i=0}^{n} (H_{n-i}A^{-i})} \tag{9.30}$$

Equations (9.17) are introduced, giving

$$n - \bar{v} = \frac{\sum\limits_{i=0}^{n} i\beta_i \dfrac{(H_nA)}{(H^+)^i}}{\sum\limits_{i=0}^{n} \beta_i \dfrac{(H_nA)}{(H^+)^i}} = \frac{\sum\limits_{i=0}^{n} \dfrac{i\beta_i}{(H^+)^i}}{\sum\limits_{i=0}^{n} \dfrac{\beta_i}{(H^+)^i}} \tag{9.31}$$

Then Equation (9.29) is used, yielding

$$n - \bar{v} = \frac{\sum\limits_{i=0}^{n} \dfrac{(i)(n!)}{i!(n-i)!} K_{1,j}{}^i \left(\dfrac{1}{(H^+)}\right)^i}{\sum\limits_{i=0}^{n} \dfrac{n!}{i!(n-i)!} K_{1,j}{}^i \left(\dfrac{1}{(H^+)}\right)^i} \tag{9.32}$$

Equation (9.32) is awesome, but it turns out to be a very simple expression in disguise. The method for simplification can be seen by comparing denominator and numerator with the binomial expansion and the differentiated binomial expansion. The binomial theorem asserts that

$$(1 + x)^n = \sum\limits_{i=0}^{n} \frac{n!}{(n-i)!i!} x^i \tag{9.33}$$

Differentiation of Equation (9.33) with respect to x gives

$$n(1 + x)^{n-1} = \sum\limits_{i=0}^{n} \frac{n!i}{(n-i)!i!} x^{i-1} \tag{9.34}$$

where it has been noted that the first term of the right-hand member of Equation (9.33) is the constant unity with its derivative equal to zero. If both sides of Equation (9.34) are multiplied by x, there results

$$nx(1 + x)^{n-1} = \sum\limits_{i=0}^{n} \frac{n!i}{(n-i)!i!} x^i \tag{9.35}$$

Setting $K_{1,j}/(H^+)$ equal to x and comparing Equations (9.35) and (9.33) with Equation (9.32), it is seen that

$$n - \bar{v} = \frac{n \dfrac{K_{1,j}}{(H^+)}\left[1 + \dfrac{K_{1,j}}{(H^+)}\right]^{n-1}}{[1 + K_{1,j}/(H^+)]^n}$$

$$= \frac{nK_{1,j}/(H^+)}{1 + K_{1,j}/(H^+)} = \frac{n K_{i,j}}{(H^+) + K_{1,j}} \tag{9.36}$$

or

$$\frac{n - \bar{v}}{\bar{v}} = \frac{K_{1,j}}{(H^+)} \tag{9.37}$$

Equation (9.37) is a surprisingly simple equation. It represents the predicted behavior for a type of ideal polyacid. Such ideal behavior will seldom be encountered experimentally, However, significant information about the chemistry of macromolecules can be obtained by studying the deviations from Equation (9.37) which are in fact observed.

Additional insight into the behavior of the idealized polyprotic acid with identical, noninteracting sites can be gained by eliminating $\bar{v}$ between Equations (9.37) and (9.9), giving

$$\frac{(H^+) - \dfrac{K_w}{(H^+)} + [M]}{n[A] - (H^+) + \dfrac{K_w}{(H^+)} - [M]} = \frac{K_{1,j}}{(H^+)} \tag{9.38}$$

Rearrangement yields

$$(H^+)^3 + (H^+)^2\{[M] + K_{1,j}\} + (H^+)\{[M]K_{1,j} - n[A]K_{1,j} - K_w\} \\ - K_{1,j}K_w = 0 \tag{9.39}$$

And this is Equation (4.8) with a change in the notation for the equilibrium constant, and with [A] replaced by $n[A]$.

Experimental Titration Curves. As more and more protons are removed from a polyacid, the polymer becomes more highly negatively charged. The increasing charge changes the energy required for removal of an additional proton, and thereby changes the microscopic equilibrium constants. One of the most straightforward ways of interpreting an experimental titration curve is to write Equation (9.37) as

$$\log_{10} \frac{n - \bar{v}}{\bar{v}} = pH - pK(\bar{v}) \tag{9.40}$$

where $K(\bar{v})$ is some sort of average microscopic equilibrium constant which will be expected to change during a titration as $\bar{v}$ changes. The theoretical problem is then a problem of relating the observed functional dependence of K and $\bar{v}$ to detailed molecular properties. This is a problem in statistical thermodynamics which is outside the scope of this case study.

Problems

9.1. Devise a graphical method for determination of $K_{1,j}$ for a linear polyacid with identical, noninteracting sites, in terms of the titration data of V_{MOH}, V_{H_nA}, M_{MOH}, M_{H_nA}, and pH.

9.2. Determine if Equation (9.9) is valid if M^+ cations can bind at any or all sites unoccupied by protons.

9.3. Show that Equation (9.37) reduces to some equation derived in Chapter 5 for the case of $n = 2$.

Suggestions for Further Study

1. Substantial insight can be gained by study of a paper by Bak[2] on the titration curve of a polyacrylic acid with about 27 identical binding sites. Careful experimental techniques were employed to obtain data for a titration curve at constant ionic strength. The data were plotted according to the equation

$$pK = pH - \log_{10} \frac{\theta}{1 - \theta} \qquad (9.1.1)$$

where θ, the degree of neutralization, is equal to $\{1 - \bar{v}/n\}$. Equations (9.38) and (9.1.1) are equivalent. A plot of pK, calculated from Equation (9.1.1), versus θ, is found experimentally to be linear at constant ionic strength. The slope of this linear plot is interpreted as an interaction energy, and from the magnitude of this interaction energy certain conclusions are made about the manner in which the polymer molecule is coiled in solution.

A student who wishes to do further study in this area is also encouraged to make a careful comparison of the paper by Bak[2] and earlier studies by Arnold and Overbeek,[3] and by Kagawa and Gregor.[5] The Arnold and Overbeek paper is discussed by Tanford in an excellent discussion of multiple equilibria.[4]

2. An important related area of chemical research is the titration of polypeptides and proteins. Two papers which treat the theory of protein titration curves, using many of the concepts treated in this chapter, are:

C. Tanford and J. G. Kirkwood, *J. Am. Chem. Soc.* **79,** 5333 (1957).

C. Tanford, *J. Am. Chem. Soc.* **79,** 5340 (1957).

[2]K. Bak, *Acta Chem. Scand.* **16,** 229 (1962). (In English).

[3]R. Arnold, and J. Th. G. Overbeek, *Rec. trav. chim.* **69,** 192 (1950). (In English).

[4]C. Tanford, *Physical Chemistry of Macromolecules.* New York: John Wiley and Sons, Inc., 1961. Chapter 8 deals with multiple equilibria; the Arnold and Overbeek paper is discussed on pp. 549–552.

[5]I. Kagawa, and H. P. Gregor, *J. Polymer Sci.* **23,** 477 (1957).

10

The Solubility of Lead Chloride

The total mount of lead (II) in an aqueous solution in equilibrium with solid $PbCl_2$ depends on the total chloride in solution. Some kind or kinds of chloride complexes are formed, and the amount of lead (II) in solution is surely determined by the simultaneous solubility and complexation equilibria. There is substantive disagreement among chemists working in this area about the nature of the equilibria and the composition of the complexes. Different chemical models turn out to be consistent with the same experimental data.

In this case study a series of derivations are presented to treat the solubility of lead chloride, beginning with a chemical model without complex formation, and continuing with more complicated models. The important question to be considered is whether the various models are operationally distinguishable. The student is asked to view critically the chemical reality of the various lead complexes which have been proposed, and to consider what sort of evidence a solution chemist needs in order to establish the existence of a complex species in solution.

A Chemical Model Without Complex Formation. The simplest chemical model which can describe a solution from which $PbCl_2$ has precipitated is

$$PbCl_2(s) \rightleftarrows Pb^{++} + 2Cl^- \qquad K_1' = (Pb^{++})(Cl^-)^2 \qquad (10.1)$$

Only the solution, the homogeneous solution, in equilibrium with the solid phase will be considered, and hence the conservation equations will be written without regard for quantities of $PbCl_2$ in the precipitate. It is only

154

required that solubility equilibrium has been established, and that the critical restraint imposed by the solubility product is operative. The experimental data can be converted directly from analyses of the solution for chloride and for lead into the quantities [Pb] and [Cl] which for this chemical model are

$$[Pb] = (Pb^{++}) \tag{10.2}$$

$$[Cl] = (Cl^-) \tag{10.3}$$

The notation [Cl] here denotes total chloride in the homogeneous solution, whereas in other chapters the same notation has denoted total chloride added to a titration flask and has then included chloride in a precipitate.

Equations (10.1), (10.2), and (10.3) give

$$K_1' = [Pb][Cl]^2 \tag{10.4}$$

Comparison of experimental data with Equation (10.4) is straightforward. If there is lack of agreement, data may be inaccurate, or perhaps it is not safe to assume constant activity coefficients in the concentration range employed, or equilibrium conditions may not have been attained. Another possibility is that additional equilibria are involved, and this possibility will now be examined.

Formation of the Complex PbCl$^+$. Inclusion of a single complexation step requires the following equilibria and apparent equilibrium constants:

$$PbCl_2(s) \rightleftarrows Pb^{++} + 2Cl^- \quad K_1' = (Pb^{++})(Cl^-)^2 \tag{10.5}$$

$$Pb^{++} + Cl^- \rightleftarrows PbCl^+ \quad K_2' = \frac{(PbCl^+)}{(Pb^{++})(Cl^-)} \tag{10.6}$$

An additional term is added to each conservation equation, with the result

$$[Pb] = (Pb^{++}) + (PbCl^+) \tag{10.7}$$

$$[Cl] = (Cl^-) + (PbCl^+) \tag{10.8}$$

Combination of Equations (10.5), (10.6), and (10.7) produces

$$(Cl^-)^2 = \frac{K_1'}{[Pb]} + \frac{K_1'K_2'(Cl^-)}{[Pb]} \tag{10.9}$$

Equations (10.5), (10.6), and (10.8) yield

$$(Cl^-)^2 = [Cl](Cl^-) - K_1'K_2' \tag{10.10}$$

Restricting this derivation to the chemically-meaningful, real, positive, roots of simultaneous Equations (10.9) and 10.10, $(Cl^-)^2$ is equated in the two equations with the result

$$(Cl^-) = \frac{K_1'\{1 + K_2'[Pb]\}}{[Pb][Cl] - K_1'K_2'} \tag{10.11}$$

Equation (10.11) can be substituted into either (10.9) or (10.10), and in either case an equation is obtained which contains only the apparent equilibrium constants and the two experimental observables, [Pb] and [Cl]. This final equation can be written as

$$[Pb][Cl]^2 = K_1' + K_2'^3 K_1'^2$$
$$+ K_1' K_2' (2[Pb] + [Cl] - K_2' \{[Pb][Cl] - [Pb]^2\}) \quad (10.12)$$

Equation (10.12) is in a form suitable for plotting experimental data obtained from analysis of saturated solutions containing varying amounts of chloride. Graphs of $[Pb][Cl]^2$ versus $(2[Pb] + [Cl] - K_2'\{[Pb][Cl] - [Pb]^2\})$ can be constructed for different trial values of K_2'. There are two criteria for consistency among the assumed value of K_2', the experimental values of [Pb] and [Cl], and Equation (10.12): the plot must be linear within the limits of experimental uncertainty, and the assumed value of K_2' must be consistent with the observed values of slope and intercept. Equation (10.12) reduces to Equation (10.4) for the case in which $K_2' = 0$.

Two complexes: $PbCl^+$ and $PbCl_2$. The next step in complexity may well be to assume formation of the uncharged species $PbCl_2$ in solution. There is no a priori requirement that the second species have the formula $PbCl_2$. It is possible to formulate chemical mechanisms for forming higher complexes without $PbCl_2$ species by having Cl^- react with the solid crystal, and at any rate it is unnecessary to postulate $PbCl_2$ as an important species in order to have appreciable equilibrium concentrations of higher complexes.

The particular model under consideration excludes higher complexes, and includes the equilibria

$$PbCl_2(s) \rightleftarrows Pb^{++} + 2Cl^- \quad K_1' = (Pb^{++})(Cl^-)^2 \quad (10.13)$$

$$Pb^{++} + Cl^- \rightleftarrows PbCl^+ \quad K_2' = \frac{(PbCl^+)}{(Pb^{++})(Cl^-)} \quad (10.14)$$

$$PbCl^+ + Cl^- \rightleftarrows PbCl_2 \quad K_3' = \frac{(PbCl_2)}{(PbCl^+)(Cl^-)} \quad (10.15)$$

The conservation equations become

$$[Pb] = (Pb^{++}) + (PbCl^+) + (PbCl_2) \quad (10.16)$$

$$[Cl] = (Cl^-) + (PbCl^+) + 2(PbCl_2) \quad (10.17)$$

The three equilibrium constant expressions can be used to eliminate $(PbCl_2)$ from the conservation equations, leaving

$$[Pb] - K_1' K_2' K_3' = (Pb^{++}) + (PbCl^+) \quad (10.18)$$

$$[Cl] - 2K_1' K_2' K_3' = (Cl^-) + (PbCl^+) \quad (10.19)$$

Equation (10.18) differs from Equation (10.7) only in that in (10.18) the quantity $\{[Pb] - K_1' K_2' K_3'\}$ functions as an effective concentration or a corrected concentration. The same consideration applies to a comparison of Equations (10.19) and (10.8). Thus there is evidence for formation of $PbCl_2$ in solution if an otherwise curved plot of data according to Equation (10.12) can be made linear by subtracting a constant quantity from all values of [Pb] and twice that amount from all values of [Cl]. This constant gives K_3' if $K_1'K_2'$ is known.

Higher Chloride Complexes. It is not difficult to obtain equations relating [Pb] and [Cl] under the assumption of more and more complexes, but it becomes increasingly more of a challenge to find ways of evaluating unambiguously the separate equilibrium constants. One method is to obtain values for K_1' and K_2' at very low values of [Cl] where the higher complexes may be present in insignificant concentrations. With certain values for K_1' and K_2' established, it is easier to evaluate the remaining constants. It usually turns out that data will be fit better by a curve with many equilibrium constants rather than by a curve with just one or two, regardless of whether or not there are in fact higher complexes.

There have been tentative suggestions for species up to $PbCl_6^{-4}$ from ion exchange experiments.[1] Some lead chloride solubility data have been interpreted in terms of a single complexation step[2]

$$PbCl_2(s) + Cl^- \rightleftarrows PbCl_3^-$$

where all other possible species were ignored and the data fit the calculated equation in a satisfactory manner. One of the most impressive demonstrations of two different chemical models fitting equally well with the experimental data is given by Papoff and Caliumi[3] who showed that their polarographic measurements on the lead chloride system can be interpreted equally well by the two sets of overall stability constants:

$$\text{Set } \text{i}: \ \beta_1 = 10, \ \beta_2 = 20, \ \beta_3 = 100, \ \beta_3 = 10$$

$$\text{Set } \text{ii}: \ \beta_1 = 13, \ \beta_2 = \ 0, \ \beta_3 = 120, \ \beta_3 = 10$$

There is a qualitative difference between the two sets, for the first gives evidence for a complex which the second set asserts does not exist.

An excellent discussion of curve-fitting procedures to correlate experimental solubility data for the lead chloride system with a chemical model which assumes all complex-ion species up to $PbCl_4^{-2}$ is given by Helgeson in a monograph[4] discussing solubility of galena, the PbS ore, in chloride-containing waters. This detailed discussion makes extensive use of the algebraic methods like the ones used in this chapter, with the complication of more equilibria and the saving grace of an IBM 709 computer.

[1]F. Nelson and K. A. Kraus, *J. Am. Chem. Soc.* **76,** 5916 (1954).

[2]A. B. Garrett, M. V. Nobel, and S. Miller, *J. Chem. Ed.* **19,** 485 (1942).

[3]P. Papoff and M. Caliumi, *Gazz. chim. ital.* **84,** 1006 (1954).

[4]H. C. Helgeson, *Complexing and Hydrothermal Ore Deposition.* New York: Pergamon Press, 1964.

Suggestion for Further Study

H. C. Helgeson, in a geochemical investigation of the variables involved in hydrothermal ore-forming processes, chose the system PbS-NaCl-HCl-H_2O as a physical-chemical model. He devotes a third of a book[4] to consideration of equilibria involving the thirteen species which predominate in acidic solutions. The entire book, and especially Chapter III, is highly recommended.

Suggestion for Experimental Investigation

1. Prepare a set of solutions of varying total chloride concentration, each in equilibrium with solid $PbCl_2$, and determine the total lead and total chloride concentrations in each solution. The aqueous and solid phases can be brought to equilibrium either by shaking solid $PbCl_2$ with a solution, or by precipitating $PbCl_2$. The additional variable amount of chloride must come from somewhere. Supernatant liquid may be removed with a sintered-polyethylene or sintered-glass filter stick. After completing a preliminary set of experiments, try to analyze the data in terms of some set of chemical equilibria, starting with the simplest case first. Obtain numerical values within upper and lower bounds for the relevant equilibrium constants.

11

Equilibria in the
Alanine-Nickel(II) System

The chemistry of aqueous solutions of nickel(II) and alanine involves complex-ion, acid-base, and solubility equilibria. Nickel(II) solubility is increased by the presence of alanine and is also a function of pH. The acid-base titration curve of alanine is changed when nickel(II) is present. Any analysis of complex formation must be concerned with simultaneous acid-base equilibria.

Even after making a few simplifying assumptions, there remain six simultaneous equilibria and a dozen chemical species to consider. The goal of this chapter is to point out some types of experiments which can yield quantitative information about the chemistry of these solutions, and to show ways in which the data of such experiments can be interpreted in terms of probable species in solution. The discussion will be based on a chemical model which takes into account the following equilibria:

$$A^+ \rightleftarrows A^\pm + H^+ \qquad\qquad K_A' = \frac{(A^\pm)(H^+)}{(A^+)} \qquad\qquad (11.1)$$

$$A^\pm \rightleftarrows A^- + H^+ \qquad\qquad K_B' = \frac{(A^-)(H^+)}{(A^\pm)} \qquad\qquad (11.2)$$

$$NiA^+ \rightleftarrows Ni^{++} + A^- \qquad\qquad K_1' = \frac{(Ni^{++})(A^-)}{(NiA^+)} \qquad\qquad (11.3)$$

$$NiA_2 \rightleftarrows NiA^+ + A^- \qquad\qquad K_2' = \frac{(NiA^+)(A^-)}{(NiA_2)} \qquad\qquad (11.4)$$

$$Ni(OH)_2(s) \rightleftarrows Ni^{++} + 2OH^- \quad K_3' = (Ni^{++})(OH^-)^2 \qquad (11.5)$$

$$H_2O \rightleftarrows H^+ + OH^- \qquad\qquad K_w' = (H^+)(OH^-) \qquad\qquad (11.6)$$

159

The species A^+, $A^\pm$, and A^- are variously protonated forms of alanine. Equilibrium (11.5) is a precipitation reaction, and $Ni(OH)_2$ is a solid precipitate. Since it will be of interest to inquire into how concentrations of the various species change as [A], [Ni], and (H^+) are independently varied, it is necessary that another cation and another anion be available, and we shall choose Na^+ and ClO_4^-.

Several approximations and restrictions have already been introduced by the failure to include additional equilibria. It has been assumed that

a. No complexes involving Na^+, ClO_4^-, or OH^- are formed,

b. The value of (A°) is insignificant compared to the value of $(A^\pm)$,

c. The various concentrations are small enough so that no precipitates are formed except $Ni(OH)_2$, and

d. There are no complexes formed with nickel(II) and alanine except NiA^+ and NiA_2.

There are two types of equilibria under consideration. Equilibria (11.1), (11.2), (11.5), and (11.6) can be studied in solutions in which either nickel(II) or alanine is missing. By their very nature, Equilibria (11.3) and (11.4) can be studied only in the presence of both nickel(II) and alanine. There are likewise two qualitatively different types of equilibria to describe; it is convenient to consider the case of *homogeneous equilibria* in the absence of precipitate independently of the case of *heterogeneous equilibria* in the presence of precipitate.

Homogeneous Case. We seek here an equation which will permit calculation of concentrations of all chemical species in a solution of known [A], [Ni], and (H^+). Unfortunately, such an equation will not be obtained. However, a straightforward calculation method will be developed, and the method will be used for some sample calculations.

The conservation equation which sums all A containing species is

$$[A] = (A^+) + (A^\pm) + (A^-) + (NiA^+) + 2(NiA_2) \qquad (11.7)$$

The nickel conservation equation, in the absence of $Ni(OH)_2$ precipitate, is

$$[Ni] = (Ni^{++}) + (NiA^+) + (NiA_2) \qquad (11.8)$$

Substitution of the appropriate equilibrium constant expressions into the conservation equations yields

$$[A] = (A^-)\left\{1 + \frac{(H^+)}{K_B'} + \frac{(H^+)^2}{K_A'K_B'}\right\} + (Ni^{++})\left\{\frac{(A^-)}{K_1'} + \frac{2(A^-)^2}{K_1'K_2'}\right\} \qquad (11.9)$$

$$[Ni] = (Ni^{++})\left\{1 + \frac{(A^-)}{K_1'} + \frac{(A^-)^2}{K_1'K_2'}\right\} \qquad (11.10)$$

The concentration of uncomplexed Ni^{++}, (Ni^{++}), can be eliminated between Equations (11.9) and (11.10), giving

$$[A] = [Ni]\left[\frac{K_2'(A^-) + 2(A^-)^2}{K_1'K_2' + K_2'(A^-) + (A^-)^2}\right] + (A^-)\left[1 + \frac{(H^+)}{K_B'} + \frac{(H^+)^2}{K_A'K_B'}\right]$$
(11.11)

Equation (11.11) forms the basis of a calculation method which permits calculation of all concentrations in a solution if (H^+), $[A]$, and $[Ni]$ are known. First, a graph is made of (A^-) vs $[A]$ at constant $[Ni]$ and (H^+) by assuming values of (A^-) until the desired range of $[A]$ is covered. Then at a particular set of values of $[A]$, $[Ni]$, and (H^+), (A^-) is read from the graph, and Equation (11.10) used to compute (Ni^{++}). Inspection of the equilibrium constant equations reveals that all remaining concentrations can be calculated directly if (A^-), (Ni^{++}), and (H^+) are known simultaneously.

For purposes for performing some illustrative calculations, the following numerical values will be assumed:

$$K_A' = 4.6 \times 10^{-3}$$
$$K_B' = 1.8 \times 10^{-10}$$
$$K_1' = 1.1 \times 10^{-6}$$
$$K_2' = 2.0 \times 10^{-5}$$
$$K_3' = 2.8 \times 10^{-16}$$
$$K_w' = 1.00 \times 10^{-14}$$
$$[Ni] = 0.100 \text{ moles per liter}$$
$$(H^+) = 1.00 \times 10^{-1} \text{ moles per liter}$$

Figure 11.1 shows the fraction $(Ni^{++})/[Ni]$ plotted from Equation (11.10) for a wide range of values of (A^-), a range so great that a logarithmic scale is required. Equation (11.11) is plotted in Figure 11.2 for the particular case of pH 7.00, $[Ni] = 0.100$ molar. The equilibria in a series of solutions will be examined under the constraint that $[Ni]$ and (H^+) have constant values, $[A]$ taking on a range of values. For the present, the restriction is retained that the equilibria be homogeneous, that $[A]$ must be high enough to prevent $Ni(OH)_2$ precipitation.

Equation (11.11) is of central importance, for at constant (H^+) and $[Ni]$ it permits calculation of the master variable for Equations (11.1) through (11.5) and Equation (11.10). This master variable, which sets the values of all other concentrations, is (A^-). Figures 11.3 and 11.4 show distribution

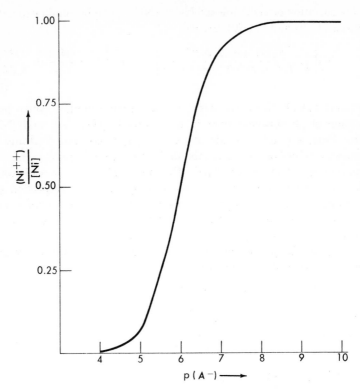

Figure 11.1. Fraction $(Ni^{++})/[Ni]$ versus $p(A^-)$ According to Equation 11.10.

curves calculated by reading values of (A^-) from the graph in Figure 11.2, obtaining the corresponding value of (Ni^{++}) from Figure 11.1, and then substituting these numbers into the equilibrium-constant expressions. Equation (11.5) places an upper limit on (Ni^{++}) for the homogeneous solution case, and a corresponding lower limit is thus placed on $[A]$.

It makes sense to talk about a type of buffer capacity in these solutions. For instance, a 0.1 molar $[A]$ solution is well-buffered with respect to changes in (NiA^+) caused by changes in $[A]$, and this maximum buffer capacity occurs in solutions in which there are comparable and appreciable concentrations of the species Ni^{++} and NiA_2 which are jointly involved in the equilibrium

$$Ni^{++} + NiA_2 \rightleftarrows 2NiA^+ \tag{11.12}$$

The coexisting species Ni^{++} and NiA_2 provide a reservoir of NiA^+, and the concentration of NiA^+ is thus stablized. The same considerations apply to buffering of (NiA_2), the equilibrium

$$NiA^+ + A^- \leftrightarrows NiA_2$$

being stabilized at high relative values of (NiA_2) at high $[A]$ because of a

reservoir of uncomplexed alanine which in turn stabilizes (A⁻) at a low but
nearly constant value.

The master variable (A⁻) is the concentration of a species which is present

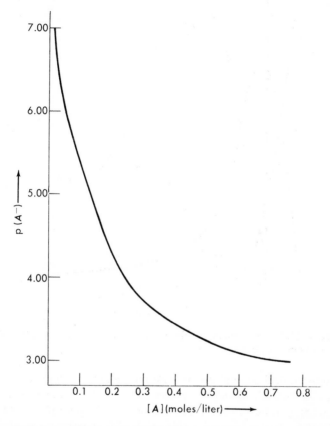

Figure 11.2. Logarithmic Plot of the Master Variable (A⁻) versus [A] at pH
7.00, [Ni] = 0.100 moles per liter.

in such small amounts that one might have been tempted to ignore it completely as an unimportant species in solution. The calculations presented
consider (A⁻) as being a controlling variable, hardly an insignificantly small
quantity. There is an arbitrary feature to this analysis which can be seen by
rewriting the complexation equilibria as

$$\text{NiA}^+ + \text{H}^+ \rightleftarrows \text{Ni}^{++} + \text{A}^{\pm} \qquad \frac{(\text{Ni}^{++})(\text{A}^{\pm})}{(\text{NiA}^+)(\text{H}^+)} = K_4' = \frac{K_1'}{K_B'}$$

$$(11.13)$$

$$\text{NiA}_2 + \text{H}^+ \rightleftarrows \text{NiA}^+ + \text{A}^{\pm} \qquad \frac{(\text{NiA}^+)(\text{A}^{\pm})}{(\text{NiA}_2)(\text{H}^+)} = K_5' = \frac{K_2'}{K_B'}$$

$$(11.14)$$

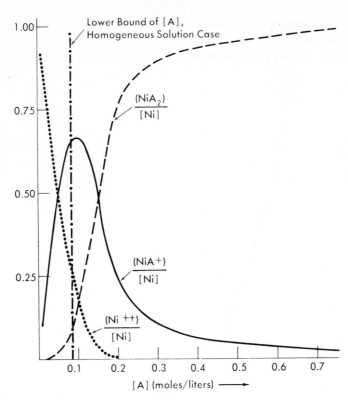

Figure 11.3. Distribution of Species Containing Nickel at pH 7.00, [Ni] = 0.100 moles per liter.

When written in this form, the predominant alanine-species at pH 7.00, $A^{\pm}$, becomes the controlling master species. In a similar manner, the equilibria can be written in terms of A^+. No additional information results from these different formulations, since the new equilibrium constants can be written in terms of the initial set of constants. Equilibria (11.13) and (11.14) are not distinguishable from Equilibria (11.3) and (11.4) by equilibrium experiments.

Acid-Base Titration of Alanine. Before considering the titration of an alanine-Ni(II) mixture, we will look at the titration curve of alanine alone. Since a solution of alanine in water is almost neutral, the two pH extremes can be reached only by separate addition of strong acid and of strong base. The chemical and mathematical models for analysis of the titration curve include equilibria (11.1), (11.2), and (11.6), as well as conservation equations,

$$[A] = (A^-) + (A^{\pm}) + (A^+) \tag{11.15}$$

$$[Na] = (Na^+) \tag{11.16}$$

$$[ClO_4] = (ClO_4^-) \tag{11.17}$$

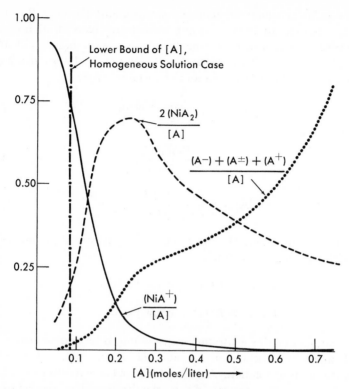

Figure 11.4. Distribution of Species Containing Alanine at pH 7.00, [Ni] = 0.100 moles per liter.

It is also necessary to include the electroneutrality equation

$$(A^+) + (Na^+) + (H^+) = (ClO_4^-) + (A^-) + (OH^-) \qquad (11.18)$$

These equations lead directly to

$$[Na] - [ClO_4] = \frac{K_w'}{(H^+)} - (H^+) + [A] \left\{ \frac{1 - \dfrac{(H^+)^2}{K_A'K_B'}}{\dfrac{(H^+)}{K_B'} + \dfrac{(H^+)^2}{K_A'K_B'} + 1} \right\}$$

$$(11.19)$$

Certain features of Equation (11.19) are worthy of note. Both quantities [Na] and [ClO₄] enter in the same manner, except for a change of sign. In fact, the left-hand member of Equation (11.19) is just the molar excess of NaOH, the added NaOH in excess of added HClO₄ in moles per liter, a quantity which can be either positive or negative. At zero [A], (11.19) is the equation for a strong acid-strong base titration curve. The coefficient of [A] is positive at high values of pH, is negative at low values of pH, and is zero when $(H^+)^2 = K_A'K_B'$; the coefficient of [A] is thus zero at the isoelectric point, the point at which all alanine concentrations cancel in the electro-neutrality equation to leave a strong acid-strong base titration curve.

In a titration performed by adding together some combination of M_{HClO_4} molar $HClO_4$ solution, M_{NaOH} molar NaOH solution, and M_A molar alanine solution, the following transformations of variables apply:

$$[ClO_4] = \frac{V_{HClO_4}M_{HClO_4}}{V_{HClO_4} + V_A + V_{NaOH}} \qquad (11.20)$$

$$[Na] = \frac{V_{NaOH}M_{NaOH}}{V_{HClO_4} + V_A + V_{NaOH}} \qquad (11.21)$$

$$[A] = \frac{V_A M_A}{V_{HClO_4} + V_A + V_{NaOH}} \qquad (11.22)$$

Substitution of Equations (11.20) through (11.22) into Equation (11.19) yields, with rearrangement, equations of the form

$$V_{NaOH} = f((H^+)), \text{ const } V_A, V_{HClO_4}$$

$$V_{HClO_4} = f((H^+)), \text{ const } V_{NaOH}, V_A$$

These equations describe a titration curve obtained by adding acid or base to an alanine solution to obtain a solution of extreme pH, and then back-titrating the resulting solution. A similar titration curve results by combining the data from two separate experiments: the titration of an alanine solution with NaOH, and the titration of an identical alanine solution with $HClO_4$. The equations we seek then are of the form

$$V_{NaOH} = f((H^+)), \text{ const } V_A, V_{HClO_4} = 0$$

$$V_{HClO_4} = f((H^+)), \text{ const } V_A, V_{NaOH} = 0$$

For the case in which $HClO_4$ is absent and NaOH is titrant, there results

$$V_{Na} = \\ -V_A \left[\frac{\begin{array}{l}(H^+)^4 + (H^+)^3[K_A' + M_A] + (H^+)^2[K_A'K_B' - K_w'] \\ + (H^+)[-K_w'K_A' - M_AK_A'K_B'] - K_w'K_A'K_B'\end{array}}{\begin{array}{l}(H^+)^4 + (H^+)^3[K_A' + M_{Na}] + (H^+)^2[K_A'K_B' - K_w' + K_A'M_{Na}] \\ + (H^+)[-K_w'K_A' + M_{Na}K_A'K_B'] - K_w'K_A'K_B'\end{array}} \right] \qquad (11.23)$$

For alanine solutions, the values of (H^+) which will satisfy this equation range from about 10^{-7} to lower values which depend on the concentration of NaOH used as titrant. Since the inequality

$$(H^+) \ll K_A'$$

is a good approximation throughout the titration, it will be used to simplify

Equation (11.23) to give, after division of both numerator and denominator by K_A',

$$V_{Na} = -V_A \left[\frac{(H^+)^3\left\{1 + \dfrac{M_A}{K_A'}\right\} + (H^+)^2 K_B' + (H^+)[-K_w' - M_A K_B'] - K_w' K_B'}{(H^+)^3 + (H^+)^2[M_{Na} - K_w'/K_A' + K_B] + (H^+)[M_{Na} K_B' - K_w'] - K_w' K_B'} \right]$$

(11.24)

Equation (11.24) is plotted in Figure 11.5. Certain features of this calculated titration curve will now be discussed.

It is evident that an analytical titration of alanine in aqueous solution with NaOH as titrant cannot have a sharp endpoint which will permit a visual indicator. When the reactant concentrations are approximately 0.1 molar, the inflection point is difficult to locate and precedes the equiv-

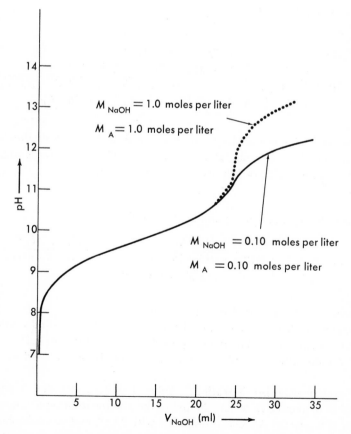

Figure 11.5. Basic Titration Curve of Alanine Calculated from Equation (11.24), $V_A = 25.00$ ml.

alence point by about one ml. Even in the more concentrated solution with reactants 1.0 molar, the inflection point precedes the equivalence point by at least 0.1 ml, and the nearly-vertical section of the titration curve extends from pH 11.4 to pH 11.6, hardly a large pH interval.

The absence of a sharp inflection point is a consequence of an important chemical feature of the alanine equilibria. When essentially all of the dissociable protons have been removed from the alanine molecules, the pH is within less than two pH units from the maximum pH attainable with 0.10 molar NaOH, and there is no chemical way to have a dramatic increase in (OH^-).

Endpoint detection in concentrated solutions can be achieved by titration to a predetermined endpoint pH value if experimental conditions are carefully controlled. A sharper inflection point can be obtained in a properly chosen nonaqueous solvent (see "Suggestions for Experimental Investigation" at end of chapter).

When NaOH is absent and $HClO_4$ is the titrant, Equations (11.19), (11.20), and (11.22) yield

$$V_{HClO_4} =$$

$$-V_A \left[\frac{\begin{array}{c} (H^+)^4 + (H^+)^3[K_A' + M_A] + (H^+)^2[K_A'K_B' - K_w'] \\ - (H^+)[K_w'K_A' + M_AK_A'K_B'] - K_w'K_A'K_B' \end{array}}{\begin{array}{c} (H^+)^4 + (H^+)^3[K_A' - M_{HClO_4}] + (H^+)^2[K_A'K_B' - K_w' - K_A'M_{HClO_4}] \\ + (H^+)[-K_w'K_A' - M_{HClO_4}K_A'K_B'] - K_w'K_A'K_B' \end{array}} \right]$$

$$(11.25)$$

This equation for the acidic titration curve differs from Equation (11.23) only in that M_{Na} is replaced by $-M_{HClO_4}$. When it is recognized that throughout the region of validity of Equation (11.25),

$$(H^+) \gg K_B'$$

it is possible to obtain the approximate equation

$$V_{HClO_4} = -V_A \left[\frac{\begin{array}{c} (H^+)^3 + (H^+)^2[K_A + M_A] - K_A[K_w' + M_AK_B] \\ \end{array}}{\begin{array}{c} (H^+)^3 + (H^+)^2[K_A - M_{HClO_4}] - (H^+)K_A'M_{HClO_4} \\ - K_A'[M_{HClO_4}K_B' + K_w'] \end{array}} \right]$$

$$(11.26)$$

Equation (11.26) is plotted in Figure 11.6.

The striking feature of Figure 11.6 is the absence of an inflection point in the titration curve. The pH of equivalence is less than one pH unit from the minimum attainable pH value if 0.10 molar $HClO_4$ is used as titrant.

Nickel(II)–Alanine Titration. When $Ni(ClO_4)_2$ solution is added to a solution of alanine in water, the pH of the alanine solution drops to lower values. The species A^- forms complexes with Ni^{++}, and re-establishment of equilibrium among the alanine species liberates protons from some A^+ ions. If values of K_w', K_A', and K_B' are known, a titration of alanine with

$Ni(ClO_4)_2$ provides the information necessary for determination of the values of K_1' and K_2'. Progress of the titration is followed with a pH meter.

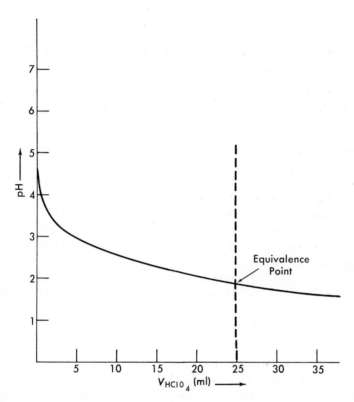

Figure 11.6. Acidic Titration Curve of Alanine Calculated from Equation (11.26). $V_A = 25.00$ ml, $M_{HClO_4} = M_A = 0.10$ moles per liter.

In this solution being titrated, conservation equations are

$$[A] = (A^+) + (A^\pm) + (A^-) + (NiA^+) + 2(NiA_2) \qquad (11.27)$$

$$(Ni) = (Ni^{++}) + (NiA^+) + (NiA_2) \qquad (11.28)$$

$$[ClO_4] = (ClO_4^-) = 2[Ni] \qquad (11.29)$$

Electroneutrality requires that

$$(A^+) + (H^+) + (NiA^+) + 2(Ni^{++}) = (A^-) + (OH^-) + (ClO_4^-) \qquad (11.30)$$

Equations (11.30), (11.29), (11.1), (11.2), and (11.6) combine to give

$$(A^-)\left\{\frac{(H^+)^2}{K_A'K_B'} - 1\right\} + (H^+) - \frac{K_w'}{(H^+)} = 2[Ni] - (Ni^{++})\left\{2 + \frac{(A^-)}{K_1'}\right\} \qquad (11.31)$$

Equations (11.28), (11.3), and (11.4) together yield

$$(Ni^{++}) = [Ni]\frac{1}{1 + \dfrac{(A^-)}{K_1'} + \dfrac{(A^-)^2}{K_1'K_2'}} \tag{11.32}$$

The quantity (Ni^{++}) can be eliminated between Equations (11.31) and (11.32), with the result

$$(A^-)\left\{\frac{(H^+)^2}{K_A'K_B'} - 1\right\} + (H^+) - \frac{K_w'}{(H^+)} = [Ni]\left\{\frac{2(A^-)^2 + (A^-)K_2'}{K_1'K_2' + K_2'(A^-) + (A^-)^2}\right\} \tag{11.33}$$

Equations (11.27) and (11.28) can be combined with the appropriate equilibrium constant expressions to give Equation (11.11).

The equation being sought is an equation giving pH of a solution of known [A] and [Ni] as a function of the known total concentrations and the equilibrium constants. Equations (11.33) and (11.11) are two simultaneous equations, which would give the desired equation if it were possible to eliminate (A^-) between the two. Since both are cubic equations in (A^-), the prospects are not hopeful.

However, it turns out that the coefficient of [Ni] is the same in both equations, and thus when (11.33) is subtracted from (11.11), there is obtained

$$[A] - (H^+) + \frac{K_w'}{(H^+)} = (A^-)\left[\frac{2(H^+)^2}{K_A'K_B'} + \frac{(H^+)}{K_B'}\right] \tag{11.34}$$

Once again (A^-) is treated as a master variable. For a solution of known [A] and measured pH, (A^-) can be calculated with no a priori knowledge of the complexation constants. This value of (A^-) can then be substituted into the left-hand member of Equation (11.33); together with the known values of (H^+) and [Ni] for the solution under consideration, it is possible to calculate a value for

$$\frac{2(A^-)^2 + (A^-)K_2'}{K_1'K_2' + K_2'(A^-) + (A^-)^2} = F \tag{11.35}$$

at a known value of (A^-). A series of solutions permits calculation of (11.35) for a wide range of (A^-), and this data may suffice for evaluation of one or both of the complexation constants. See "Suggestions for Experimental Investigation" at the end of this chapter for some initial approximation methods useful in analysis of data.

Heterogeneous Equilibria. When precipitation of $Ni(OH)_2$ occurs, the condition of conservation of Ni-containing species in solution fails. It is precisely at this point, however, that the solubility product equation places a condition on (Ni^{++}). If the solution is in equilibrium with solid $Ni(OH)_2$, and if there is no alanine contained in the precipitate, the alanine conservation equation can be combined with Equations (11.1) through (11.6) as follows:

$$[A] = (A^-) + (A^\pm) + (A^+) + (NiA^+) + 2(NiA_2)$$

$$= (A^-)\left\{1 + \frac{(H^+)}{K_B'} + \frac{(H^+)^2}{K_A'K_B'}\right\} + (Ni^{++})\left\{\frac{(A^-)}{K_1'} + \frac{2(A^-)^2}{K_1'K_2'}\right\}$$

$$= (A^-)\left\{1 + \frac{(H^+)}{K_B'} + \frac{(H^+)^2}{K_A'K_B'}\right\} + (H^+)^2\frac{K_3'}{(K_w')^2}\left\{\frac{(A^-)}{K_1'} + \frac{2(A^-)^2}{K_1'K_2'}\right\}$$

$$= (A^-)\left[1 + \frac{(H^+)}{K_B'} + (H^+)^2\left\{\frac{1}{K_A'K_B'} + \frac{K_3'}{(K_w')^2K_1'}\right\}\right]$$

$$+ (A^-)^2\left\{\frac{2(H^+)^2K_3'}{(K_w')^2K_1'K_2'}\right\} \tag{11.36}$$

It is straightforward to compute any or all of the concentrations, given [A] and (H^+). There is no dependence on [Ni]. Equation (11.36) permits calculation of [A] for any pair of values of (A^-) and (H^+). A plot of [A] versus (A^-) at some pH makes convenient a reading of (A^-) for a pair $\{(H^+),$ [A]$\}$. Once (A^-) is known, all other concentrations can be calculated using equations derived from the equilibrium constant equations.

Problems

11.1. Show that (A°) is insignificant with respect to $(A^\pm)$ under all conditions at 25°C., and that failure to include A° as a species in solution has no measurable effect on calculated values of the other concentrations.

11.2. Inspection of Figure 11.5 reveals that the pH value at the macroscopic half-equivalence point is approximately equal to the value of pK_B' for alanine. Perhaps the macroscopic half-equivalence point locates pK_B' with sufficient accuracy to permit experimental evaluation of the equilibrium constant. Using algebraic or numerical arguments, find the error introduced by evaluation of K_B' for alanine by this method. Do the same considerations apply to determination of K_A'?

11.3. Plot a distribution curve showing the fraction of [A] present as A^-, $A^\pm$, and A^+ at various values of pH in the absence of nickel(II). (Hint: Less calculation is required if it is remembered that the sum of the three fractions must be unity.) Where will best acid-base buffering occur? What is the predominant ·alanine species in acidic solution? in basic solution? Under the conditions of the titration represented in Figure 11.6, how nearly is all alanine converted to a single chemical species at the equivalence point?

11.4. Equation (11.36) shows that in the presence of $Ni(OH)_2$ precipitate, the value of (A^-) depends only on (H^+) and [A]. Show that under the same conditions, the value of the same concentration (A^-) depends only on the values of (H^+) and [Ni]. Formation of the precipitate has created a new phase and the chemical system has lost one degree of freedom. There are no longer as many independent variables as there were before precipitation occurred.

Suggestions for Experimental Investigation

1. Pick several likely nonaqueous solvents which would be predicted to yield sharp inflection points in an alanine-strong base titration. Then perform the titrations, using some electrode pair and a pH meter to follow the course of the titration. Evaluate the results in terms of two important criteria for a useful analytical titration: can a reproducible endpoint be accurately detected? does this endpoint correspond to the equivalence point?

2. Figures 11.5 and 11.6 together suggest that a titration of NaAlaninate or of AlanineHClO$_4$ throughout a wide pH range should yield a sharp inflection point between pH 5.0 and pH 7.5. Endpoint detection should be straightforward, and it would appear that here is the basis for a good analytical method of titration of alanine. Can stoichiometric NaAlaninate or AlanineHClO$_4$ be prepared quantitatively from a small sample of the amino acid? Try some procedures which seem feasible.

3. Evaluate K_1' and K_2' by analysis of a pH titration curve, using some combination of Ni(ClO$_4$)$_2$ and alanine as the titrant solution and the solution being titrated. The methods described in this chapter permit conversion of the titration data into values of F as a function of (A$^-$) given by Equation (11.34). If the fraction F is less than unity, then $K_1'K_2'$ is greater than (A$^-$)^2, and it is then possible to write Equation (11.34) as

$$\frac{1}{F} = 1 + \frac{K_1'K_2'}{(A^-)}$$

A plot of $1/F$ versus $1/(A^-)$ at low values of (A$^-$) should yield a straight line of slope equal to $K_1'K_2'$. After finding a value for the product $K_1'K_2'$, it is useful to plot the data at higher values of (A$^-$) according to

$$\frac{(A^-)^2[2 - F] - K_1K_2F}{(F - 1)} = (A^-)K_2'$$

which is an equation derived from (11.34) without approximation. The left-hand member contains only known quantities, and when it is plotted versus (A$^-$), a linear plot of slope K_2' results. When $F = 1$, the equation is indeterminate, as written.

4. Design an experiment for the determination of Ni(II) solubility in solutions containing alanine. How can the composition of the solid phase be established? Will the solid-phase composition affect the results? How much information about values of the several equilibrium constants can be obtained from solubility data?

12

Complexation Equilibria in
Silver Chloride Precipitation
Titrations

This chapter consists of two case studies involving simultaneous complexion and solubility equilibria. The first is an examination of equilibria important in the titration of chloride with silver nitrate in the presence of iron(III) and thiocyanate. The second is a discussion of the effect of complexes like $AgCl_2^-$ and $AgCl_3^{--}$ on the shape of a silver chloride precipitation titration curve. In both cases experimental details are included.

Modified Volhard Titration. A visual endpoint detection technique for the silver chloride precipitation titration was described by Swift,[1] et al., in 1950. The method is a modification of the classical Volhard titration[2] introduced in 1874. The modified procedure involves preparation of a sample containing 25 ml of approximately 0.1 molar chloride mixed with 10 ml of 2 molar iron (III) nitrate and 1 ml 0.01 molar potassium thiocyanate. The solution must be acidic to prevent formation of hydroxy complexes or precipitates. This solution is reddish pink due to formation of the colored $FeSCN^{++}$ complex ion. Titrant is 0.1 molar silver nitrate. At or near the equivalence point, there occurs a color change, interpreted as due to dissociation of the $FeSCN^{++}$ complex.

Included in the chemical model are the following equilibria and apparent equilibrium constants:

$$AgCl(s) \rightleftarrows Ag^+ + Cl^- \qquad K_1' = (Ag^+)(Cl^-) \qquad (12.1)$$

$$AgSCN(s) \rightleftarrows Ag^+ + SCN^- \qquad K_2' = (Ag^+)(SCN^-) \qquad (12.2)$$

$$FeSCN^{++} \rightleftarrows Fe^{3+} + SCN^- \qquad K_3' = \frac{(Fe^{3+})(SCN^-)}{(FeSCN^{++})} \qquad (12.3)$$

[1]E. H. Swift, G. M. Arcand, R. Lutwack, and D. J. Meier, *Anal. Chem.* **22**, 306 (1950).
[2]J. Volhard, *J. prakt. Chem.* **9**, 217 (1874).

There will be no discussion of the initial portion of the titration before AgCl precipitates. The titration is thus conveniently divided into the region in which the solid phase is entirely AgCl, and the region in which both AgCl and AgSCN have precipitated. It will be assumed, with surely some error, that AgCl and AgSCN are present as separate solids, each in its most stable crystalline form, and that coprecipitation, occlusion, solid solution formation, and adsorption do not occur. The possibility of chloride complexes with silver is ignored; the discussion later in this chapter can serve as a guide to whether or not it is justifiable to ignore such complexes.

Before AgSCN Precipitates. In the presence of AgCl(s) and the absence of AgSCN(s), Equations (12.1) and (12.3) apply, although initially only (12.3) will be used. The goal in this derivation is to obtain an equation which shows, or fails to show, that the visual color change corresponds to the equivalence point. Since the colored species being considered is $FeSCN^{++}$, the equation sought is a relation between V_{AgNO_3} and $(FeSCN^{++})$. Only two conservation equations are needed,

$$[SCN] = (SCN^-) + (FeSCN^{++}) \qquad (12.4)$$

$$[Fe] = (Fe^{3+}) + (FeSCN^{++}) \qquad (12.5)$$

Substitution of Equations (12.4) and (12.5) into Equation (12.3) yields

$$(FeSCN^{++})^2 - (FeSCN^{++})\{[Fe] + [SCN] + K_3'\} + [Fe][SCN] = 0 \quad (12.6)$$

Table 12.1. TABULATION OF SELECTED VALUES OF [Cl], [SCN], [Ag], AND [Fe] AT VARIOUS VALUES OF V_{AgNO_3}.

V_{AgNO_3}	V_{total}	[Cl]	[SCN]	[Ag]	[Fe]
0.00 ml	36.0 ml	0.06944	0.0002778	0.00000	0.55555
5.00	41.0	0.06098	0.0002439	0.01220	0.48780
10.00	46.0	0.05435	0.0002174	0.02174	0.43478
18.00	54.0	0.04630	0.0001852	0.03333	0.37037
24.00	60.0	0.041667	0.0001667	0.040000	0.33333
24.50	60.5	0.0413223	0.0001653	0.0404959	0.33058
24.70	60.7	0.0411862	0.0001647	0.0406919	0.32949
24.80	60.8	0.0411184	0.0001645	0.0407895	0.32895
24.90	60.9	0.0410509	0.0001642	0.0408867	0.32841
25.00	61.0	0.0409836	0.0001639	0.0409836	0.32787
25.07	61.07	0.04093663	0.00016375	0.04105125	0.32749
25.08	61.08	0.04092992	0.00016372	0.04106090	0.32744
25.09	61.09	0.0409232	0.0001637	0.0410706	0.32739
25.10	61.10	0.0409165	0.0001637	0.0410802	0.32733
25.15	61.15	0.0408831	0.0001635	0.0411284	0.32706
25.20	61.20	0.0408497	0.0001634	0.0411765	0.32680
25.50	61.50	0.0406504	0.0001626	0.0414634	0.32520
30.00	66.00	0.037879	0.0001515	0.045455	0.30303

Transformation to volume variables is not very useful in this case, since the resulting equation would be a quadratic in both $(FeSCN^{++})$ and V_{AgNO_3}. A satisfactory computation method involves calculation of $[Fe]$ and $[SCN]$ at each value of V_{AgNO_3}, and use of these values, Equation (12.6), and the quadratic formula to obtain values of $(FeSCN^{++})$. Table 12.1 gives the quantities in [ ] for various titrant volumes. Quantities $[Ag]$, $[Cl]$, $[Fe]$, and $[SCN]$ represent total Ag^+, Cl^-, Fe^{3+}, and SCN^- added to the reaction flask, and are not necessarily equal to the total concentrations of the respective species in homogeneous solution if precipitation has occurred. The quadratic formula converts (12.6) into

$$2(FeSCN^{++}) = [Fe] + [SCN] + K_3'$$
$$\pm \sqrt{\{[Fe] + [SCN] + K_3'\}^2 - 4[Fe][SCN]} \qquad (12.7)$$

Equation (12.7) is plotted in Figures 12.1 and 12.2.

In the Presence of AgSCN Precipitate. When the first particles of AgSCN precipitate, the conservation equation (12.4) fails, and the constraint of Equation (12.2) is imposed. Let us suppose that the chloride in the initial sample was potassium chloride; this assumption does not affect the final result, but it makes setting up of the starting equations a bit easier. Then, since NO_3^-, K^+, and all $Fe(III)$ species remain in solution and do not precipitate, three conservation equations can be written as follows:

$$(NO_3^-) = 3[Fe] + [Ag] \qquad (12.8)$$

$$(K^+) = [Cl] + [SCN] \qquad (12.9)$$

$$[Fe] = (Fe^{3+}) + (FeSCN^{++}) \qquad (12.10)$$

Electroneutrality requires that

$$(NO_3^-) + (Cl^-) + (SCN^-) = 3(Fe^{3+}) + (Ag^+) + (K^+) + 2(FeSCN^{++}) \qquad (12.11)$$

All three equilibrium constant expressions, (12.1), (12.2), and (12.3), will be required.

Equations (12.8), (12.9), and (12.10) can be combined with (12.11) to eliminate the concentrations of NO_3^- and K^+, removing all explicit reference to these ions and giving

$$3[Fe] + [Ag] - [Cl] - [SCN]$$
$$= 3(Fe^{++}) + (Ag^+) + 2(FeSCN^{++}) - (Cl^-) - (SCN^-) \qquad (12.12)$$

Introduction of Equation (12.10) gives

$$[Ag] - [Cl] - [SCN] = -(FeSCN^{++}) + (Ag^+) - (Cl^-) - (SCN^-) \qquad (12.13)$$

The concentrations of Ag^+ and Cl^- can be eliminated with the use of Equations (12.1) and (12.2) to leave

$$[Ag] - [Cl] - [SCN] = -(FeSCN^{++}) + \frac{K_2'}{(SCN^-)} - (SCN^-)\left[\frac{K_1'}{K_2'} + 1\right]$$

(12.14)

The next step is to eliminate (SCN^-), and this requires an equation for (SCN^-) obtained by combination of (12.3) and (12.10):

$$(SCN^-) = \frac{K_3'(FeSCN^{++})}{[Fe] - (FeSCN^{++})}$$

(12.15)

Generality is lost, but for the experimental conditions being considered no significant accuracy is lost, by the approximation

$$(FeSCN^{++}) \ll [Fe]$$

(12.16)

Justification for (12.16) rests on the facts that $(FeSCN^{++})$ can never exceed

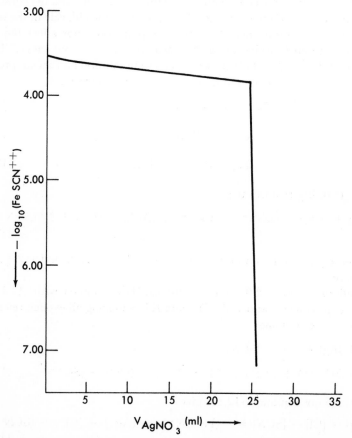

Figure 12.1. Variation of $(FeSCN^{++})$ in Silver Chloride Precipitation Titration.

[SCN], and that the ratio [Fe]/[SCN] is 2×10^3 throughout the titration. Equation (12.15) is therefore approximated by

$$(SCN^-) = \frac{K_3'(FeSCN^{++})}{[Fe]} \tag{12.17}$$

Equations (12.14) and (12.17) can finally be combined to yield

$$(FeSCN^{++})^2 \left[1 + \frac{\dfrac{K_1'K_3'}{K_2'} + K_3'}{[Fe]} \right] + (FeSCN^{++}) \{[Ag] - [Cl] - [SCN]\}$$

$$- \frac{K_2'}{K_3'}[Fe] = 0 \tag{12.18}$$

Equation (12.18) is plotted in Figures 12.1 and 12.2.

Some Notes on the Computations. Following Swift, the value of K_3' is taken to be 7.25×10^{-3} as reported by Frank and Oswalt.[3] The value of K_2' is taken as 1.00×10^{-12} as determined by Vanderzee and

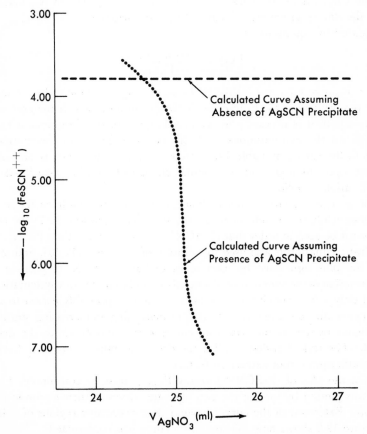

Figure 12.2. Variation of (FeSCN^{++}) Near Equivalence Point in Silver Chloride Precipitation Titration.

[3] H. S. Frank and R. L. Oswalt, *J. Am. Chem. Soc.* **69,** 1321 (1947).

Smith.[4] The value of K_1' is taken as 1.78×10^{-10} as determined by Davies and Jones.[5] The following volumes and concentrations are used:

$$V_{KCl} = 25.00 \text{ ml}$$

$$M_{KCl} = 0.100 \text{ molar}$$

$$V_{Fe(NO_3)_3} = 10.0 \text{ ml}$$

$$M_{Fe(NO_3)_3} = 2.00 \text{ molar}$$

$$V_{KSCN} = 1.00 \text{ ml}$$

$$M_{KSCN} = 0.0100 \text{ molar}$$

$$M_{AgNO_3} = 0.100 \text{ molar}$$

The calculations are carried out in terms [Ag], [Cl], [SCN], and [Fe], and the values presented in Table 12.1 for various values of V_{AgNO_3} were calculated by equations like

$$[Ag] = \frac{V_{AgNO_3} M_{AgNO_3}}{V_{total}}$$

where $V_{total} = V_{KCl} + V_{Fe(NO_3)_3} + V_{KSCN} + V_{AgNO_3}$. Since the computations require use of the differences between numbers which themselves are nearly equal, it is necessary to retain a large number of significant figures throughout the computations, and this fact is reflected in the number of digits in the entries of Table 12.1. It is assumed that there is no volume change upon mixing, and no volume change of solution associated with precipitation of solid.

The ± sign appears to offer a choice, but in fact there is in each case only one chemically reasonable algebraic solution. In Equation (12.7) the minus sign must be used in order that (FeSCN^{++}) be no greater than [SCN]. The quadratic equation is also used for solution of Equation (12.18), and in this case the plus sign must be used so as to have (FeSCN^{++}) positive.

Extraction of the square root of a number can be carried out systematically, but if only a few calculations are to be made it is probably easiest to use a desk calculator to make several trial squarings, using an increasing number of significant figures as the trial root comes closer and closer to the desired result. The task is easiest of all if the desk calculator happens to have an automatic square root extraction feature.

Since the plot of (FeSCN^{++}) versus V_{AgNO_3} must be continuous, Figure 12.1 was plotted by joining the two separate curves at their common intersection. Extension of the curves beyond their respective regions of validity in Figure 12.2 shows how the composite curve was constructed.

[4] C. E. Vanderzee and W. E. Smith, *J. Am. Chem. Soc.* **78**, 721 (1956).
[5] C. W. Davies and A. L. Jones, *Trans. Faraday Soc.* **51**, 812 (1955).

Discussion of the Titration.   The virtual step-function shown in Figure 12.1 indicates that this method makes possible an excellent means of endpoint detection. It turns out that in practice the method is convenient, accurate, and precise. But there are two complicating factors which must be considered, factors which can cause difficulty if ignored.

The expanded portion of the titration curve plotted in Figure 12.2 shows that the inflection point in the curve of $(FeSCN^{++})$ versus V_{AgNO_3} does not lie at the equivalence point, but rather follows the equivalence point by about 0.1 ml. This causes no problem if the analyst sees the color of the complex disappear when $(FeSCN^{++})$ falls just below $10^{-4.5}$. It does cause an important titration error if the analyst detects the loss of color at $(FeSCN^{++})$ equal to $10^{-5.5}$.

This derivation is predicated on equilibrium existing at the equivalence point between solution and each of two separate solid phases composed individually of pure AgCl and AgSCN. There are reasons to believe that such pure phases do not constitute the equilibrium state. Whatever the equilibrium state, it is unlikely that the state will be achieved unless equivalence is approached slowly with vigorous shaking. Some SCN^- or $FeSCN^{++}$ may be adsorbed on the AgCl crystals early in the titration, and it is likely that when substantial precipitation of AgSCN does occur the new crystals will be formed on the surfaces of existing AgCl crystals, probably altering the activity of AgSCN from the value of the pure crystal.

No matter how attractive an analytical method appears to be on the basis of a priori equilibrium calculations, an empirical experimental validation is essential. The paper by Swift *et al.* contains a description of experiments which illustrate how an analytical method can be evaluated.

Effect of Chloride Complexes on the Silver Chloride Titration Curve. The discussion of the silver chloride precipitation titration in Chapter 2 which led to Equations (2.27) and (2.28) failed to consider the effect of such species in solution as $AgCl$, $AgCl_2^-$, $AgCl_3^{--}$, and so forth. Chemical models for the titration curve which include complex formation will now be examined.

Consider first a titration characterized by the following equilibria:

$$AgCl(s) \rightleftarrows Ag^+ + Cl^- \qquad K_1' = (Ag^+)(Cl^-) \qquad (12.19)$$

$$Ag^+ + 2Cl^- \rightleftarrows AgCl_2^- \qquad \beta_2 = \frac{(Ag^+)(Cl^-)^2}{(AgCl_2^-)} \qquad (12.20)$$

If the sample is a solution of KCl and the titrant is a solution of $AgNO_3$, then the electroneutrality and conservation equations are

$$(NO_3^-) + (Cl^-) + (AgCl_2^-) = (Ag^+) + (K^+) \qquad (12.21)$$

$$[Cl] = (K^+) \qquad (12.22)$$

$$[Ag] = (NO_3^-) \qquad (12.23)$$

Substitution of Equations (12.19) to (12.23) into Equation (12.21) yields

$$(Ag^+)^2 + (Ag^+)\{[Cl] - [Ag]\} - K_1'\left[1 + \frac{K_1'}{\beta_2}\right] = 0 \qquad (12.24)$$

This result is of exactly the same form as Equation (2.20). Although the constant terms look different, it must be remembered that values of K_1' and β_2 must be obtained from experiments like these. If the only information available is the data from titration curves, Equations (2.20) and (12.24) appear operationally indistinguishable.

However, Equations (12.19) through (12.23) can be combined so as to yield a quadratic equation in (Cl^-):

$$(Cl^-)^2\left\{\frac{K_1'}{\beta_2} + 1\right\} + (Cl^-)\{[Ag] - [Cl]\} - K_1' = 0 \qquad (12.25)$$

This result should be compared with Equation (2.19), the titration curve equation derived without assuming complex formation. When expressed in terms of the concentration (Cl^-), the derived titration curves have different shapes for the two different chemical models.

Why should the formation of $AgCl_2^-$ have no effect on the functional form of the titration curve when the curve is a plot of (Ag^+) vs V_{AgNO_3}, but alter the shape when the titration curve is a plot of (Cl^-) vs V_{AgNO_3}? The answer to this question can be found by examining four chemical reactions:

$$Ag^+ + \ Cl^- \rightleftarrows AgCl(s)$$

$$Ag^+ + \ Cl^- \rightleftarrows AgCl$$

$$2Ag^+ + \ Cl^- \leftrightarrows Ag_2Cl^+$$

$$Ag^+ + 2Cl^- \rightleftarrows AgCl_2^-$$

The formation of the Ag_2Cl^+ complex is no doubt hypothetical; the uncharged AgCl species is probably present in solution. These four reactions are alike in that each removes uncomplexed Cl^- and uncomplexed Ag^+ from solution. Formation of AgCl complex in solution has no effect on the form of the titration curve, since (AgCl) does not enter the electroneutrality equation; formation of AgCl removes equimolar amounts of Cl^- and Ag^+, leaving the electroneutrality equation unchanged. The AgCl concentration depends only on the product $(Cl^-)(Ag^+)$ which is a constant, so that (AgCl) remains constant throughout the titration.

Inclusion of higher chloride complexes would be expected to change the shape of the titration curve. Presence of Ag_2Cl^+ in the chemical model results in a titration curve in (Cl^-) differing from (2.19) only by an altered constant term, but a titration curve in (Ag^+) which is a two-parameter equation.

Problems

12.1. E. Rabinowitch and W. H. Stockmayer [*J. Am. Chem. Soc.* **64**, 335 (1942)] demonstrated complex formation involving $Fe(III)$ and Cl^-. Consult this paper, and then discuss the effect of such complexes on the derivation of Equations (12.13) and (12.18). H. S. Frank and R. L. Oswalt [*J. Am. Chem. Soc.* **69**, 1321 (1947)] suggest that in solutions of $Fe(III)$ and SCN^-, complexes containing more than one SCN^- per complex may occur. They also suggest the possibility of the species $FeClSCN^+$ when both SCN^- and Cl^- are present. What implications, qualitative and quantitative, do such complexes have on the derivation of Equations (12.13) and (12.18)?

12.2. Derive an equation for the titration of KCl with $AgNO_3$, assuming the formation of the complexes $AgCl_2^-$ and $AgCl_3^{--}$. What combination of values of the formation constants and of concentrations is necessary for presence of $AgCl_3^{--}$ to have a demonstratable effect on the shape of the titration curve? Can the formation constant for $AgCl_3^{--}$ be evaluated from titration data?

Suggestions for Experimental Investigation

1. Devise some experiments to evaluate the modified Volhard titration. Does the $FeSCN^{++}$ endpoint coincide with an endpoint detected with a Ag^+-sensitive glass electrode or a Ag-AgCl electrode? Does the method give the calculated results for a series of pure chlorides, such as KCl, $SrCl_2$, $AlCl_3$, and so forth? How can such chlorides be prepared in a pure, known, stoichiometric state for weighing? Over how wide a range of concentrations is the titration method valid? What happens if other halides, or other anions, are present in either trace or larger concentrations? Are equilibrium conditions established more quickly at elevated temperatures so as to give a better endpoint, or are there other complications not suspected at high temperatures?

2. Devise experiments to determine the formulas of the chloride complexes which exist in equilibrium with AgCl. An excellent guiding discussion is R. Ramette, *J. Chem. Ed.* **37**, 348 (1960).

3. Using an appropriate electrode combination, determine (Ag^+) and/or (Cl^-) throughout a AgCl titration, and see if this experimental titration curve gives any evidence of complex formation. Can complex formation be excluded? Can the existence of any specific complexes be proved?

13

EDTA Titrations

One of the most important complexometric titration reagents is ethylene-diaminetetraacetic acid, EDTA,

$$\begin{array}{ccccc}
\text{HOOCCH}_2 & & \text{H} \quad \text{H} & & \text{CH}_2\text{COOH} \\
& \diagdown & | \quad\; | & \diagup & \\
& \text{N}\!\!-\!\!\text{C}\!\!-\!\!\text{C}\!\!-\!\!\text{N} & & \\
& \diagup & | \quad\; | & \diagdown & \\
\text{HOOCCH}_2 & & \text{H} \quad \text{H} & & \text{CH}_2\text{COOH}
\end{array}$$

EDTA forms complexes with a great many cations. Selectivity can often be achieved by taking advantage of competitive complexing reactions and acid-base equilibria. Analysis of equilibria in a typical EDTA titration represents a practical example of many simultaneous equilibria being treated under appropriate experimental conditions so as to yield a very simple titration curve. Even though a dozen reactions are considered at the same time, the titration curve equation which results has practically the same functional form as the equation for an uncomplicated titration of a metal B and a ligand X to form BX.

Conditional Equilibrium Constants. It is the purpose of this section to demonstrate how the effects of many simultaneous equilibria can be summarized for certain purposes by one or two parameters which may be functions of most of the experimental conditions. Since these condition-dependent parameters function as apparent equilibrium constants, they are commonly called *conditional equilibrium constants*.

EDTA is a polyprotic acid, and so the proportions of variously-protonated species will depend on (H^+). In order to prevent precipitation of metal hydroxide at high pH, and in order to change the conditional constants to more favorable values, a complex-forming salt is often included in the solutions. Often this salt is also a good acid-base buffer, and thus H^+ equilibria must be considered here. The possibility must be considered that any one of the protonated forms of EDTA may form complexes, although it is to be expected a priori that the formation constants will be different in each case. The chemical model for an EDTA titration considered below will include many of these possibilities.

The chemical model considers the metal ion M; EDTA in five differently-protonated forms designated H_4Y, H_3Y, H_2Y, HY, and Y; metal-EDTA complexes MY, MHY, and MH_2Y; and buffer with metal-buffer complexes A, MA, MA_2, $\cdots$, MA_n. In order to reduce the number of pages for the derivation, acid-base equilibria involving A, and complexation of M with other forms of EDTA will not be considered; inclusion of these equilibria will not affect the *form* of the final result.

Equilibria and equilibrium constants to be considered are given below. Explicit charges are given on no species; electroneutrality condition is not required, and charges clutter the nomenclature unnecessarily.

$$\beta_0 = 1$$

$$M + A \rightleftarrows MA \qquad K_1' = \frac{(MA)}{(M)(A)} \qquad \beta_1 = \frac{(MA)}{(M)(A)}$$

$$MA + A \rightleftarrows MA_2 \qquad K_2' = \frac{(MA_2)}{(MA)(A)} \qquad \beta_2 = K_1'K_2' = \frac{(MA_2)}{(M)(A)^2}$$

$$MA_{i-1} + A \rightleftarrows MA_i \qquad K_i' = \frac{(MA_i)}{(MA_{i-1})(A)} \qquad \beta_i = \prod_{j=1}^{i} K_j' = \frac{(MA_i)}{(M)(A)^i}$$

$$\cdots \qquad\qquad \cdots \qquad\qquad \cdots$$

$$MA_{n-1} + A \rightleftarrows MA_n \qquad K_n' = \frac{(MA_n)}{(MA_{n-1})(A)} \qquad \beta_n = \prod_{j=1}^{n} K_j' = \frac{(MA_n)}{(M)(A)^n}$$

$$\alpha_0 = 1$$

$$HY \rightleftarrows H + Y \qquad K_A' = \frac{(H)(Y)}{(HY)} \qquad \alpha_1 = \frac{(H)(Y)}{(HY)}$$

$$H_2Y \rightleftarrows H + HY \qquad K_B' = \frac{(H)(HY)}{(H_2Y)} \qquad \alpha_2 = K_A'K_B' = \frac{(H)^2(Y)}{(H_2Y)}$$

$$H_3Y \rightleftarrows H + H_2Y \qquad K_C' = \frac{(H)(H_2Y)}{(H_3Y)} \qquad \alpha_3 = K_A'K_B'K_C' = \frac{(H)^3(Y)}{(H_3Y)}$$

$$H_4Y \rightleftarrows H + H_3Y \qquad K_D' = \frac{(H)(H_3Y)}{(H_4Y)} \qquad \alpha_4 = K_A'K_B'K_C'K_D' = \frac{(H)^4(Y)}{(H_4Y)}$$

$$Y + M \rightleftarrows MY \qquad K_I' = \frac{(MY)}{(Y)(M)}$$

$$HY + M \rightleftarrows MHY \qquad K_{II}' = \frac{(MHY)}{(HY)(M)}$$

$$H_2Y + M \rightleftarrows MH_2Y \qquad K_{III}' = \frac{(MH_2Y)}{(H_2Y)(M)}$$

Conservation equations for the metal species and the EDTA species are

$$[M] = (M) + (MA) + (MA_2) + \cdots + (MA_n)$$
$$+ (MY) + (MHY) + (MH_2Y) \qquad (13.1)$$

$$[Y] = (Y) + (HY) + (H_2Y) + (H_3Y) + (H_4Y)$$
$$+ (MY) + (MHY) + (MH_2Y) \qquad (13.2)$$

Substitution of appropriate equilibrium-constant equations into the two conservation equations yields

$$[M] = (M)\{1 + \beta_1(A) + \beta_2(A)^2 + \cdots + \beta_n(A)^n\}$$
$$+ (M)(Y)\left\{K_I' + \frac{K_{II}'(H)}{\alpha_1} + \frac{K_{III}'(H)^2}{\alpha_2}\right\} \qquad (13.3)$$

$$[Y] = (Y)\left\{1 + \frac{(H)}{\alpha_1} + \frac{(H)^2}{\alpha_2} + \frac{(H)^3}{\alpha_3} + \frac{(H)^4}{\alpha_4}\right\}$$
$$+ (M)(Y)\left\{K_I' + \frac{K_{II}'(H)}{\alpha_1} + \frac{K_{III}'(H)^2}{\alpha_2}\right\} \qquad (13.4)$$

Elimination of (Y) between Equations (13.3) and (13.4) results in, after rearrangement,

$$(M)^2 + (M)\left\{\frac{[Y] - [M]}{\sum\limits_{i=0}^{n} \beta_i(A)^i} + \frac{\sum\limits_{i=0}^{4} \frac{(H)^i}{\alpha_i}}{K_I' + \frac{K_{II}'(H)}{\alpha_1} + \frac{K_{III}'(H)^2}{\alpha_2}}\right\}$$
$$- \frac{[M] \sum\limits_{i=0}^{4} \frac{(H)^i}{\alpha_i}}{\left\{\sum\limits_{i=0}^{n} \beta_i(A)^i\right\}\left\{K_I' + \frac{K_{II}'(H)}{\alpha_1} + \frac{K_{III}'(H)^2}{\alpha_2}\right\}} \qquad (13.5)$$

If experimental conditions can be so arranged as to permit a titration at constant (H) and (A), many of the fractors in Equation (13.5) will be constant throughout the titration. At constant (H) and (A), Equation (13.5) is

$$(M)^2 + (M)\left\{\frac{[Y] - [M]}{K_a'} + K_b'\right\} - [M]\frac{K_b'}{K_a'} = 0 \qquad (13.6)$$

where $K_a' = f((A))$ and $K_b' = f((H))$. Constant (H) is achieved by using a buffer solution, perhaps having the buffer components in the sample solution, or sometimes having buffer in both sample and titrant. Constant (A) can be assured if [A] is substantially greater than n[M], so that even if every M cation were complexed with n molecules of A, only a small percentage of [A] would be involved in metal complexes. Problem (13.1) deals with the effect on K_a' and K_b' of allowing A to react with H and act as an acid-base buffer.

The parameters K_a' and K_b' are conditional constants. A titration curve will take on a simple and familiar form if the conditional constants are constant. An important consideration of experimental design in complexation titrations is to be sure that the variables on which the conditional constants depend are constant throughout the titration. Improvement of a particular titrimetric method can oftentimes be made by changing conditions so as to change the value of the conditional constants.

EDTA as a Polyprotic Acid. EDTA can exist as five different species, varying only in the number of bound protons. A distribution diagram is instructive. Five equations for the fraction of [Y] present as each of the species can be derived by beginning with the conservation equation

$$[Y] = (H_4Y) + (H_3Y) + (H_2Y) + (HY) + (Y) \qquad (13.7)$$

and substituting the overall dissociation constants. Calculations are simplified by writing each of the fractions with the same denominator. If the common denominator, D is given by

$$D = \frac{(H^+)^4}{\alpha_4} + \frac{(H^+)^3}{\alpha_3} + \frac{(H^+)^2}{\alpha_2} + \frac{(H^+)}{\alpha_1} + 1 \qquad (13.8)$$

then the five distribution fractions are

$$\frac{(Y)}{[Y]} = \frac{1}{D} \qquad (13.9)$$

$$\frac{(HY)}{[Y]} = \frac{(H^+)}{D\alpha_1} \qquad (13.10)$$

$$\frac{(H_2Y)}{[Y]} = \frac{(H^+)^2}{D\alpha_2} \qquad (13.11)$$

$$\frac{(H_3Y)}{[Y]} = \frac{(H^+)^3}{D\alpha_3} \qquad (13.12)$$

$$\frac{(H_4Y)}{[Y]} = \frac{(H^+)^4}{D\alpha_4} \qquad (13.13)$$

Equations (13.9) through (13.13) are plotted in Figure 13.1. The parameters used in the calculation are

$$1/\alpha_1 = 1.828 \times 10^{10}$$

$$1/\alpha_2 = 2.648 \times 10^{16}$$

$$1/\alpha_3 = 1.245 \times 10^{19}$$

$$1/\alpha_4 = 1.233 \times 10^{21}$$

These reciprocal overall dissociation constants are calculated from data reported by Schwarzenbach and Ackermann.[1]

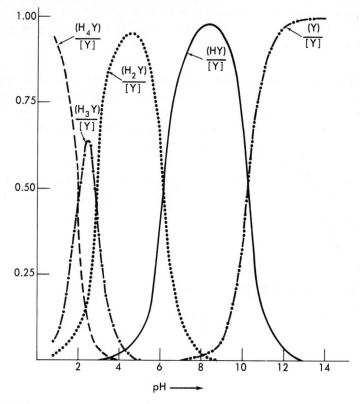

Figure 13.1. Distribution Function for the Variously-Protonated Forms of EDTA.

The problem of determining four equilibrium constants from titration data may seem staggering. Inspection of Figure 13.1 shows that at values of pH equal to 4 and less, the only species present are H_4Y, H_3Y, and H_2Y. Thus in this acid region EDTA can be considered a diprotic acid. In the region from pH 5 to pH 8 only H_2Y and HY are present and the acid must act as a monoprotic acid. In solutions more basic than pH 8 only HY and Y

[1]G. Schwarzenbach and H. Ackermann, *Helv. Chim. Acta* **30,** 1798 (1947).

are in solution, and again the EDTA must behave in this region as a monoprotic acid. See problem (13.3) for determination of dissociation constants
from titration data.

The pure acid is a white crystalline solid which is only slightly soluble in
water. The disodium salt, a dihydrate, is a white crystalline solid which
dissolves in water easily. It is available commercially in such high purity
that standard EDTA solutions may be prepared by direct weighing of the
disodium salt.

Problems

13.1. The derivation of Equation (13.6) proceeds without discussion of the
chemical nature of secondary complexing species A. It is likely that A
is a species like CN^-, NH_3, or CH_3COO^-, in which case it participates
in proton equilibria and can help buffer the solution near a given pH
value. Show how the inclusion of acid-base equilibria involving A
affects the functional dependence of K_a' and K_b' on (H) and (A). Is it
necessary to assume [A] large compared to [M]?

13.2. Equilibria assumed in deriving Equation (13.6) do not include

$$MY + H \rightleftharpoons MHY$$

$$MHY + H \rightleftharpoons MH_2Y$$

Express the equilibrium constants for these two reactions in terms of the
equilibrium constants which appear on Pages 183 and 184.

13.3. Procedures have been developed in previous chapters for the determination of dissociation constants for both monoprotic and diprotic
acids from titration data. Figure 13.1 reveals that within certain regions
of pH, EDTA can be considered to be a monoprotic or diprotic acid.
Determine as many dissociation constants as you can from the following
titration data:

pH	$\dfrac{[KOH]}{[EDTA]}$	pH	$\dfrac{[KOH]}{[EDTA]}$
2.833	0.00	5.816	2.30
2.876	0.20	6.011	2.40
2.934	0.40	6.186	2.50
2.998	0.60	6.375	2.60
3.070	0.80	6.561	2.70
3.156	1.00	9.567	3.20
3.259	1.20	9.928	3.40
3.403	1.40	10.160	3.60
3.594	1.60	10.352	3.80
3.922	1.80		

Apparently the titration was performed with rather concentrated KOH solution so
that there was very little volume change. Temperature was 20°C., ionic strength was
0.1 with KCl, K_w' was taken as 1.14×10^{-14}, and [EDTA] = 9.8×10^{-4} moles per liter.
The data is from a paper by Schwarzenbach and Ackermann [*Helv. Chim. Acta* **30**,
1798 (1947)].

Suggestion for Experimental Investigations

Examine, both experimentally and theoretically, the titration of Zn^{++} with EDTA in the presence of NH_3. Use Eriochrome Blue Black R indicator. Obtain an equation, making only such approximations which you can justify, for the optical absorbance due to indicator species as a function of volume of added titrant. Compare the predictions of this equation with experimental curves obtained using a colorimeter or a spectrophotometer. Refer to C. N. Reilley and R. W. Schmid, *Anal. Chem.* **31**, 887 (1959).

Bibliographical Note

Two excellent little books dealing with the theory and practice of EDTA titrations are:

G. Schwarzenbach, *Complexometric Titrations*, H. Irving, trans., London: Methuen and Co. Ltd., 1957.

H. A. Flaschka, *EDTA Titrations*, London: Pergamon Press, 1959.

A comprehensive compilation of quantitative analytical methods using EDTA is F. J. Welcher, *The Analytical Uses of Ethylenediamine Tetraacetic Acid*, Princeton: D. van Nostrand Company, Inc., 1958.

Appendix I

Annotated Compilation of Selected Equilibrium Constants

Tables of numerical values of equilibrium constants can be very misleading. Some experiments reported in the chemical literature represent the results of several years of careful research, and other values of equilibrium constants are, at best, guesses based on quite limited experimentation. Some chemical systems are especially well suited for precise equilibrium measurements, whereas other interesting chemical reactions defy quantitative measurement and tax the ingenuity of the very best chemist. All this is by way of saying that whenever the numerical value of an equilibrium constant is needed, original research papers should be consulted.

Some research papers make good reading for the student. The references cited in this appendix were selected because they represent good presentations of both experimental results and methods of data treatment. These papers are suggested as additional study material for learning about chemical equilibria in solution.

Acetic Acid. The dissociation constant of acetic acid [CH_3—COOH] was determined potentiometrically with a cell composed of a hydrogen electrode and a silver-silver chloride electrode. At 25 °C, K was found to vary from 1.726×10^{-5} at 0.18 ionic strength to 1.752×10^{-5} at 0.01 ionic strength, with an extrapolated value for zero ionic strength being 1.754×10^{-5} [H. S. Harned and R. W. Ehlers, *J. Am. Chem. Soc.* **54**, 1350 (1932)]. K was determined as a function of temperature from 0 to 60 °C at 5° intervals, and it was found that the value of K passes through a maximum at about 23 °C [H. S. Harned and R. W. Ehlers, *J. Am. Chem. Soc.* **55**, 652 (1933)].

189

Aliphatic Dicarboxylic Acids. Two dissociation constants for each of the series oxalic acid [HOOC—COOH], succinic acid [HOOC—$(CH_2)_2$ —COOH], glutaric acid [HOOC—$(CH_2)_3$—COOH], and adipic acid [HOOC—$(CH_2)_4$—COOH] were determined potentiometrically with a cell composed of a glass electrode and a silver-silver chloride electrode. A straightforward graphical method using titration data is used to obtain K_1 and $K_1 K_2$. A typical set of numerical titration data is presented. Values obtained at 20°C are:

Oxalic acid: $pK_1 = 1.25$, $pK_2 = 4.23$

Succinic acid: $pK_1 = 4.22$, $pK_2 = 5.67$.

Glutaric acid: $pK_1 = 4.39$, $pK_2 = 5.50$.

Adipic acid: $pK_1 = 4.43$, $pK_2 = 5.42$.

[J. C. Speakman, *J. Chem. Soc.* **1940**, 855].

The two dissociation constants of malonic acid [HOOC—CH_2—COOH] were determined at 25°C by analysis of a titration curve by considering the solution of diprotic acid to be a mixture of two monoprotic acids. The pH was determined using a hydrogen electrode. Titration data and detailed calculations from this data are reported. Values reported are $pK_1 = 2.79$ and $pK_2 = 5.38$.

[H. S. Simms, *J. Am. Chem. Soc.* **48**, 1239 (1926)].

Cycloalkane 1, 1-dicarboxylic Acids. Two dissociation constants for each of the series cyclopropane-1,1-dicarboxylic acid (ɪ), cyclobutane-1, 1-dicarboxylic acid (ɪɪ), cyclopentane-1,1-dicarboxylic acid (ɪɪɪ), and cyclo-hexane-1,1-dicarboxylic acid (ɪᴠ) have been determined by analysis of titra-tion data [W. L. German, G. H. Jeffery, and A. I. Vogel, *J. Chem. Soc.* **1935**,

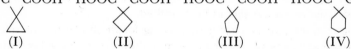

1624], and similar values from conductance data were reported in the same paper. Experimental values of pH and of V_{NaOH} are tabulated for the titration of each of the four acids. Apparent equilibrium constants are calculated at various points in the titration, and these are converted to a thermodynamic K by use of the Debye-Hückel limiting-law equation. There is no actual extrapolation of data to infinite dilution. Values reported are:

Cyclopropane-1,1-dicarboxylic acid: $K_1 = 1.5 \times 10^{-2}$ (from conductance measurements, since the value could not be obtained reliably from titration data), $K_2 = 3.71 \times 10^{-8}$.

Cyclobutane-1,1-dicarboxylic acid: $K_1 = 7.47 \times 10^{-4}$, $K_2 = 1.32 \times 10^{-6}$

Cyclopentane-1,1-dicarboxylic acid: $K_1 = 5.88 \times 10^{-4}$, $K_2 = 8.28 \times 10^{-7}$.

Cyclohexane-1,1-dicarboxylic acid: $K_1 = 3.54 \times 10^{-4}$, $K_2 = 7.78 \times 10^{-7}$.

Sulfonphthalein Acid-Base Indicators. Dissociation constants for bromcresol green, bromcresol purple, and phenol red, each a sulfonphthalein derivative, have been reported in a 50-page paper [J. Sendroy and A. B. Hastings, *J. Biol. Chem.* **82,** 197 (1929)] as a function of ionic strength of the different electrolytes used to attain a particular ionic strength. Values of pK' were determined colorimetrically. Data at 20 °C is given in detail in the paper. Extrapolated values of pK at zero ionic strength, determined by experiments in solutions of NaCl, KCl, Na_2SO_4, K_2SO_4, $MgCl_2$, and in some cases $MgSO_4$, $CaCl_2$, and a mixture of phosphates, are:

Bromcresol green: $pK = 4.92$.

Bromcresol purple: $pK = 6.46$.

Phenol red: $pK = 8.04$.

After reading this paper, a student may find interesting the following two short notes:

Mary Kilpatrick and Martin Kilpatrick, Jr., "Note on the Dissociation Constants of Certain Sulfonphthalein Indicators," *J. Phys. Chem.* **34,** 211 (1930).

J. Sendroy and A. B. Hastings, "Reply to Note on the Dissociation Constants of Certain Sulfonphthalein Indicators," *J. Phys. Chem.* **34,** 1607 (1930).

Benzene Seleninic Acids. A survey of the dissociation constants of benzene selenic acid (i) and twelve substituted benzene seleninic acids at 25 °C yielded the following values:

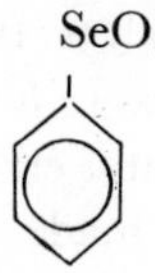

(i)

Substituent	pK
None	4.79
p-CH$_3$	4.88
m-CH$_3$	4.80
p-F	4.50
m-F	4.34
p-Cl	4.48
m-Cl	4.47
p-Br	4.50
m-Br	4.43
p-CH$_3$O	5.05
m-CH$_3$O	4.65
m-NO$_2$	4.07
o-C$_6$H$_5$	4.67

Titration curves were plotted in each case, using a pH meter and presumably a glass electrode and a calomel reference electrode. The value of pH at the macroscopic half-equivalence point was taken to be equal numerically to pK'. Conversion to values at zero ionic strength was made by a calculation utilizing the Debye-Hückel limiting law [J. D. McCullough and E. S. Gould, *J. Am. Chem. Soc.* **71**, 674 (1949)].

Alanine. Two dissociation constants of the amino acid alanine (I) have been determined by each of several researchers.

$$\begin{array}{c} H \\ | \\ H_2N-C-COOH \\ | \\ CH_3 \end{array}$$

(I)

Five investigations, reported during the period 1924 to 1938, are summarized here. Branch and Miyamoto [G. E. K. Branch and S. Miyamoto, *J. Am. Chem. Soc.* **52**, 863 (1930)] determined dissociation constants at 0 and 20°C and, assuming that pK is a linear function of $1/T$, reported pK at 25°C. Hirsch [P. Hirsch, *Biochem. Z.* **147**, 433 (1924)] determined dissociation constants at 18°C and his results were corrected to 25°C by Branch and Miyamoto. Nims and Smith [L. F. Nims and P. K. Smith, *J. Biol. Chem.* **101**, 401 (1933)] utilized emf measurements in cells without liquid junction and extrapolated their data to infinite dilution. These experiments were repeated by Smith, Taylor, and Smith [P. K. Smith, A. C. Taylor, and E. R. B. Smith, *J. Biol. Chem.* **122**, 109 (1937–38)] under the same conditions, although "certain simplifications were introduced into the procedure, which probably increased the experimental errors." Harris [L. J. Harris, *Pro. Roy. Soc. (London)* **95B**, 440 (1924)] made measurements at 25°C and ionic strength 0.025. These experimental results are tabulated together.

pK_1	pK_2	Ionic strength	Investigators
2.34	9.69	0.109	Branch and Miyamoto
2.25	9.66	0.100	Hirsch
2.39	9.74	0.025	Harris
2.340 ± 0.003	9.870 ± 0.003	0.000	Nims and Smith
2.348 ± 0.005	9.866 ± < 0.005	0.000	Smith, Taylor, and Smith

5-Arylthiopyrimidines. From photometric data, pK values differing by only 1.4 to 1.7 pK units have been determined for four compounds of the structure (1),

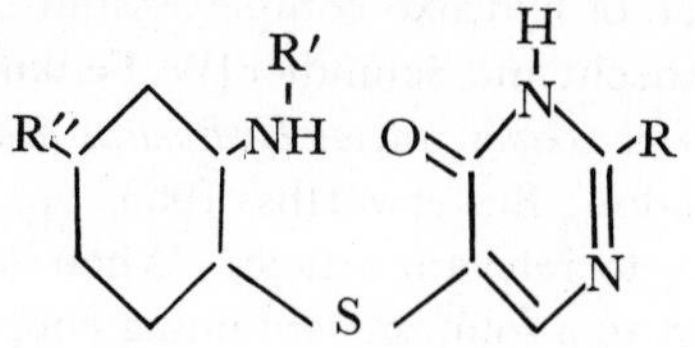

(1)

where the substituents are

Ia: $R = NH_2$, R', $R'' = H$

Ic: $R = NH_2$, $R' = H$, $R'' = Cl$

Id: $R = -N(CH_2)_5-$, $R' = H$, $R'' = Cl$

Ie: $R = NH_2$, $R' = CH_3$, $R'' = H$

A very good discussion of the use of an electronic computer in evaluating the equilibrium constants is included in the paper. The reported pK values are:

Ia: 2.1 ± 0.2, 3.6 ± 0.2, 8.7 ± 0.1

Ic: 1.5 ± 0.2, 3.2 ± 0.2, 8.6 ± 0.1

Id: 1.4 ± 0.2, 2.8 ± 0.2, 8.5 ± 0.1

Ie: 2.1 ± 0.2, 3.6 ± 0.2, 8.7 ± 0.1

[B. Roth and J. F. Bunnett, *J. Am. Chem. Soc.* **87**, 334 (1965)].

Uranyl Phosphates. Most salts of the alkali metals are quite soluble in aqueous media. An interesting series of exceptions is the uranyl phosphates. Determination of the solubility products requires consideration of multiple equilibria involving the variously-protonated phosphate species and a variety of uranyl phosphate complexes. V. Vesely, V. Pekarek, and M. Abbrent [*J. Inorg. Nucl. Chem.* **27**, 1159 (1965)] have reported experimental solubility data and details of their mathematical methods used in obtaining the following solubility products at $20 \pm 1\,°C$, ionic strength in the range 0.22 to 0.32:

$$(UO_2^{++})(HPO_4^{2-}) = 10^{-12.17 \pm 0.07}$$

$$(Na^+)(UO_2^{++})(PO_4^{3-}) = 10^{-24.21 \pm 0.07}$$

$$(Rb^+)(UO_2^{++})(PO_4^{3-}) = 10^{-25.72 \pm 0.15}$$

$$(K^+)(UO_2^{++})(PO_4^{3-}) = 10^{-25.50 \pm 0.1}$$

$$(Cs^+)(UO_2^{++})(PO_4^{3-}) = 10^{-25.41 \pm 0.2}$$

$$(NH_4^+)(UO_2^{++})(PO_4^{3-}) = 10^{-26.23 \pm 0.2}$$

$$(UO_2^{++})^3(PO_4^{3-})^2 = 10^{-49.7 \pm 0.3}$$

Copper (II) Oxide, Copper (II) Hydroxide, and Copper (II) Hydroxide Salts. Solubility of copper(II) in basic aqueous solution is complicated by the existence of hydroxo complexes and by extreme variability of the solid phase. Feitknecht and Schindler [W. Feitknecht and P. Schindler, *Solubility Constants of Metal Oxides, Metal Hydroxides and Metal Hydroxide Salts in Aqueous Solution.* London: Butterworths, 1963, pp. 172–175.] discuss the literature with reference to relevant articles. When less than an equivalent amount of base is added to a solution containing copper(II) salts, hydroxide salts are precipitated, whereas when an equivalent amount of base is added, active $Cu(OH)_2$ precipitates. The active $Cu(OH_2)$ ages into either CuO or inactive $Cu(OH)_2$. Depending on the solid phase, the solubility product can range from $10^{-16.4}$ to $10^{-20.5}$, a range of four orders of magnitude. In addition to complexes $Cu(OH)_3^-$ and $Cu(OH)_4^{--}$, a variety of polynuclear complexes is also thought to exist.

Appendix II

APPENDIX TABLE

Common Logarithms (Five-Place) of the Natural Numbers 1 to 10,000

N	Log	N	Log	N	Log	N	Log	N	Log
0	—	20	1.30 103	40	1.60 206	60	1.77 815	80	1.90 309
1	0.00 000	21	1.32 222	41	1.61 278	61	1.78 533	81	1.90 849
2	0.30 103	22	1.34 242	42	1.62 325	62	1.79 239	82	1.91 381
3	0.47 712	23	1.36 173	43	1.63 347	63	1.79 934	83	1.91 908
4	0.60 206	24	1.38 021	44	1.64 345	64	1.80 618	84	1.92 428
5	0.69 897	25	1.39 794	45	1.65 321	65	1.81 291	85	1.92 942
6	0.77 815	26	1.41 497	46	1.66 276	66	1.81 954	86	1.93 450
7	0.84 510	27	1.43 136	47	1.67 210	67	1.82 607	87	1.93 952
8	0.90 309	28	1.44 716	48	1.68 124	68	1.83 251	88	1.94 448
9	0.95 424	29	1.46 240	49	1.69 020	69	1.83 885	89	1.94 939
10	1.00 000	30	1.47 712	50	1.69 897	70	1.84 510	90	1.95 424
11	1.04 139	31	1.49 136	51	1.70 757	71	1.85 126	91	1.95 904
12	1.07 918	32	1.50 515	52	1.71 600	72	1.85 733	92	1.96 379
13	1.11 394	33	1.51 851	53	1.72 428	73	1.86 332	93	1.96 848
14	1.14 613	34	1.53 148	54	1.73 239	74	1.86 923	94	1.97 313
15	1.17 609	35	1.54 407	55	1.74 036	75	1.87 506	95	1.97 772
16	1.20 412	36	1.55 630	56	1.74 819	76	1.88 081	96	1.98 227
17	1.23 045	37	1.56 820	57	1.75 587	77	1.88 649	97	1.98 677
18	1.25 527	38	1.57 978	58	1.76 343	78	1.89 209	98	1.99 123
19	1.27 875	39	1.59 106	59	1.77 085	79	1.89 763	99	1.99 564
20	1.30 103	40	1.60 206	60	1.77 815	80	1.90 309	100	2.00 000

V. 1000—FIVE-PLACE LOGARITHMS OF NUMBERS—1509

N	0	1	2	3	4	5	6	7	8	9
100	00 000	043	087	130	173	217	260	303	346	389
101	00 432	475	518	561	604	647	689	732	775	817
102	00 860	903	945	988	*030	*072	*115	*157	*199	*242
103	01 284	326	368	410	452	494	536	578	620	662
104	01 703	745	787	828	870	912	953	995	*036	*078
105	02 119	160	202	243	284	325	366	407	449	490
106	02 531	572	612	653	694	735	776	816	857	898
107	02 938	979	*019	*060	*100	*141	*181	*222	*262	*302
108	03 342	383	423	463	503	543	583	623	663	703
109	03 743	782	822	862	902	941	981	*021	*060	*100
110	04 139	179	218	258	297	336	376	415	454	493
111	04 532	571	610	650	689	727	766	805	844	883
112	04 922	961	999	*038	*077	*115	*154	*192	*231	*269
113	05 308	346	385	423	461	500	538	576	614	652
114	05 690	729	767	805	843	881	918	956	994	*032
115	06 070	108	145	183	221	258	296	333	371	408
116	06 446	483	521	558	595	633	670	707	744	781
117	06 819	856	893	930	967	*004	*041	*078	*115	*151
118	07 188	225	262	298	335	372	408	445	482	518
119	07 555	591	628	664	700	737	773	809	846	882
120	07 918	954	990	*027	*063	*099	*135	*171	*207	*243
121	08 279	314	350	386	422	458	493	529	565	600
122	08 636	672	707	743	778	814	849	884	920	955
123	08 991	*026	*061	*096	*132	*167	*202	*237	*272	*307
124	09 342	377	412	447	482	517	552	587	621	656
125	09 691	726	760	795	830	864	899	934	968	*003
126	10 037	072	106	140	175	209	243	278	312	346
127	10 380	415	449	483	517	551	585	619	653	687
128	10 721	755	789	823	857	890	924	958	992	*025
129	11 059	093	126	160	193	227	261	294	327	361
130	11 394	428	461	494	528	561	594	628	661	694
131	11 727	760	793	826	860	893	926	959	992	*024
132	12 057	090	123	156	189	222	254	287	320	352
133	12 385	418	450	483	516	548	581	613	646	678
134	12 710	743	775	808	840	872	905	937	969	*001
135	13 033	066	098	130	162	194	226	258	290	322
136	13 354	386	418	450	481	513	545	577	609	640
137	13 672	704	735	767	799	830	862	893	925	956
138	13 988	*019	*051	*082	*114	*145	*176	*208	*239	*270
139	14 301	333	364	395	426	457	489	520	551	582
140	14 613	644	675	706	737	768	799	829	860	891
141	14 922	953	983	*014	*045	*076	*106	*137	*168	*198
142	15 229	259	290	320	351	381	412	442	473	503
143	15 534	564	594	625	655	685	715	746	776	806
144	15 836	866	897	927	957	987	*017	*047	*077	*107
145	16 137	167	197	227	256	286	316	346	376	406
146	16 435	465	495	524	554	584	613	643	673	702
147	16 732	761	791	820	850	879	909	938	967	997
148	17 026	056	085	114	143	173	202	231	260	289
149	17 319	348	377	406	435	464	493	522	551	580
150	17 609	638	667	696	725	754	782	811	840	869
N	0	1	2	3	4	5	6	7	8	9

Prop. Parts

	44	43	42
1	4.4	4.3	4.2
2	8.8	8.6	8.4
3	13.2	12.9	12.6
4	17.6	17.2	16.8
5	22.0	21.5	21.0
6	26.4	25.8	25.2
7	30.8	30.1	29.4
8	35.2	34.4	33.6
9	39.6	38.7	37.8

	41	40	39
1	4.1	4.0	3.9
2	8.2	8.0	7.8
3	12.3	12.0	11.7
4	16.4	16.0	15.6
5	20.5	20.0	19.5
6	24.6	24.0	23.4
7	28.7	28.0	27.3
8	32.8	32.0	31.2
9	36.9	36.0	35.1

	38	37	36
1	3.8	3.7	3.6
2	7.6	7.4	7.2
3	11.4	11.1	10.8
4	15.2	14.8	14.4
5	19.0	18.5	18.0
6	22.8	22.2	21.6
7	26.6	25.9	25.2
8	30.4	29.6	28.8
9	34.2	33.3	32.4

	35	34	33
1	3.5	3.4	3.3
2	7.0	6.8	6.6
3	10.5	10.2	9.9
4	14.0	13.6	13.2
5	17.5	17.0	16.5
6	21.0	20.4	19.8
7	24.5	23.8	23.1
8	28.0	27.2	26.4
9	31.5	30.6	29.7

	32	31	30
1	3.2	3.1	3.0
2	6.4	6.2	6.0
3	9.6	9.3	9.0
4	12.8	12.4	12.0
5	16.0	15.5	15.0
6	19.2	18.6	18.0
7	22.4	21.7	21.0
8	25.6	24.8	24.0
9	28.8	27.9	27.0

IV. 1500—FIVE–PLACE LOGARITHMS OF NUMBERS—2009

Prop. Parts	N	0	1	2	3	4	5	6	7	8	9
	150	17 609	638	667	696	725	754	782	811	840	869
	151	17 898	926	955	984	*013	*041	*070	*099	*127	*156
	152	18 184	213	241	270	298	327	355	384	412	441
	153	18 469	498	526	554	583	611	639	667	696	724
	154	18 752	780	808	837	865	893	921	949	977	*005
	155	19 033	061	089	117	145	173	201	229	257	285
	156	19 312	340	368	396	424	451	479	507	535	562
	157	19 590	618	645	673	700	728	756	783	811	838
	158	19 866	893	921	948	976	*003	*030	*058	*085	*112
	159	20 140	167	194	222	249	276	303	330	358	385
	160	20 412	439	466	493	520	548	575	602	629	656
	161	20 683	710	737	763	790	817	844	871	898	925
	162	20 952	978	*005	*032	*059	*085	*112	*139	*165	*192
	163	21 219	245	272	299	325	352	378	405	431	458
	164	21 484	511	537	564	590	617	643	669	696	722
	165	21 748	775	801	827	854	880	906	932	958	985
	166	22 011	037	063	089	115	141	167	194	220	246
	167	22 272	298	324	350	376	401	427	453	479	505
	168	22 531	557	583	608	634	660	686	712	737	763
	169	22 789	814	840	866	891	917	943	968	994	*019
	170	23 045	070	096	121	147	172	198	223	249	274
	171	23 300	325	350	376	401	426	452	477	502	528
	172	23 553	578	603	629	654	679	704	729	754	779
	173	23 805	830	855	880	905	930	955	980	*005	*030
	174	24 055	080	105	130	155	180	204	229	254	279
	175	24 304	329	353	378	403	428	452	477	502	527
	176	24 551	576	601	625	650	674	699	724	748	773
	177	24 797	822	846	871	895	920	944	969	993	*018
	178	25 042	066	091	115	139	164	188	212	237	261
	179	25 285	310	334	358	382	406	431	455	479	503
	180	25 527	551	575	600	624	648	672	696	720	744
	181	25 768	792	816	840	864	888	912	935	959	983
	182	26 007	031	055	079	102	126	150	174	198	221
	183	26 245	269	293	316	340	364	387	411	435	458
	184	26 482	505	529	553	576	600	623	647	670	694
	185	26 717	741	764	788	811	834	858	881	905	928
	186	26 951	975	998	*021	*045	*068	*091	*114	*138	*161
	187	27 184	207	231	254	277	300	323	346	370	393
	188	27 416	439	462	485	508	531	554	577	600	623
	189	27 646	669	692	715	738	761	784	807	830	852
	190	27 875	898	921	944	967	989	*012	*035	*058	*081
	191	28 103	126	149	171	194	217	240	262	285	307
	192	28 330	353	375	398	421	443	466	488	511	533
	193	28 556	578	601	623	646	668	691	713	735	758
	194	28 780	803	825	847	870	892	914	937	959	981
	195	29 003	026	048	070	092	115	137	159	181	203
	196	29 226	248	270	292	314	336	358	380	403	425
	197	29 447	469	491	513	535	557	579	601	623	645
	198	29 667	688	710	732	754	776	798	820	842	863
	199	29 885	907	929	951	973	994	*016	*038	*060	*081
	200	30 103	125	146	168	190	211	233	255	276	298
Prop. Parts	**N**	**0**	**1**	**2**	**3**	**4**	**5**	**6**	**7**	**8**	**9**

Prop. Parts

	29	28
1	2.9	2.8
2	5.8	5.6
3	8.7	8.4
4	11.6	11.2
5	14.5	14.0
6	17.4	16.8
7	20.3	19.6
8	23.2	22.4
9	26.1	25.2

	27	26
1	2.7	2.6
2	5.4	5.2
3	8.1	7.8
4	10.8	10.4
5	13.5	13.0
6	16.2	15.6
7	18.9	18.2
8	21.6	20.8
9	24.3	23.4

	25
1	2.5
2	5.0
3	7.5
4	10.0
5	12.5
6	15.0
7	17.5
8	20.0
9	22.5

	24	23
1	2.4	2.3
2	4.8	4.6
3	7.2	6.9
4	9.6	9.2
5	12.0	11.5
6	14.4	13.8
7	16.8	16.1
8	19.2	18.4
9	21.6	20.7

	22	21
1	2.2	2.1
2	4.4	4.2
3	6.6	6.3
4	8.8	8.4
5	11.0	10.5
6	13.2	12.6
7	15.4	14.7
8	17.6	16.8
9	19.8	18.9

IV. 2000—FIVE-PLACE LOGARITHMS OF NUMBERS—2509

N	0	1	2	3	4	5	6	7	8	9
200	30 103	125	146	168	190	211	233	255	276	298
201	30 320	341	363	384	406	428	449	471	492	514
202	30 535	557	578	600	621	643	664	685	707	728
203	30 750	771	792	814	835	856	878	899	920	942
204	30 963	984	*006	*027	*048	*069	*091	*112	*133	*154
205	31 175	197	218	239	260	281	302	323	345	366
206	31 387	408	429	450	471	492	513	534	555	576
207	31 597	618	639	660	681	702	723	744	765	785
208	31 806	827	848	869	890	911	931	952	973	994
209	32 015	035	056	077	098	118	139	160	181	201
210	32 222	243	263	284	305	325	346	366	387	408
211	32 428	449	469	490	510	531	552	572	593	613
212	32 634	654	675	695	715	736	756	777	797	818
213	32 838	858	879	899	919	940	960	980	*001	*021
214	33 041	062	082	102	122	143	163	183	203	224
215	33 244	264	284	304	325	345	365	385	405	425
216	33 445	465	486	506	526	546	566	586	606	626
217	33 646	666	686	706	726	746	766	786	806	826
218	33 846	866	885	905	925	945	965	985	*005	*025
219	34 044	064	084	104	124	143	163	183	203	223
220	34 242	262	282	301	321	341	361	380	400	420
221	34 439	459	479	498	518	537	557	577	596	616
222	34 635	655	674	694	713	733	753	772	792	811
223	34 830	850	869	889	908	928	947	967	986	*005
224	35 025	044	064	083	102	122	141	160	180	199
225	35 218	238	257	276	295	315	334	353	372	392
226	35 411	430	449	468	488	507	526	545	564	583
227	35 603	622	641	660	679	698	717	736	755	774
228	35 793	813	832	851	870	889	908	927	946	965
229	35 984	*003	*021	*040	*059	*078	*097	*116	*135	*154
230	36 173	192	211	229	248	267	286	305	324	342
231	36 361	380	399	418	436	455	474	493	511	530
232	36 549	568	586	605	624	642	661	680	698	717
233	36 736	754	773	791	810	829	847	866	884	903
234	36 922	940	959	977	996	*014	*033	*051	*070	*088
235	37 107	125	144	162	181	199	218	236	254	273
236	37 291	310	328	346	365	383	401	420	438	457
237	37 475	493	511	530	548	566	585	603	621	639
238	37 658	676	694	712	731	749	767	785	803	822
239	37 840	858	876	894	912	931	949	967	985	*003
240	38 021	039	057	075	093	112	130	148	166	184
241	38 202	220	238	256	274	292	310	328	346	364
242	38 382	399	417	435	453	471	489	507	525	543
243	38 561	578	596	614	632	650	668	686	703	721
244	38 739	757	775	792	810	828	846	863	881	899
245	38 917	934	952	970	987	*005	*023	*041	*058	*076
246	39 094	111	129	146	164	182	199	217	235	252
247	39 270	287	305	322	340	358	375	393	410	428
248	39 445	463	480	498	515	533	550	568	585	602
249	39 620	637	655	672	690	707	724	742	759	777
250	39 794	811	829	846	863	881	898	915	933	950
N	0	1	2	3	4	5	6	7	8	9

Prop. Parts

	22	21
1	2.2	2.1
2	4.4	4.2
3	6.6	6.3
4	8.8	8.4
5	11.0	10.5
6	13.2	12.6
7	15.4	14.7
8	17.6	16.8
9	19.8	18.9

	20
1	2.0
2	4.0
3	6.0
4	8.0
5	10.0
6	12.0
7	14.0
8	16.0
9	18.0

	19
1	1.9
2	3.8
3	5.7
4	7.6
5	9.5
6	11.4
7	13.3
8	15.2
9	17.1

	18
1	1.8
2	3.6
3	5.4
4	7.2
5	9.0
6	10.8
7	12.6
8	14.4
9	16.2

	17
1	1.7
2	3.4
3	5.1
4	6.8
5	8.5
6	10.2
7	11.9
8	13.6
9	15.3

IV. 2500—FIVE-PLACE LOGARITHMS OF NUMBERS—3009

Prop. Parts

18	
1	1.8
2	3.6
3	5.4
4	7.2
5	9.0
6	10.8
7	12.6
8	14.4
9	16.2

17	
1	1.7
2	3.4
3	5.1
4	6.8
5	8.5
6	10.2
7	11.9
8	13.6
9	15.3

16	
1	1.6
2	3.2
3	4.8
4	6.4
5	8.0
6	9.6
7	11.2
8	12.8
9	14.4

15	
1	1.5
2	3.0
3	4.5
4	6.0
5	7.5
6	9.0
7	10.5
8	12.0
9	13.5

14	
1	1.4
2	2.8
3	4.2
4	5.6
5	7.0
6	8.4
7	9.8
8	11.2
9	12.6

N	0	1	2	3	4	5	6	7	8	9
250	39 794	811	829	846	863	881	898	915	933	950
251	39 967	985	*002	*019	*037	*054	*071	*088	*106	*123
252	40 140	157	175	192	209	226	243	261	278	·295
253	40 312	329	346	364	381	398	415	432	449	466
254	40 483	500	518	535	552	569	586	603	620	637
255	40 654	671	688	705	722	739	756	773	790	807
256	40 824'	841	858	875	892	909	926	943	960	976
257	40 993	*010	*027	*044	*061	*078	*095	*111	*128	*145
258	41 162	179	196	212	229	246	263	280	296	313
259	41 330	347	363	380	397	414	430	447	464	481
260	41 497	514	531	547	564	581	597	614	631	647
261	41 664	681	697	714	731	747	764	780	797	814
262	41 830	847	863	880	896	913	929	946	963	979
263	41 996	*012	*029	*045	*062	*078	*095	*111	*127	*144
264	42 160	177	193	210	226	243	259	275	292	308
265	42 325	341	357	374	390	406	423	439	455	472
266	42 488	504	521	537	553	570	586	602	619	635
267	42 651	667	684	700	716	732	749	765	781	797
268	42 813	830	846	862	878	894	911	927	943	959
269	42 975	991	*008	*024	*040	*056	*072	*088	*104	*120
270	43 136	152	169	185	201	217	233	249	265	281
271	43 297	313	329	345	361	377	393	409	425	441
272	43 457	473	489	505	521	537	553	569	584	600
273	43 616	632	648	664	680	696	712	727	743	759
274	43 775	791	807	823	838	854	870	886	902	917
275	43 933	949	965	981	996	*012	*028	*044	*059	*075
276	44 091	107	122	138	154	170	185	201	217	232
277	44 248	264	279	295	311	326	342	358	373	389
278	44 404	420	436	451	467	483	498	514	529	545
279	44 560	576	592	607	623	638	654	669	685	700
280	44 716	731	747	762	778	793	809	824	840	855
281	44 871	886	902	917	932	948	963	979	994	*010
282	45 025	040	056	071	086	102	117	133	148	163
283	45 179	194	209	225	240	255	271	286	301	317
284	45 332	347	362	378	393	408	423	439	454	469
285	45 484	500	515	530	545	561	576	591	606	621
286	45 637	652	667	682	697	712	728	743	758	773
287	45 788	803	818	834	849	864	879	894	909	924
288	45 939	954	969	984	*000	*015	*030	*045	*060	*075
289	46 090	105	120	135	150	165	180	195	210	225
290	46 240	255	270	285	300	315	330	345	359	374
291	46 389	404	419	434	449	464	479	494	509	523
292	46 538	553	568	583	598	613	627	642	657	672
293	46 687	702	716	731	746	761	776	790	805	820
294	46 835	850	864	879	894	909	923	938	953	967
295	46 982	997	*012	*026	*041	*056	*070	*085	*100	*114
296	47 129	144	159	173	188	202	217	232	246	261
297	47 276	290	305	319	334	349	363	378	392	407
298	47 422	436	451	465	480	494	509	524	538	553
299	47 567	582	596	611	625	640	654	669	683	698
300	47 712	727	741	756	770	784	799	813	828	842

Prop. Parts	N	0	1	2	3	4	5	6	7	8	9

IV. 3000—FIVE-PLACE LOGARITHMS OF NUMBERS—3509

N	0	1	2	3	4	5	6	7	8	9
300	47 712	727	741	756	770	784	799	813	828	842
301	47 857	871	885	900	914	929	943	958	972	986
302	48 001	015	029	044	058	073	087	101	116	130
303	48 144	159	173	187	202	216	230	244	259	273
304	48 287	302	316	330	344	359	373	387	401	416
305	48 430	444	458	473	487	501	515	530	544	558
306	48 572	586	601	615	629	643	657	671	686	700
307	48 714	728	742	756	770	785	799	813	827	841
308	48 855	869	883	897	911	926	940	954	968	982
309	48 996	*010	*024	*038	*052	*066	*080	*094	*108	*122
310	49 136	150	164	178	192	206	220	234	248	262
311	49 276	290	304	318	332	346	360	374	388	402
312	49 415	429	443	457	471	485	499	513	527	541
313	49 554	568	582	596	610	624	638	651	665	679
314	49 693	707	721	734	748	762	776	790	803	817
315	49 831	845	859	872	886	900	914	927	941	955
316	49 969	982	996	*010	*024	*037	*051	*065	*079	*092
317	50 106	120	133	147	161	174	188	202	215	229
318	50 243	256	270	284	297	311	325	338	352	365
319	50 379	393	406	420	433	447	461	474	488	501
320	50 515	529	542	556	569	583	596	610	623	637
321	50 651	664	678	691	705	718	732	745	759	772
322	50 786	799	813	826	840	853	866	880	893	907
323	50 920	934	947	961	974	987	*001	*014	*028	*041
324	51 055	068	081	095	108	121	135	148	162	175
325	51 188	202	215	228	242	255	268	282	295	308
326	51 322	335	348	362	375	388	402	415	428	441
327	51 455	468	481	495	508	521	534	548	561	574
328	51 587	601	614	627	640	654	667	680	693	706
329	51 720	733	746	759	772	786	799	812	825	838
330	51 851	865	878	891	904	917	930	943	957	970
331	51 983	996	*009	*022	*035	*048	*061	*075	*088	*101
332	52 114	127	140	153	166	179	192	205	218	231
333	52 244	257	270	284	297	310	323	336	349	362
334	52 375	388	401	414	427	440	453	466	479	492
335	52 504	517	530	543	556	569	582	595	608	621
336	52 634	647	660	673	686	699	711	724	737	750
337	52 763	776	789	802	815	827	840	853	866	879
338	52 892	905	917	930	943	956	969	982	994	*007
339	53 020	033	046	058	071	084	097	110	122	135
340	53 148	161	173	186	199	212	224	237	250	263
341	53 275	288	301	314	326	339	352	364	377	390
342	53 403	415	428	441	453	466	479	491	504	517
343	53 529	542	555	567	580	593	605	618	631	643
344	53 656	668	681	694	706	719	732	744	757	769
345	53 782	794	807	820	832	845	857	870	882	895
346	53 908	920	933	945	958	970	983	995	*008	*020
347	54 033	045	058	070	083	095	108	120	133	145
348	54 158	170	183	195	208	220	233	245	258	270
349	54 283	295	307	320	332	345	357	370	382	394
350	54 407	419	432	444	456	469	481	494	506	518
N	0	1	2	3	4	5	6	7	8	9

Prop. Parts

15
1	1.5
2	3.0
3	4.5
4	6.0
5	7.5
6	9.0
7	10.5
8	12.0
9	13.5

14
1	1.4
2	2.8
3	4.2
4	5.6
5	7.0
6	8.4
7	9.8
8	11.2
9	12.6

13
1	1.3
2	2.6
3	3.9
4	5.2
5	6.5
6	7.8
7	9.1
8	10.4
9	11.7

12
1	1.2
2	2.4
3	3.6
4	4.8
5	6.0
6	7.2
7	8.4
8	9.6
9	10.8

IV. 3500—FIVE-PLACE LOGARITHMS OF NUMBERS—4009

N	0	1	2	3	4	5	6	7	8	9
350	54 407	419	432	444	456	469	481	494	506	518
351	54 531	543	555	568	580	593	605	617	630	642
352	54 654	667	679	691	704	716	728	741	753	765
353	54 777	790	802	814	827	839	851	864	876	888
354	54 900	913	925	937	949	962	974	986	998	*011
355	55 023	035	047	060	072	084	096	108	121	133
356	55 145	157	169	182	194	206	218	230	242	255
357	55 267	279	291	303	315	328	340	352	364	376
358	55 388	400	413	425	437	449	461	473	485	497
359	55 509	522	534	546	558	570	582	594	606	618
360	55 630	642	654	666	678	691	703	715	727	739
361	55 751	763	775	787	799	811	823	835	847	859
362	55 871	883	895	907	919	931	943	955	967	979
363	55 991	*003	*015	*027	*038	*050	*062	*074	*086	*098
364	56 110	122	134	146	158	170	182	194	205	217
365	56 229	241	253	265	277	289	301	312	324	336
366	56 348	360	372	384	396	407	419	431	443	455
367	56 467	478	490	502	514	526	538	549	561	573
368	56 585	597	608	620	632	644	656	667	679	691
369	56 703	714	726	738	750	761	773	785	797	808
370	56 820	832	844	855	867	879	891	902	914	926
371	56 937	949	961	972	984	996	*008	*019	*031	*043
372	57 054	066	078	089	101	113	124	136	148	159
373	57 171	183	194	206	217	229	241	252	264	276
374	57 287	299	310	322	334	345	357	368	380	392
375	57 403	415	426	438	449	461	473	484	496	507
376	57 519	530	542	553	565	576	588	600	611	623
377	57 634	646	657	669	680	692	703	715	726	738
378	57 749	761	772	784	795	807	818	830	841	852
379	57 864	875	887	898	910	921	933	944	955	967
380	57 978	990	*001	*013	*024	*035	*047	*058	*070	*081
381	58 092	104	115	127	138	149	161	172	184	195
382	58 206	218	229	240	252	263	274	286	297	309
383	58 320	331	343	354	365	377	388	399	410	422
384	58 433	444	456	467	478	490	501	512	524	535
385	58 546	557	569	580	591	602	614	625	636	647
386	58 659	670	681	692	704	715	726	737	749	760
387	58 771	782	794	805	816	827	838	850	861	872
388	58 883	894	906	917	928	939	950	961	973	984
389	58 995	*006	*017	*028	*040	*051	*062	*073	*084	*095
390	59 106	118	129	140	151	162	173	184	195	207
391	59 218	229	240	251	262	273	284	295	306	318
392	59 329	340	351	362	373	384	395	406	417	428
393	59 439	450	461	472	483	494	506	517	528	539
394	59 550	561	572	583	594	605	616	627	638	649
395	59 660	671	682	693	704	715	726	737	748	759
396	59 770	780	791	802	813	824	835	846	857	868
397	59 879	890	901	912	923	934	945	956	966	977
398	59 988	999	*010	*021	*032	*043	*054	*065	*076	*086
399	60 097	108	119	130	141	152	163	173	184	195
400	60 206	217	228	239	249	260	271	282	293	304

Prop. Parts

13		12		11		10	
1	1.3	1	1.2	1	1.1	1	1.0
2	2.6	2	2.4	2	2.2	2	2.0
3	3.9	3	3.6	3	3.3	3	3.0
4	5.2	4	4.8	4	4.4	4	4.0
5	6.5	5	6.0	5	5.5	5	5.0
6	7.8	6	7.2	6	6.6	6	6.0
7	9.1	7	8.4	7	7.7	7	7.0
8	10.4	8	9.6	8	8.8	8	8.0
9	11.7	9	10.8	9	9.9	9	9.0

IV. 4000—FIVE–PLACE LOGARITHMS OF NUMBERS—4509

N	0	1	2	3	4	5	6	7	8	9
400	60 206	217	228	239	249	260	271	282	293	304
401	60 314	325	336	347	358	369	379	390	401	412
402	60 423	433	444	455	466	477	487	498	509	520
403	60 531	541	552	563	574	584	595	606	617	627
404	60 638	649	660	670	681	692	703	713	724	735
405	60 746	756	767	778	788	799	810	821	831	842
406	60 853	863	874	885	895	906	917	927	938	949
407	60 959	970	981	991	*002	*013	*023	*034	*045	*055
408	61 066	077	087	098	109	119	130	140	151	162
409	61 172	183	194	204	215	225	236	247	257	268
410	61 278	289	300	310	321	331	342	352	363	374
411	61 384	395	405	416	426	437	448	458	469	479
412	61 490	500	511	521	532	542	553	563	574	584
413	61 595	606	616	627	637	648	658	669	679	690
414	61 700	711	721	731	742	752	763	773	784	794
415	61 805	815	826	836	847	857	868	878	888	899
416	61 909	920	930	941	951	962	972	982	993	*003
417	62 014	024	034	045	055	066	076	086	097	107
418	62 118	128	138	149	159	170	180	190	201	211
419	62 221	232	242	252	263	273	284	294	304	315
420	62 325	335	346	356	366	377	387	397	408	418
421	62 428	439	449	459	469	480	490	500	511	521
422	62 531	542	552	562	572	583	593	603	613	624
423	62 634	644	655	665	675	685	696	706	716	726
424	62 737	747	757	767	778	788	798	808	818	829
425	62 839	849	859	870	880	890	900	910	921	931
426	62 941	951	961	972	982	992	*002	*012	*022	*033
427	63 043	053	063	073	083	094	104	114	124	134
428	63 144	155	165	175	185	195	205	215	225	236
429	63 246	256	266	276	286	296	306	317	327	337
430	63 347	357	367	377	387	397	407	417	428	438
431	63 448	458	468	478	488	498	508	518	528	538
432	63 548	558	568	579	589	599	609	619	629	639
433	63 649	659	669	679	689	699	709	719	729	739
434	63 749	759	769	779	789	799	809	819	829	839
435	63 849	859	869	879	889	899	909	919	929	939
436	63 949	959	969	979	988	998	*008	*018	*028	*038
437	64 048	058	068	078	088	098	108	118	128	137
438	64 147	157	167	177	187	197	207	217	227	237
439	64 246	256	266	276	286	296	306	316	326	335
440	64 345	355	365	375	385	395	404	414	424	434
441	64 444	454	464	473	483	493	503	513	523	532
442	64 542	552	562	572	582	591	601	611	621	631
443	64 640	650	660	670	680	689	699	709	719	729
444	64 738	748	758	768	777	787	797	807	816	826
445	64 836	846	856	865	875	885	895	904	914	924
446	64 933	943	953	963	972	982	992	*002	*011	*021
447	65 031	040	050	060	070	079	089	099	108	118
448	65 128	137	147	157	167	176	186	196	205	215
449	65 225	234	244	254	263	273	283	292	302	312
450	65 321	331	341	350	360	369	379	389	398	408
N	0	1	2	3	4	5	6	7	8	9

Prop. Parts

	11		10		9
1	1.1	1	1.0	1	0.9
2	2.2	2	2.0	2	1.8
3	3.3	3	3.0	3	2.7
4	4.4	4	4.0	4	3.6
5	5.5	5	5.0	5	4.5
6	6.6	6	6.0	6	5.4
7	7.7	7	7.0	7	6.3
8	8.8	8	8.0	8	7.2
9	9.9	9	9.0	9	8.1

IV. 4500—FIVE-PLACE LOGARITHMS OF NUMBERS—5009

N	0	1	2	3	4	5	6	7	8	9
450	65 321	331	341	350	360	369	379	389	398	408
451	65 418	427	437	447	456	466	475	485	495	504
452	65 514	523	533	543	552	562	571	581	591	600
453	65 610	619	629	639	648	658	667	677	686	696
454	65 706	715	725	734	744	753	763	772	782	792
455	65 801	811	820	830	839	849	858	868	877	887
456	65 896	906	916	925	935	944	954	963	973	982
457	65 992	*001	*011	*020	*030	*039	*049	*058	*068	*077
458	66 087	096	106	115	124	134	143	153	162	172
459	66 181	191	200	210	219	229	238	247	257	266
460	66 276	285	295	304	314	323	332	342	351	361
461	66 370	380	389	398	408	417	427	436	445	455
462	66 464	474	483	492	502	511	521	530	539	549
463	66 558	567	577	586	596	605	614	624	633	642
464	66 652	661	671	680	689	699	708	717	727	736
465	66 745	755	764	773	783	792	801	811	820	829
466	66 839	848	857	867	876	885	894	904	913	922
467	66 932	941	950	960	969	978	987	997	*006	*015
468	67 025	034	043	052	062	071	080	089	099	108
469	67 117	127	136	145	154	164	173	182	191	201
470	67 210	219	228	237	247	256	265	274	284	293
471	67 302	311	321	330	339	348	357	367	376	385
472	67 394	403	413	422	431	440	449	459	468	477
473	67 486	495	504	514	523	532	541	550	560	569
474	67 578	587	596	605	614	624	633	642	651	660
475	67 669	679	688	697	706	715	724	733	742	752
476	67 761	770	779	788	797	806	815	825	834	843
477	67 852	861	870	879	888	897	906	916	925	934
478	67 943	952	961	970	979	988	997	*006	*015	*024
479	68 034	043	052	061	070	079	088	097	106	115
480	68 124	133	142	151	160	169	178	187	196	205
481	68 215	224	233	242	251	260	269	278	287	296
482	68 305	314	323	332	341	350	359	368	377	386
483	68 395	404	413	422	431	440	449	458	467	476
484	68 485	494	502	511	520	529	538	547	556	565
485	68 574	583	592	601	610	619	628	637	646	655
486	68 664	673	681	690	699	708	717	726	735	744
487	68 753	762	771	780	789	797	806	815	824	833
488	68 842	851	860	869	878	886	895	904	913	922
489	68 931	940	949	958	966	975	984	993	*002	*011
490	69 020	028	037	046	055	064	073	082	090	099
491	69 108	117	126	135	144	152	161	170	179	188
492	69 197	205	214	223	232	241	249	258	267	276
493	69 285	294	302	311	320	329	338	346	355	364
494	69 373	381	390	399	408	417	425	434	443	452
495	69 461	469	478	487	496	504	513	522	531	539
496	69 548	557	566	574	583	592	601	609	618	627
497	69 636	644	653	662	671	679	688	697	705	714
498	69 723	732	740	749	758	767	775	784	793	801
499	69 810	819	827	836	845	854	862	871	880	888
500	69 897	906	914	923	932	940	949	958	966	975

Prop. Parts

10		9		8	
1	1.0	1	0.9	1	0.8
2	2.0	2	1.8	2	1.6
3	3.0	3	2.7	3	2.4
4	4.0	4	3.6	4	3.2
5	5.0	5	4.5	5	4.0
6	6.0	6	5.4	6	4.8
7	7.0	7	6.3	7	5.6
8	8.0	8	7.2	8	6.4
9	9.0	9	8.1	9	7.2

IV. 5000—FIVE–PLACE LOGARITHMS OF NUMBERS—5509

N	0	1	2	3	4	5	6	7	8	9	Prop. Parts
500	69 897	906	914	923	932	940	949	958	966	975	
501	69 984	992	*001	*010	*018	*027	*036	*044	*053	*062	
502	70 070	079	088	096	105	114	122	131	140	148	
503	70 157	165	174	183	191	200	209	217	226	234	
504	70 243	252	260	269	278	286	295	303	312	321	
505	70 329	338	346	355	364	372	381	389	398	406	
506	70 415	424	432	441	449	458	467	475	484	492	
507	70 501	509	518	526	535	544	552	561	569	578	
508	70 586	595	603	612	621	629	638	646	655	663	
509	70 672	680	689	697	706	714	723	731	740	749	
510	70 757	766	774	783	791	800	808	817	825	834	
511	70 842	851	859	868	876	885	893	902	910	919	
512	70 927	935	944	952	961	969	978	986	995	*003	
513	71 012	020	029	037	046	054	063	071	079	088	
514	71 096	105	113	122	130	139	147	155	164	172	
515	71 181	189	198	206	214	223	231	240	248	257	
516	71 265	273	282	290	299	307	315	324	332	341	
517	71 349	357	366	374	383	391	399	408	416	425	
518	71 433	441	450	458	466	475	483	492	500	508	
519	71 517	525	533	542	550	559	567	575	584	592	
520	71 600	609	617	625	634	642	650	659	667	675	
521	71 684	692	700	709	717	725	734	742	750	759	
522	71 767	775	784	792	800	809	817	825	834	842	
523	71 850	858	867	875	883	892	900	908	917	925	
524	71 933	941	950	958	966	975	983	991	999	*008	
525	72 016	024	032	041	049	057	066	074	082	090	
526	72 099	107	115	123	132	140	148	156	165	173	
527	72 181	189	198	206	214	222	230	239	247	255	
528	72 263	272	280	288	296	304	313	321	329	337	
529	72 346	354	362	370	378	387	395	403	411	419	
530	72 428	436	444	452	460	469	477	485	493	501	
531	72 509	518	526	534	542	550	558	567	575	583	
532	72 591	599	607	616	624	632	640	648	656	665	
533	72 673	681	689	697	705	713	722	730	738	746	
534	72 754	762	770	779	787	979	803	811	819	827	
535	72 835	843	852	860	868	876	884	892	900	908	
536	72 916	925	933	941	949	957	965	973	981	989	
537	72 997	*006	*014	*022	*030	*038	*046	*054	*062	*070	
538	73 078	086	094	102	111	119	127	135	143	151	
539	73 159	167	175	183	191	199	207	215	223	231	
540	73 239	247	255	263	272	280	288	296	304	312	
541	73 320	328	336	344	352	360	368	376	384	392	
542	73 400	408	416	424	432	440	448	456	464	472	
543	73 480	488	496	504	512	520	528	536	544	552	
544	73 560	568	576	584	592	600	608	616	624	632	
545	73 640	648	656	664	672	679	687	695	703	711	
546	73 719	727	735	743	751	759	767	775	783	791	
547	73 799	807	815	823	830	838	846	854	862	870	
548	73 878	886	894	902	910	918	926	933	941	949	
549	73 957	965	973	981	989	997	*005	*013	*020	*028	
550	74 036	044	052	060	068	076	084	092	099	107	
N	0	1	2	3	4	5	6	7	8	9	Prop. Parts

Prop. Parts

9
1   0.9
2   1.8
3   2.7
4   3.6
5   4.5
6   5.4
7   6.3
8   7.2
9   8.1

8
1   0.8
2   1.6
3   2.4
4   3.2
5   4.0
6   4.8
7   5.6
8   6.4
9   7.2

7
1   0.7
2   1.4
3   2.1
4   2.8
5   3.5
6   4.2
7   4.9
8   5.6
9   6.3

IV. 5500—FIVE-PLACE LOGARITHMS OF NUMBERS—6009

Prop. Parts	N	0	1	2	3	4	5	6	7	8	9
	550	74 036	044	052	060	068	076	084	092	099	107
	551	74 115	123	131	139	147	155	162	170	178	186
	552	74 194	202	210	218	225	233	241	249	257	265
	553	74 273	280	288	296	304	312	320	327	335	343
	554	74 351	359	367	374	382	390	398	406	414	421
	555	74 429	437	445	453	461	468	476	484	492	500
	556	74 507	515	523	531	539	547	554	562	570	578
	557	74 586	593	601	609	617	624	632	640	648	656
	558	74 663	671	679	687	695	702	710	718	726	733
	559	74 741	749	757	764	772	780	788	796	803	811
	560	74 819	827	834	842	850	858	865	873	881	889
	561	74 896	904	912	920	927	935	943	950	958	966
	562	74 974	981	989	997	*005	*012	*020	*028	*035	*043
	563	75 051	059	066	074	082	089	097	105	113	120
	564	75 128	136	143	151	159	166	174	182	189	197
	565	75 205	213	220	228	236	243	251	259	266	274
	566	75 282	289	297	305	312	320	328	335	343	351
	567	75 358	366	374	381	389	397	404	412	420	427
	568	75 435	442	450	458	465	473	481	488	496	504
	569	75 511	519	526	534	542	549	557	565	572	580
	570	75 587	595	603	610	618	626	633	641	648	656
	571	75 664	671	679	686	694	702	709	717	724	732
	572	75 740	747	755	762	770	778	785	793	800	808
	573	75 815	823	831	838	846	853	861	868	876	884
	574	75 891	899	906	914	921	929	937	944	952	959
	575	75 967	974	982	989	997	*005	*012	*020	*027	*035
	576	76 042	050	057	065	072	080	087	095	103	110
	577	76 118	125	133	140	148	155	163	170	178	185
	578	76 193	200	208	215	223	230	238	245	253	260
	579	76 268	275	283	290	298	305	313	320	328	335
	580	76 343	350	358	365	373	380	388	395	403	410
	581	76 418	425	433	440	448	455	462	470	477	485
	582	76 492	500	507	515	522	530	537	545	552	559
	583	76 567	574	582	589	597	604	612	619	626	634
	584	76 641	649	656	664	671	678	686	693	701	708
	585	76 716	723	730	738	745	753	760	768	775	782
	586	76 790	797	805	812	819	827	834	842	849	856
	587	76 864	871	879	886	893	901	908	916	923	930
	588	76 938	945	953	960	967	975	982	989	997	*004
	589	77 012	019	026	034	041	048	056	063	070	078
	590	77 085	093	100	107	115	122	129	137	144	151
	591	77 159	166	173	181	188	195	203	210	217	225
	592	77 232	240	247	254	262	269	276	283	291	298
	593	77 305	313	320	327	335	342	349	357	364	371
	594	77 379	386	393	401	408	415	422	430	437	444
	595	77 452	459	466	474	481	488	495	503	510	517
	596	77 525	532	539	546	554	561	568	576	583	590
	597	77 597	605	612	619	627	634	641	648	656	663
	598	77 670	677	685	692	699	706	714	721	728	735
	599	77 743	750	757	764	772	779	786	793	801	808
	600	77 815	822	830	837	844	851	859	866	873	880
Prop. Parts	N	0	1	2	3	4	5	6	7	8	9

Prop. Parts:

8
1	0.8
2	1.6
3	2.4
4	3.2
5	4.0
6	4.8
7	5.6
8	6.4
9	7.2

7
1	0.7
2	1.4
3	2.1
4	2.8
5	3.5
6	4.2
7	4.9
8	5.6
9	6.3

IV. 6000—FIVE-PLACE LOGARITHMS OF NUMBERS—6509

N	0	1	2	3	4	5	6	7	8	9
600	77 815	822	830	837	844	851	859	866	873	880
601	77 887	895	902	909	916	924	931	938	945	952
602	77 960	967	974	981	988	996	*003	*010	*017	*025
603	78 032	039	046	053	061	068	075	082	089	097
604	78 104	111	118	125	132	140	147	154	161	168
605	78 176	183	190	197	204	211	219	226	233	240
606	78 247	254	262	269	276	283	290	297	305	312
607	78 319	326	333	340	347	355	362	369	376	383
608	78 390	398	405	412	419	426	433	440	447	455
609	78 462	469	476	483	490	497	504	512	519	526
610	78 533	540	547	554	561	569	576	583	590	597
611	78 604	611	618	625	633	640	647	654	661	668
612	78 675	682	689	696	704	711	718	725	732	739
613	78 746	753	760	767	774	781	789	796	803	810
614	78 817	824	831	838	845	852	859	866	873	880
615	78 888	895	902	909	916	923	930	937	944	951
616	78 958	965	972	979	986	993	*000	*007	*014	*021
617	79 029	036	043	050	057	064	071	078	085	092
618	79 099	106	113	120	127	134	141	148	155	162
619	79 169	176	183	190	197	204	211	218	225	232
620	79 239	246	253	260	267	274	281	288	295	302
621	79 309	316	323	330	337	344	351	358	365	372
622	79 379	386	393	400	407	414	421	428	435	442
623	79 449	456	463	470	477	484	491	498	505	511
624	79 518	525	532	539	546	553	560	567	574	581
625	79 588	595	602	609	616	623	630	637	644	650
626	79 657	664	671	678	685	692	699	706	713	720
627	79 727	734	741	748	754	761	768	775	782	789
628	79 796	803	810	817	824	831	837	844	851	858
629	79 865	872	879	886	893	900	906	913	920	927
630	79 934	941	948	955	962	969	975	982	989	996
631	80 003	010	017	024	030	037	044	051	058	065
632	80 072	079	085	092	099	106	113	120	127	134
633	80 140	147	154	161	168	175	182	188	195	202
634	80 209	216	223	229	236	243	250	257	264	271
635	80 277	284	291	298	305	312	318	325	332	339
636	80 346	353	359	366	373	380	387	393	400	407
637	80 414	421	428	434	441	448	455	462	468	475
638	80 482	489	496	502	509	516	523	530	536	543
639	80 550	557	564	570	577	584	591	598	604	611
640	80 618	625	632	638	645	652	659	665	672	679
641	80 686	693	699	706	713	720	726	733	740	747
642	80 754	760	767	774	781	787	794	801	808	814
643	80 821	828	835	841	848	855	862	868	875	882
644	80 889	895	902	909	916	922	929	936	943	949
645	80 956	963	969	976	983	990	996	*003	*010	*017
646	81 023	030	037	043	050	057	064	070	077	084
647	81 090	097	104	111	117	124	131	137	144	151
648	81 158	164	171	178	184	191	198	204	211	218
649	81 224	231	238	245	251	258	265	271	278	285
650	81 291	298	305	311	318	325	331	338	345	351
N	0	1	2	3	4	5	6	7	8	9

Prop. Parts

	8		7		6
1	0.8	1	0.7	1	0.6
2	1.6	2	1.4	2	1.2
3	2.4	3	2.1	3	1.8
4	3.2	4	2.8	4	2.4
5	4.0	5	3.5	5	3.0
6	4.8	6	4.2	6	3.6
7	5.6	7	4.9	7	4.2
8	6.4	8	5.6	8	4.8
9	7.2	9	6.3	9	5.4

IV. 6500—FIVE–PLACE LOGARITHMS OF NUMBERS—7009

Prop. Parts	N	0	1	2	3	4	5	6	7	8	9
	650	81 291	298	305	311	318	325	331	338	345	351
	651	81 358	365	371	378	385	391	398	405	411	418
	652	81 425	431	438	445	451	458	465	471	478	485
	653	81 491	498	505	511	518	525	531	538	544	551
	654	81 558	564	571	578	584	591	598	604	611	617
	655	81 624	631	637	644	651	657	664	671	677	684
	656	81 690	697	704	710	717	723	730	737	743	750
	657	81 757	763	770	776	783	790	796	803	809	816
	658	81 823	829	836	842	849	856	862	869	875	882
	659	81 889	895	902	908	915	921	928	935	941	948
	660	81 954	961	968	974	981	987	994	*000	*007	*014
	661	82 020	027	033	040	046	053	060	066	073	079
	662	82 086	092	099	105	112	119	125	132	138	145
	663	82 151	158	164	171	178	184	191	197	204	210
	664	82 217	223	230	236	243	249	256	263	269	276
	665	82 282	289	295	302	308	315	321	328	334	341
	666	82 347	354	360	367	373	380	387	393	400	406
	667	82 413	419	426	432	439	445	452	458	465	471
	668	82 478	484	491	497	504	510	517	523	530	536
	669	82 543	549	556	562	569	575	582	588	595	601
	670	82 607	614	620	627	633	640	646	653	659	666
	671	82 672	679	685	692	698	705	711	718	724	730
	672	82 737	743	750	756	763	769	776	782	789	795
	673	82 802	808	814	821	827	834	840	847	853	860
	674	82 866	872	879	885	892	898	905	911	918	924
	675	82 930	937	943	950	956	963	969	975	982	988
	676	82 995	*001	*008	*014	*020	*027	*033	*040	*046	*052
	677	83 059	065	072	078	085	091	097	104	110	117
	678	83 123	129	136	142	149	155	161	168	174	181
	679	83 187	193	200	206	213	219	225	232	238	245
	680	83 251	257	264	270	276	283	289	296	302	308
	681	83 315	321	327	334	340	347	353	359	366	372
	682	83 378	385	391	398	404	410	417	423	429	436
	683	83 442	448	455	461	467	474	480	487	493	499
	684	83 506	512	518	525	531	537	544	550	556	563
	685	83 569	575	582	588	594	601	607	613	620	626
	686	83 632	639	645	651	658	664	670	677	683	689
	687	83 696	702	708	715	721	727	734	740	746	753
	688	83 759	765	771	778	784	790	797	803	809	816
	689	83 822	828	835	841	847	853	860	866	872	879
	690	83 885	891	897	904	910	916	923	929	935	942
	691	83 948	954	960	967	973	979	985	992	998	*004
	692	84 011	017	023	029	036	042	048	055	061	067
	693	84 073	080	086	092	098	105	111	117	123	130
	694	84 136	142	148	155	161	167	173	180	186	192
	695	84 198	205	211	217	223	230	236	242	248	255
	696	84 261	267	273	280	286	292	298	305	311	317
	697	84 323	330	336	342	348	354	361	367	373	379
	698	84 386	392	398	404	410	417	423	429	435	442
	699	84 448	454	460	466	473	479	485	491	497	504
	700	84 510	516	522	528	535	541	547	553	559	566
Prop. Parts	N	0	1	2	3	4	5	6	7	8	9

Prop. Parts:

7
1	0.7
2	1.4
3	2.1
4	2.8
5	3.5
6	4.2
7	4.9
8	5.6
9	6.3

6
1	0.6
2	1.2
3	1.8
4	2.4
5	3.0
6	3.6
7	4.2
8	4.8
9	5.4

IV. 7000—FIVE-PLACE LOGARITHMS OF NUMBERS—7509

N	0	1	2	3	4	5	6	7	8	9
700	84 510	516	522	528	535	541	547	553	559	566
701	84 572	578	584	590	597	603	609	615	621	628
702	84 634	640	646	652	658	665	671	677	683	689
703	84 696	702	708	714	720	726	733	739	745	751
704	84 757	763	770	776	782	788	794	800	807	813
705	84 819	825	831	837	844	850	856	862	868	874
706	84 880	887	893	899	905	911	917	924	930	936
707	84 942	948	954	960	967	973	979	985	991	997
708	85 003	009	016	022	028	034	040	046	052	058
709	85 065	071	077	083	089	095	101	107	114	120
710	85 126	132	138	144	150	156	163	169	175	181
711	85 187	193	199	205	211	217	224	230	236	242
712	85 248	254	260	266	272	278	285	291	297	303
713	85 309	315	321	327	333	339	345	352	358	364
714	85 370	376	382	388	394	400	406	412	418	425
715	85 431	437	443	449	455	461	467	473	479	485
716	85 491	497	503	509	516	522	528	534	540	546
717	85 552	558	564	570	576	582	588	594	600	606
718	85 612	618	625	631	637	643	649	655	661	667
719	85 673	679	685	691	697	703	709	715	721	727
720	85 733	739	745	751	757	763	769	775	781	788
721	85 794	800	806	812	818	824	830	836	842	848
722	85 854	860	866	872	878	884	890	896	902	908
723	85 914	920	926	932	938	944	950	956	962	968
724	85 974	980	986	992	998	*004	*010	*016	*022	*028
725	86 034	040	046	052	058	064	070	076	082	088
726	86 094	100	106	112	118	124	130	136	141	147
727	86 153	159	165	171	177	183	189	195	201	207
728	86 213	219	225	231	237	243	249	255	261	267
729	86 273	279	285	291	297	303	308	314	320	326
730	86 332	338	344	350	356	362	368	374	380	386
731	86 392	398	404	410	415	421	427	433	439	445
732	86 451	457	463	469	475	481	487	493	499	504
733	86 510	516	522	528	534	540	546	552	558	564
734	86 570	576	581	587	593	599	605	611	617	623
735	86 629	635	641	646	652	658	664	670	676	682
736	86 688	694	700	705	711	717	723	729	735	741
737	86 747	753	759	764	770	776	782	788	794	800
738	86 806	812	817	823	829	835	841	847	853	859
739	86 864	870	876	882	888	894	900	906	911	917
740	86 923	929	935	941	947	953	958	964	970	976
741	86 982	988	994	999	*005	*011	*017	*023	*029	*035
742	87 040	046	052	058	064	070	075	081	087	093
743	87 099	105	111	116	122	128	134	140	146	151
744	87 157	163	169	175	181	186	192	198	204	210
745	87 216	221	227	233	239	245	251	256	262	268
746	87 274	280	286	291	297	303	309	315	320	326
747	87 332	338	344	349	355	361	367	373	379	384
748	87 390	396	402	408	413	419	425	431	437	442
749	87 448	454	460	466	471	477	483	489	495	500
750	87 506	512	518	523	529	535	541	547	552	558
N	0	1	2	3	4	5	6	7	8	9

Prop. Parts

	7		6		5
1	0.7	1	0.6	1	0.5
2	1.4	2	1.2	2	1.0
3	2.1	3	1.8	3	1.5
4	2.8	4	2.4	4	2.0
5	3.5	5	3.0	5	2.5
6	4.2	6	3.6	6	3.0
7	4.9	7	4.2	7	3.5
8	5.6	8	4.8	8	4.0
9	6.3	9	5.4	9	4.5

IV. 7500—FIVE-PLACE LOGARITHMS OF NUMBERS—8009

N	0	1	2	3	4	5	6	7	8	9
750	87 506	512	518	523	529	535	541	547	552	558
751	87 564	570	576	581	587	593	599	604	610	616
752	87 622	628	633	639	645	651	656	662	668	674
753	87 679	685	691	697	703	708	714	720	726	731
754	87 737	743	749	754	760	766	772	777	783	789
755	87 795	800	806	812	818	823	829	835	841	846
756	87 852	858	864	869	875	881	887	892	898	904
757	87 910	915	921	927	933	938	944	950	955	961
758	87 967	973	978	984	990	996	*001	*007	*013	*018
759	88 024	030	036	041	047	053	058	064	070	076
760	88 081	087	093	098	104	110	116	121	127	133
761	88 138	144	150	156	161	167	173	178	184	190
762	88 195	201	207	213	218	224	230	235	241	247
763	88 252	258	264	270	275	281	287	292	298	304
764	88 309	315	321	326	332	338	343	349	355	360
765	88 366	372	377	383	389	395	400	406	412	417
766	88 423	429	434	440	446	451	457	463	468	474
767	88 480	485	491	497	502	508	513	519	525	530
768	88 536	542	547	553	559	564	570	576	581	587
769	88 593	598	604	610	615	621	627	632	638	643
770	88 649	655	660	666	672	677	683	689	694	700
771	88 705	711	717	722	728	734	739	745	750	756
772	88 762	767	773	779	784	790	795	801	807	812
773	88 818	824	829	835	840	846	852	857	863	868
774	88 874	880	885	891	897	902	908	913	919	925
775	88 930	936	941	947	953	958	964	969	975	981
776	88 986	992	997	*003	*009	*014	*020	*025	*031	*037
777	89 042	048	053	059	064	070	076	081	087	092
778	89 098	104	109	115	120	126	131	137	143	148
779	89 154	159	165	170	176	182	187	193	198	204
780	89 209	215	221	226	232	237	243	248	254	260
781	89 265	271	276	282	287	293	298	304	310	315
782	89 321	326	332	337	343	348	354	360	365	371
783	89 376	382	387	393	398	404	409	415	421	426
784	89 432	437	443	448	454	459	465	470	476	481
785	89 487	492	498	504	509	515	520	526	531	537
786	89 542	548	553	559	564	570	575	581	586	592
787	89 597	603	609	614	620	625	631	636	642	647
788	89 653	658	664	669	675	680	686	691	697	702
789	89 708	713	719	724	730	735	741	746	752	757
790	89 763	768	774	779	785	790	796	801	807	812
791	89 818	823	829	834	840	845	851	856	862	867
792	89 873	878	883	889	894	900	905	911	916	922
793	89 927	933	938	944	949	955	960	966	971	977
794	89 982	988	993	998	*004	*009	*015	*020	*026	*031
795	90 037	042	048	053	059	064	069	075	080	086
796	90 091	097	102	108	113	119	124	129	135	140
797	90 146	151	157	162	168	173	179	184	189	195
798	90 200	206	211	217	222	227	233	238	244	249
799	90 255	260	266	271	276	282	287	293	298	304
800	90 309	314	320	325	331	336	342	347	352	358

Prop. Parts

6		**5**	
1	0.6	1	0.5
2	1.2	2	1.0
3	1.8	3	1.5
4	2.4	4	2.0
5	3.0	5	2.5
6	3.6	6	3.0
7	4.2	7	3.5
8	4.8	8	4.0
9	5.4	9	4.5

IV. 8000—FIVE–PLACE LOGARITHMS OF NUMBERS—8509

N	0	1	2	3	4	5	6	7	8	9	Prop. Parts
800	90 309	314	320	325	331	336	342	347	352	358	
801	90 363	369	374	380	385	390	396	401	407	412	
802	90 417	423	428	434	439	445	450	455	461	466	
803	90 472	477	482	488	493	499	504	509	515	520	
804	90 526	531	536	542	547	553	558	563	569	574	
805	90 580	585	590	596	601	607	612	617	623	628	
806	90 634	639	644	650	655	660	666	671	677	682	
807	90 687	693	698	703	709	714	720	725	730	736	
808	90 741	747	752	757	763	768	773	779	784	789	
809	90 795	800	806	811	816	822	827	832	838	843	
810	90 849	854	859	865	870	875	881	886	891	897	
811	90 902	907	913	918	924	929	934	940	945	950	
812	90 956	961	966	972	977	982	988	993	998	*004	**6**
813	91 009	014	020	025	030	036	041	046	052	057	1 0.6 / 2 1.2
814	91 062	068	073	078	084	089	094	100	105	110	3 1.8 / 4 2.4
815	91 116	121	126	132	137	142	148	153	158	164	5 3.0 / 6 3.6
816	91 169	174	180	185	190	196	201	206	212	217	7 4.2
817	91 222	228	233	238	243	249	254	259	265	270	8 4.8
818	91 275	281	286	291	297	302	307	312	318	323	9 5.4
819	91 328	334	339	344	350	355	360	365	371	376	
820	91 381	387	392	397	403	408	413	418	424	429	
821	91 434	440	445	450	455	461	466	471	477	482	
822	91 487	492	498	503	508	514	519	524	529	535	
823	91 540	545	551	556	561	566	572	577	582	587	
824	91 593	598	603	609	614	619	624	630	635	640	
825	91 645	651	656	661	666	672	677	682	687	693	
826	91 698	703	709	714	719	724	730	735	740	745	
827	91 751	756	761	766	772	777	782	787	793	798	
828	91 803	808	814	819	824	829	834	840	845	850	
829	91 855	861	866	871	876	882	887	892	897	903	
830	91 908	913	918	924	929	934	939	944	950	955	
831	91 960	965	971	976	981	986	991	997	*002	*007	**5**
832	92 012	018	023	028	033	038	044	049	054	059	1 0.5 / 2 1.0
833	92 065	070	075	080	085	091	096	101	106	111	3 1.5 / 4 2.0
834	92 117	122	127	132	137	143	148	153	158	163	5 2.5 / 6 3.0
835	92 169	174	179	184	189	195	200	205	210	215	7 3.5
836	92 221	226	231	236	241	247	252	257	262	267	8 4.0
837	92 273	278	283	288	293	298	304	309	314	319	9 4.5
838	92 324	330	335	340	345	350	355	361	366	371	
839	92 376	381	387	392	397	402	407	412	418	423	
840	92 428	433	438	443	449	454	459	464	469	474	
841	92 480	485	490	495	500	505	511	516	521	526	
842	92 531	536	542	547	552	557	562	567	572	578	
843	92 583	588	593	598	603	609	614	619	624	629	
844	92 634	639	645	650	655	660	665	670	675	681	
845	92 686	691	696	701	706	711	716	722	727	732	
846	92 737	742	747	752	758	763	768	773	778	783	
847	92 788	793	799	804	809	814	819	824	829	834	
848	92 840	845	850	855	860	865	870	875	881	886	
849	92 891	896	901	906	911	916	921	927	932	937	
850	92 942	947	952	957	962	967	973	978	983	988	
N	0	1	2	3	4	5	6	7	8	9	Prop. Parts

IV. 8500—FIVE–PLACE LOGARITHMS OF NUMBERS—9009

Prop. Parts

6
1 | 0.6
2 | 1.2
3 | 1.8
4 | 2.4
5 | 3.0
6 | 3.6
7 | 4.2
8 | 4.8
9 | 5 4

5
1 | 0.5
2 | 1.0
3 | 1.5
4 | 2.0
5 | 2.5
6 | 3.0
7 | 3.5
8 | 4.0
9 | 4.5

4
1 | 0.4
2 | 0.8
3 | 1.2
4 | 1.6
5 | 2.0
6 | 2.4
7 | 2.8
8 | 3.2
9 | 3.6

N	0	1	2	3	4	5	6	7	8	9
850	92 942	947	952	957	962	967	973	978	983	988
851	92 993	998	*003	*008	*013	*018	*024	*029	*034	*039
852	93 044	049	054	059	064	069	075	080	085	090
853	93 095	100	105	110	115	120	125	131	136	141
854	93·146	151	156	161	166	171	176	181	186	192
855	93 197	202	207	212	217	222	227	232	237	242
856	93 247	252	258	263	268	273	278	283	288	293
857	93 298	303	308	313	318	323	328	334	339	344
858	93 349	354	359	364	369	374	379	384	389	394
859	93 399	404	409	414	420	425	430	435	440	445
860	93 450	455	460	465	470	475	480	485	490	495
861	93 500	505	510	515	520	526	531	536	541	546
862	93 551	556	561	566	571	576	581	586	591	596
863	93 601	606	611	616	621	626	631	636	641	646
864	93 651	656	661	666	671	676	682	687	692	697
865	93 702	707	712	717	722	727	732	737	742	747
866	93 752	757	762	767	772	777	782	787	792	797
867	93 802	807	812	817	822	827	832	837	842	847
868	93 852	857	862	867	872	877	882	887	892	897
869	93 902	907	912	917	922	927	932	937	942	947
870	93 952	957	962	967	972	977	982	987	992	997
871	94 002	007	012	017	022	027	032	037	042	047
872	94 052	057	062	067	072	077	082	086	091	096
873	94 101	106	111	116	121	126	131	136	141	146
874	94 151	156	161	166	171	176	181	186	191	196
875	94 201	206	211	216	221	226	231	236	240	245
876	94 250	255	260	265	270	275	280	285	290	295
877	94 300	305	310	315	320	325	330	335	340	345
878	94 349	354	359	364	369	374	379	384	389	394
879	94 399	404	409	414	419	424	429	433	438	443
880	94 448	453	458	463	468	473	478	483	488	493
881	94 498	503	507	512	517	522	527	532	537	542
882	94 547	552	557	562	567	571	576	581	586	591
883	94 596	601	606	611	616	621	626	630	635	640
884	94 645	650	655	660	665	670	675	680	685	689
885	94 694	699	704	709	714	719	724	729	734	738
886	94 743	748	753	758	763	768	773	778	783	787
887	94 792	797	802	807	812	817	822	827	832	836
888	94 841	846	851	856	861	866	871	876	880	885
889	94 890	895	900	905	910	915	919	924	929	934
890	94 939	944	949	954	959	963	968	973	978	983
891	94 988	993	998	*002	*007	*012	*017	*022	*027	*032
892	95 036	041	046	051	056	061	066	071	075	080
893	95 085	090	095	100	105	109	114	119	124	129
894	95 134	139	143	148	153	158	163	168	173	177
895	95 182	187	192	197	202	207	211	216	221	226
896	95 231	236	240	245	250	255	260	265	270	274
897	95 279	284	289	294	299	303	308	313	318	323
898	95 328	332	337	342	347	352	357	361	366	371
899	95 376	381	386	390	395	400	405	410	415	419
900	95 424	429	434	439	444	448	453	458	463	468

Prop. Parts	N	0	1	2	3	4	5	6	7	8	9

IV. 9000—FIVE-PLACE LOGARITHMS OF NUMBERS—9509

N	0	1	2	3	4	5	6	7	8	9
900	95 424	429	434	439	444	448	453	458	463	468
901	95 472	477	482	487	492	497	501	506	511	516
902	95 521	525	530	535	540	545	550	554	559	564
903	95 569	574	578	583	588	593	598	602	607	612
904	95 617	622	626	631	636	641	646	650	655	660
905	95 665	670	674	679	684	689	694	698	703	708
906	95 713	718	722	727	732	737	742	746	751	756
907	95 761	766	770	775	780	785	789	794	799	804
908	95 809	813	818	823	828	832	837	842	847	852
909	95 856	861	866	871	875	880	885	890	895	899
910	95 904	909	914	018	923	928	933	938	942	947
911	95 952	957	961	966	971	976	980	985	990	995
912	95 999	*004	*009	*014	*019	*023	*028	*033	*038	*042
913	96 047	052	057	061	066	071	076	080	085	090
914	96 095	099	104	109	114	118	123	128	133	137
915	96 142	147	152	156	161	166	171	175	180	185
916	96 190	194	199	204	209	213	218	223	227	232
917	96 237	242	246	251	256	261	265	270	275	280
918	96 284	289	294	298	303	308	313	317	322	327
919	96 332	336	341	346	350	355	360	365	369	374
920	96 379	384	388	393	398	402	407	412	417	421
921	96 426	431	435	440	445	450	454	459	464	468
922	96 473	478	483	487	492	497	501	506	511	515
923	96 520	525	530	534	539	544	548	553	558	562
924	96 567	572	577	581	586	591	595	600	605	609
925	96 614	619	624	628	633	638	642	647	652	656
926	96 661	666	670	675	680	685	689	694	699	703
927	96 708	713	717	722	727	731	736	741	745	750
928	96 755	759	764	769	774	778	783	788	792	797
929	96 802	806	811	816	820	825	830	834	839	844
930	96 848	853	858	862	867	872	876	881	886	890
931	96 895	900	904	909	914	918	923	928	932	937
932	96 942	946	951	956	960	965	970	974	979	984
933	96 988	993	997	*002	*007	*011	*016	*021	*025	*030
934	97 035	039	044	049	053	058	063	067	072	077
935	97 081	086	090	095	100	104	109	114	118	123
936	97 128	132	137	142	146	151	155	160	165	169
937	97 174	179	183	188	192	197	202	206	211	216
938	97 220	225	230	234	239	243	248	253	257	262
939	97 267	271	276	280	285	290	294	299	304	308
940	97 313	317	322	327	331	336	340	345	350	354
941	97 359	364	368	373	377	382	387	391	396	400
942	97 405	410	414	419	424	428	433	437	442	447
943	97 451	456	460	465	470	474	479	483	488	493
944	97 497	502	506	511	516	520	525	529	534	539
945	97 543	548	552	557	562	566	571	575	580	585
946	97 589	594	598	603	607	612	617	621	626	630
947	97 635	640	644	649	653	658	663	667	672	676
948	97 681	685	690	695	699	704	708	713	717	722
949	97 727	731	736	740	745	749	754	759	763	768
950	97 772	777	782	786	791	795	800	804	809	813

Prop. Parts

	5		4
1	0.5	1	0.4
2	1.0	2	0.8
3	1.5	3	1.2
4	2.0	4	1.6
5	2.5	5	2.0
6	3.0	6	2.4
7	3.5	7	2.8
8	4.0	8	3.2
9	4.5	9	3.6

IV. 9500—FIVE–PLACE LOGARITHMS OF NUMBERS—10009

N	0	1	2	3	4	5	6	7	8	9
950	97 772	777	782	786	791	795	800	804	809	813
951	97 818	823	827	832	836	841	845	850	855	859
952	97 864	868	873	877	882	886	891	896	900	905
953	97 909	914	918	923	928	932	937	941	946	950
954	97 955	959	964	968	973	978	982	987	991	996
955	98 000	005	009	014	019	023	028	032	037	041
956	98 046	050	055	059	064	068	073	078	082	087
957	98 091	096	100	105	109	114	118	123	127	132
958	98 137	141	146	150	155	159	164	168	173	177
959	98 182	186	191	195	200	204	209	214	218	223
960	98 227	232	236	241	245	250	254	259	263	268
961	98 272	277	281	286	290	295	299	304	308	313
962	98 318	322	327	331	336	340	345	349	354	358
963	98 363	367	372	376	381	385	390	394	399	403
964	98 408	412	417	421	426	430	435	439	444	448
965	98 453	457	462	466	471	475	480	484	489	493
966	98 498	502	507	511	516	520	525	529	534	538
967	98 543	547	552	556	561	565	570	574	579	583
968	98 588	592	597	601	605	610	614	619	623	628
969	98 632	637	641	646	650	655	659	664	668	673
970	98 677	682	686	691	695	700	704	709	713	717
971	98 722	726	731	735	740	744	749	753	758	762
972	98 767	771	776	780	784	789	793	798	802	807
973	98 811	816	820	825	829	834	838	843	847	851
974	98 856	860	865	869	874	878	883	887	892	896
975	98 900	905	909	914	918	923	927	932	936	941
976	98 945	949	954	958	963	967	972	976	981	985
977	98 989	994	998	*003	*007	*012	*016	*021	*025	*029
978	99 034	038	043	047	052	056	061	065	069	074
979	99 078	083	087	092	096	100	105	109	114	118
980	99 123	127	131	136	140	145	149	154	158	162
981	99 167	171	176	180	185	189	193	198	202	207
982	99 211	216	220	224	229	233	238	242	247	251
983	99 255	260	264	269	273	277	282	286	291	295
984	99 300	304	308	313	317	322	326	330	335	339
985	99 344	348	352	357	361	366	370	374	379	383
986	99 388	392	396	401	405	410	414	419	423	427
987	99 432	436	441	445	449	454	458	463	467	471
988	99 476	480	484	489	493	498	502	506	511	515
989	99 520	524	528	533	537	542	546	550	555	559
990	99 564	568	572	577	581	585	590	594	599	603
991	99 607	612	616	621	625	629	634	638	642	647
992	99 651	656	660	664	669	673	677	682	686	691
993	99 695	699	704	708	712	717	721	726	730	734
994	99 739	743	747	752	756	760	765	769	774	778
995	99 782	787	791	795	800	804	808	813	817	822
996	99 826	830	835	839	843	848	852	856	861	865
997	99 870	874	878	883	887	891	896	900	904	909
998	99 913	917	922	926	930	935	939	944	948	952
999	99 957	961	965	970	974	978	983	987	991	996
1000	00 000	004	009	013	017	022	026	030	035	039

Prop. Parts

5
1 | 0.5
2 | 1.0
3 | 1.5
4 | 2.0
5 | 2.5
6 | 3.0
7 | 3.5
8 | 4.0
9 | 4.5

4
1 | 0.4
2 | 0.8
3 | 1.2
4 | 1.6
5 | 2.0
6 | 2.4
7 | 2.8
8 | 3.2
9 | 3.6

Index

215